Ready® Common Core

Mathematics Teacher Resource Book ❷

▲ Curriculum Associates®

Teacher Advisors

Crystal Bailey, Math Impact Teacher, Eastern Guilford Middle School, Guilford County Schools, Gibsonville, NC

Max Brand, Reading Specialist, Indian Run Elementary, Dublin City School District, Dublin, OH

Helen Comba, Supervisor of Basic Skills & Language Arts, School District of the Chathams, Chatham, NJ

Cindy Dean, Classroom Teacher, Mt. Diablo Unified School District, Concord, CA

Randall E. Groth, Ph.D, Associate Professor of Mathematics Education, Salisbury University, Salisbury, MD

Bill Laraway, Classroom Teacher, Silver Oak Elementary, Evergreen School District, San Jose, CA

Jennifer Lerner, Classroom Teacher, PS 57, New York City Public Schools, New York, NY

Susie Legg, Elementary Curriculum Coordinator, Kansas City Public Schools, Kansas City, KS

Sarah Levine, Classroom Teacher, Springhurst Elementary School, Dobbs Ferry School District, Dobbs Ferry, NY

Nicole Peirce, Classroom Teacher, Eleanor Roosevelt Elementary, Pennsbury School District, Morrisville, PA

Donna Phillips, Classroom Teacher, Farmington R-7 School District, Farmington, MO

Maria Rosati, Classroom Teacher, Harwood Elementary School, Warren Consolidated Schools, Warren, MI

Kari Ross, Reading Specialist, MN

Sunita Sangari, Math Coach, PS/MS 29, New York City Public Schools, New York, NY

Eileen Seybuck, Classroom Teacher, PS 57, New York City Public Schools, New York, NY

Mark Hoover Thames, Research Scientist, University of Michigan, Ann Arbor, MI

Shannon Tsuruda, Classroom Teacher, Mt. Diablo Unified School District, Concord, CA

Acknowledgments

Project Manager: Todd Hamer
Cover Designers, Illustrators: Julia Bourque, Matt Pollock
Book Designer: Scott Hoffman
Production Manager: Jenny Sorenson

Executive Editor: Danielle Curran
Director–Product Development: Daniel J. Smith
Vice President–Product Development: Adam Berkin

Common Core State Standards © 2010. National Governors Association Center for Best Practices and Council of Chief State School Officers. All rights reserved.

ISBN 978-0-7609-8644-8
©2014—Curriculum Associates, LLC
North Billerica, MA 01862

No part of this book may be reproduced by any means without written permission from the publisher.
All Rights Reserved. Printed in USA.
15 14 13 12 11 10 9 8 7 6 5 4 3

Table of Contents

		CCSS Emphasis
Unit 1: Operations and Algebraic Thinking	1	
Lesson 1 *Understand* Mental Math Strategies (Fact Families)	3	M
CCSS Focus - 2.OA.B.2 Embedded SMPs - 2, 3, 4, 7, 8		
Lesson 2 Solve One-Step Word Problems	12	M
CCSS Focus - 2.OA.A.1 Embedded SMPs - 1, 2, 3, 4, 5, 7		
Lesson 3 *Understand* Mental Math Strategies (Make a Ten)	23	M
CCSS Focus -2.OA.B.2 Embedded SMPs - 1, 3, 4, 5, 7, 8		
Lesson 4 *Understand* Even and Odd Numbers	32	S/A
CCSS Focus -2.OA.C.3 Embedded SMPs - 2, 3, 4, 7		
Lesson 5 Add Using Arrays	41	S/A
CCSS Focus -2.OA.C.4, 2.NBT.A.2 Embedded SMPs - 1, 3, 4, 5, 7, 8		
Lesson 6 Solve Two-Step Word Problems	50	M
CCSS Focus - 2.OA.A.1 Embedded SMPs - 1, 2, 4, 7, 8		
Unit 1 Interim Assessment	61	

M = Lessons that have a major emphasis in the Common Core Standards
S/A = Lessons that have supporting/additional emphasis in the Common Core Standards

M = Lessons that have a major emphasis in the Common Core Standards
S/A = Lessons that have supporting/additional emphasis in the Common Core Standards

M = Lessons that have a major emphasis in the Common Core Standards
S/A = Lessons that have supporting/additional emphasis in the Common Core Standards

Ready® Common Core is an integrated program of assessment and data-driven instruction designed to teach your students the Common Core State Standards (CCSS) for Mathematics. The program also teaches and assesses the Standards for Mathematical Practice. You can use the program in a supplemental way to address specific standards where your students need instruction and practice, or in a more comprehensive way to engage students in all the CCSS.

Built for the Common Core. Not just aligned.

Ready Common Core Instruction and Ready Practice

Ready Common Core Instruction provides differentiated instruction and independent practice of key concepts and skills that builds student confidence. Interim assessments give frequent opportunities to monitor progress.

Ready Common Core Practice provides extensive practice on the high-rigor items required by the Common Core, giving you a measure of student growth. The two full-length tests will strengthen students' skills, build their confidence, and ensure that they are ready to show their mastery of the Common Core.

Teacher Resource Book and Teacher Toolbox

Ready Common Core Teacher Resource Books support teachers with strong professional development, step-by-step lesson plans, and best practices for implementing the CCSS.

Ready Common Core Teacher Toolbox provides online lessons, prerequisite lessons from previous grades, and targeted best-practice teaching strategies.

i-Ready® Diagnostic

Built to support the Common Core and integrated with the **Ready** program, the *i-Ready Diagnostic* helps teachers track student growth and identify areas that need more work, pointing teachers to **Ready** lessons to use for remediation. See page A20 for details. (*i-Ready* sold separately.)

Features

 Built with all-new content written specifically for the Common Core

 Uses a research-based, gradual-release instructional model

 Requires higher-order thinking and complex reasoning to solve multi-step problems and problems with more than one answer

 Integrates Standards for Mathematical Practice throughout every lesson

 Embeds thoughtful professional development

 Encourages students to develop deeper understanding of concepts and to understand and use a variety of mathematical strategies and models

 Includes preliminary practice with high-rigor test items reflecting latest guidance from SBAC and PARCC

 Identifies Depth of Knowledge (DOK) levels throughout the Teacher's Resource Book

©Curriculum Associates, LLC   Copying is not permitted.

Supporting the Implementation of the Common Core

The Common Core State Standards (CCSS) were developed to make sure that by the time students graduate from high school, they are college- and career-ready. Therefore, the creators of the standards started with the expectations they had for students at the end of 12th grade and worked down to kindergarten. As a result of this backward design approach, the CCSS are more rigorous than most current standards. The creators of the standards want students at every grade to develop a deep mastery of fundamental math concepts; learn the coherence among seemingly different math concepts; demonstrate complex, higher-order thinking by solving more rigorous problems; and learn the mathematical practices that allow them to become confident, successful math students. *Ready® Common Core* is here to help.

Because every Common Core mathematics standard has been addressed with a clear, thoughtful pedagogy, you can use the *Ready* program as the main structure of a year-long program. Any other materials aligned to the CCSS can be easily woven into the curriculum.

Each *Ready* lesson covers the entirety of a particular skill, so classrooms can work through any lesson independently from the rest of the book. This gives teachers transitioning to the CCSS enormous flexibility, knowing that *Ready* lessons can be pulled out and applied to any implementation plan.

Keep Up to Date with the *Ready® Teacher Toolbox*

The online *Ready Teacher Toolbox* gives you access to a host of multilevel resources, such as instructional support, online lessons, and lessons for prerequisite skills. (See pages A18 and A19 for more.) You can access the latest version of *Ready Practice* there, as well.

Smarter Balanced Assessment Consortium (SBAC) and the Partnership for Assessment of Readiness for College and Career (PARCC) are state-led consortia developing assessments aligned to the Common Core. They are creating higher-rigor, innovative item types and assessments that can measure a student's mastery of the Common Core. (See page A10 to see the higher-level DOK items in *Ready*, matching the consortia approach.) To match the differing approaches of the two consortia, we have created custom versions of *Ready Practice*, one for PARCC and one for SBAC.

The situation will be changing rapidly as the consortia complete their work. We will make sure that *Ready Practice* addresses the most recent information released by the consortia. You can ensure you have access to the latest updates by visiting the *Ready Teacher Toolbox* (*www.teacher-toolbox.com*).

Helpful Resources for the Transition to the Common Core

http://www.corestandards.org/
The main website for the Common Core. Here you'll find the full text of the standards, plus frequently asked questions and resources.

http://www.smarterbalanced.org/ and *http://www.parcconline.org/*
The testing consortia creating Common Core assessments for future implementation.

http://www.ascd.org/common-core-state-standards/common-core.aspx
A helpful list of all of ASCD's Common Core resources. A repository of evidence-based strategies, videos, and supporting documents that help educators transition to the Common Core.

http://commoncoretools.me/category/progressions/   *http://www.smarterbalanced.org/*

http://www.parcconline.org/classroom-resources   *http://illustrativemathematics.org/*

http://www.utdanacenter.org/ccss/index.php   *http://www.hepg.org/hel/article/543#home*

©Curriculum Associates, LLC   Copying is not permitted.

Answering the Demands of the Common Core with *Ready*®

THE DEMANDS OF THE COMMON CORE	HOW *READY*® DELIVERS
Focus: The Common Core Standards for Mathematics focus on fewer topics each year, allowing more time to truly learn a topic. Lessons need to go into more depth to help students to build better foundations and understanding.	*Ready* lessons reflect the same focus as the Common Core standards. In fact, the majority of the lessons in each grade directly address the major focus of the year. Furthermore, each lesson was newly-written specifically to address the Common Core Standards. There is at least one lesson for each standard and only lessons that address the Common Core Standards are included.
Coherent Connections (Building on Prior Knowledge): Instruction needs to provide logical ways for students to make connections between topics within a grade as well as across multiple grades. Instruction must **build on prior knowledge** and be organized to take advantage of the natural connections among standards within each cluster as well as connections across clusters or domains. This coherence is required for students to make sense of mathematics.	*Ready* units are organized by domains following the cluster headings of the Common Core. Each lesson starts by referencing prior knowledge and making connections to what students already know, particularly reinforcing algebraic thinking and problem-solving. These connections are highlighted for teachers in the Learning Progressions of the Teachers Resource Book so teachers can see at a glance how the lesson connects to previous and future learning.
Rigor and Higher-Order Thinking: To meet the Standards, equal attention must be given to conceptual understanding, procedural skill and fluency, and applications in each grade. Students need to use **strategic thinking** in order to answer questions of varying difficulty requiring different cognitive strategies and higher-order thinking skills.	*Ready* lessons balance conceptual understanding, skill and procedural fluency, and applications. Students are asked higher-order thinking questions throughout the lessons. They are asked to understand, interpret, or explain concepts, applications, skills and strategies. Practice questions match the diversity and rigor of the Common Core standards.
Conceptual Understanding: In the past, a major emphasis in mathematics was on procedural knowledge with less attention paid to understanding math concepts. The Common Core explicitly identifies standards that focus on conceptual understanding. Conceptual understanding allows students to see math as more than just a set of rules and isolated procedures and develop a deeper knowledge of mathematics.	*Ready* includes conceptual understanding in every lesson through questions that ask students to explain models, strategies, and their mathematical thinking. In addition, a "Focus on Math Concepts" lesson is included for every Common Core standard that focuses on conceptual development—those standards that begin with the word "understand."
Mathematical Practices: The Standards for Mathematical Practice (SMP) must support content standards and be integrated into instruction. The content standards must be taught through intentional, appropriate use of the practice standards.	The Standards for Mathematical Practice are fully integrated in an age-appropriate way throughout each lesson. The Teachers Resource Book includes SMP Tips that provide more in-depth information for select practice standards addressed in the lesson. See pages A9 and A26 for more details.
Mathematical Reasoning: Mathematical reasoning must play a major role in student learning. Students must be able to analyze problems, determine effective strategies to use to solve them, and evaluate the reasonableness of their solutions. They must be able to explain their thinking, critique the reasoning of others, and generalize their results.	*Ready* lessons build on problem-solving as a main component of instruction. Students work through a problem, discuss it, draw conclusions, make generalizations, and determine the reasonableness of their solutions. Guided Practice problems ask students to critique arguments presented by fictional characters and justify their own solutions.

©Curriculum Associates, LLC   Copying is not permitted.

The Standards for Mathematical Practice

Mastery of the Standards for Mathematical Practice (SMP) is vital for educating students who can recognize and be proficient in the mathematics they will encounter in college and careers. As the chart below shows, the SMPs are built into the foundation of **Ready® Instruction**.

1. Make sense of problems and persevere in solving them:

Try more than one approach, think strategically, and succeed in solving problems that seem very difficult.

Each **Ready** lesson leads students through new problems by using what they already know, demonstrates multiple approaches and access points, and gives encouraging tips and opportunities for cooperative dialogue.

2. Reason abstractly and quantitatively:

Represent a word problem with an equation, or other symbols, solve the math, and then interpret the solution to answer the question posed.

Ready lessons lead students to see mathematical relationships connecting equations, visual representations, and problem situations. Each lesson challenges students to analyze the connection between an abstract representation and pictorial or real-world situations.

3. Construct viable arguments and critique the reasoning of others:

Discuss, communicate reasoning, create explanations, and critique the reasoning of others.

In **Ready**, the teacher-led Mathematical Discourse feature guides students through collaborative reasoning and the exchange of ideas and mathematical arguments. **Ready** lessons also provide error-analysis exercises that ask students to examine a fictional student's wrong answer, as well as multiple opportunities to explain and communicate reasoning.

4. Model with mathematics:

Use math to solve actual problems.

Students create a mathematical model using pictures, diagrams, tables, or equations to solve problems in each **Ready** lesson. In the Teacher Resource Book, the Real-World Connection feature adds another dimension to understanding application of a skill.

5. Use appropriate tools strategically:

Make choices about which tools, if any, to use to solve a problem.

Ready lessons model the use of a variety of tools, including diagrams, tables, or number lines; Guided Practice problems may be solved with a variety of strategies.

6. Attend to precision:

Explain and argue, draw, label, and compute carefully and accurately.

Ready lessons guide students to focus on precision in both procedures *and* communication, including special error-analysis tasks and group discussion questions that motivate students to employ precise, convincing arguments.

7. Look for and make use of structure:

Build mathematical understanding by recognizing structures such as place value, decomposition of numbers, and the structure of fractions.

Each **Ready** Focus on Math Concepts lesson builds understanding of new concepts by explicitly reviewing prior knowledge of mathematical structure.

8. Look for and express regularity in repeated reasoning:

Recognize regularity in repeated reasoning and make generalizations or conjectures about other situations.

Each **Ready** lesson leads students to focus attention on patterns that reflect regularity. Where appropriate, students draw a conclusion or make a generalization and explain their reasoning by referencing the observed pattern.

©Curriculum Associates, LLC   Copying is not permitted.

Depth of Knowledge Level 3 Items in *Ready® Common Core*

The following table shows the **Ready®** lessons and sections with higher-complexity items, as measured by Webb's Depth of Knowledge index.

Lesson	Section	Item	Lesson	Section	Item
1	Guided Practice	12	13	Guided Practice	14
1	Guided Practice	14	13	Common Core Practice	6
1	Performance Task	15	14	Guided Practice	15
2	Guided Practice	15	15	Guided Practice	10
2	Common Core Practice	1	15	Common Core Practice	6
2	Common Core Practice	5	Unit 2	Interim Assessment	6
2	Common Core Practice	6	16	Guided Practice	16
3	Guided Practice	12	16	Performance Task	17
3	Guided Practice	13	17	Guided Practice	17
3	Guided Practice	14	18	Guided Practice	12
3	Performance Task	15	18	Guided Practice	13
4	Guided Practice	12	18	Guided Practice	14
4	Guided Practice	13	19	Guided Practice	13
4	Guided Practice	14	19	Guided Practice	14
4	Performance Task	15	19	Guided Practice	15
5	Guided Practice	10	19	Performance Task	16
5	Common Core Practice	3	20	Guided Practice	17
5	Common Core Practice	4	20	Common Core Practice	5
5	Common Core Practice	6	21	Guided Practice	16
6	Guided Practice	18	21	Common Core Practice	4
6	Common Core Practice	3	21	Common Core Practice	6
6	Common Core Practice	6	22	Guided Practice	15
Unit 1	Interim Assessment	6	22	Guided Practice	16
7	Guided Practice	15	22	Performance Task	17
7	Common Core Practice	5	23	Guided Practice	16
8	Guided Practice	17	24	Guided Practice	9
8	Common Core Practice	5	25	Guided Practice	15
9	Guided Practice	14	Unit 3	Interim Assessment	6
10	Guided Practice	11	26	Guided Practice	13
10	Guided Practice	12	27	Guided Practice	14
10	Performance Task	14	27	Performance Task	15
11	Guided Practice	9	28	Guided Practice	14
11	Common Core Practice	4	28	Guided Practice	15
11	Common Core Practice	6	28	Guided Practice	16
12	Guided Practice	13	28	Performance Task	17
12	Guided Practice	15	Unit 4	Interim Assessment	5
12	Common Core Practice	5			

©Curriculum Associates, LLC   Copying is not permitted.

Cognitive Rigor Matrix

The following table combines the hierarchies of learning from both Webb and Bloom. For each level of hierarchy, descriptions of student behaviors that would fulfill expectations at each of the four DOK levels are given. For example, when students compare solution methods, there isn't a lower-rigor (DOK 1 or 2) way of truly assessing this skill.

Depth of Thinking (Webb) + Type of Thinking (Revised Bloom)	DOK Level 1 Recall & Reproduction	DOK Level 2 Basic Skills & Concepts	DOK Level 3 Strategic Thinking & Reasoning	DOK Level 4 Extended Thinking
Remember	• Recall conversations, terms, facts			
Understand	• Evaluate an expression • Locate points on a grid or number on number line • Solve a one-step problem • Represent math relationships in words, pictures, or symbols	• Specify, explain relationships • Make basic inferences or logical predictions from data/observations • Use models/diagrams to explain concepts • Make and explain estimates	• Use concepts to solve non-routine problems • Use supporting evidence to justify conjectures, generalize, or connect ideas • Explain reasoning when more than one response is possible • Explain phenomena in terms of concepts	• Relate mathematical concepts to other content areas, other domains • Develop generalizations of the results obtained and the strategies used and apply them to new problem situations
Apply	• Follow simple procedures • Calculate, measure, apply a rule (e.g.,rounding) • Apply algorithm or formula • Solve linear equations • Make conversions	• Select a procedure and perform it • Solve routine problem applying multiple concepts or decision points • Retrieve information to solve a problem • Translate between representations	• Design investigation for a specific purpose or research question • Use reasoning, planning, and supporting evidence • Translate between problem and symbolic notation when not a direct translation	• Initiate, design, and conduct a project that specifies a problem, identifies solution paths, solves the problem, and reports results
Analyze	• Retrieve information from a table or graph to answer a question • Identify a pattern/trend	• Categorize data, figures • Organize, order data • Select appropriate graph and organize and display data • Interpret data from a simple graph • Extend a pattern	• Compare information within or across data sets or texts • Analyze and draw conclusions from data, citing evidence • Generalize a pattern • Interpret data from complex graph	• Analyze multiple sources of evidence or data sets
Evaluate			• Cite evidence and develop a logical argument • Compare/contrast solution methods • Verify reasonableness	• Apply understanding in a novel way, provide argument or justification for the new application
Create	• Brainstorm ideas, concepts, problems, or perspectives related to a topic or concept	• Generate conjectures or hypotheses based on observations or prior knowledge and experience	• Develop an alternative solution • Synthesize information within one data set	• Synthesize information across multiple sources or data sets • Design a model to inform and solve a practical or abstract situation

SBAC, 2012; adapted from Hess et al., 2009

©Curriculum Associates, LLC   Copying is not permitted.

Use *Ready*® as Your Primary Instructional Program

Because every Common Core Standard is addressed with clear, thoughtful instruction and practice, you can use *Ready® Common Core* as your primary instructional program for a year-long mathematics course. The lesson sequence is based on the learning progressions of the Common Core to help students build upon earlier learning, develop conceptual understanding, use mathematical practices, and make connections among concepts.

Instruct

Teach one *Ready*® *Common Core Instruction* lesson per week, using the Pacing Guides on pages A14 and A15 for planning.

Use the web-based, electronic resources found in the *Teacher Toolbox* to review prerequisite skills and access on-level lessons as well as lessons from previous grades. See pages A18 and A19 for more information.

Assess and Monitor Progress

Assess student understanding using the Common Core Practice and Interim Assessments in *Ready Common Core Instruction*. See pages A29 and A46 for more information.

Monitor progress using the benchmark tests in *Ready*® *Practice* to assess cumulative understanding, identify student weaknesses for reteaching, and prepare for Common Core assessments.

Differentiate Instruction

Identify struggling students and differentiate instruction using the Assessment and Remediation pages at the end of each lesson in the *Teacher Resource Book*. See page A23 for a sample.

Access activities and prerequisite lessons (including lessons from other grades) in the *Teacher Toolbox* to reteach and support students who are still struggling. See pages A18 and A19 for more details.

Use *Ready*® with the *i-Ready*® *Diagnostic*

You can add the *i-Ready Diagnostic* as part of your *Ready* solution.

- Administer the *i-Ready Diagnostic* as a cross-grade-level assessment to pinpoint what students know and what they need to learn.

- Use the detailed individual and classroom diagnostic reports to address individual and classroom instructional needs using the lessons in *Ready Common Core Instruction* and the *Teacher Toolbox*.

See pages A20 and A21 for more information.

©Curriculum Associates, LLC   Copying is not permitted.

Using *Ready®* to Supplement Your Current Math Program

If your instructional program was not written specifically to address the Common Core Standards, then your textbook likely does not include the concepts, skills, and strategies your students need to be successful. By supplementing with *Ready® Common Core Instruction*, you'll be able to address these concerns:

- Filling gaps in mathematics content that has shifted from another grade

- Incorporating Common Core models and strategies into instruction

- Integrating the habits of mind that are in the Standards for Mathematical Practice

- Asking questions requiring students to engage in higher-level thinking, such as questions that ask students to explain effective strategies used to solve problems, critique the reasoning of others, and generalize their results

- Including lessons and questions that develop conceptual understanding

- Providing rigorous questions modeled on the latest Common Core assessment frameworks

Step-by-Step Implementation Plan

STEP 1
IDENTIFY CONTENT NEEDS
	How do I know what to teach?
	
	• Identify the *Ready* lessons you need to include in your instructional plan.
	
	  – First identify the *Ready* lessons that address standards that are a major emphasis in the Common Core. See page A16 or the Table of Contents to easily identify these *Ready* lessons.
	
	  – Next, identify the Common Core standards in the table on page A17 that are not addressed in your current math program.
	
	• Identify the place in your scope and sequence to insert the *Ready* lessons. "Focus on Math Concepts" lessons should come before the lesson in your current book.

STEP 2 **INTEGRATE READY**	**How do I make time to teach the *Ready* lessons?** • Remove lessons or units from your current instructional plan that are no longer covered in the Common Core standards at that grade level. • Replace lessons or units that do not teach topics using the models, strategies, and rigor of the Common Core with the appropriate *Ready* lessons.
STEP 3 **MEASURE STUDENT PROGRESS**	**How can I address gaps in student knowledge?** • Use the Interim Assessments in *Ready* to make sure your students are successfully able to meet the rigorous demands of the Common Core. • Use the benchmark tests in *Ready® Practice* to identify student weaknesses and gaps in students' knowledge. • Use the *Ready® Teacher Toolbox* to access activities, on-level lessons, and lessons from other grades to address gaps in students' background and learning. See pages A18 and A19 for more on the *Teacher Toolbox*.

©Curriculum Associates, LLC   Copying is not permitted.

Teaching with *Ready® Common Core Instruction*

Ready Instruction Year-Long Pacing Guide

Week	*Ready® Common Core Instruction* Lesson	Days	Minutes/day
1	Practice Test 1 or *i-Ready* Baseline Diagnostic	3	60
2	L1: Understand Math Strategies (Fact Families)	5	30–45
3	L2: Solve One-Step Word Problems	5	30–45
4	L3: Understand Mental Math Strategies (Make a Ten)	5	30–45
5	L4: Understand Even and Odd Numbers	5	30–45
6	L5: Add Using Arrays	5	30–45
7	L6: Solve Two-Step Word Problems	5	30–45
	Unit 1 Interim Assessment	1	**30–45**
8	L7: Add Two-Digit Numbers	5	30–45
9	L8: Subtract Two-Digit Numbers	5	30–45
10	L9: Solve One-Step Word Problems With Two-Digit Numbers	5	30–45
11	L10: Understand Three-Digit Numbers	5	30–45
12	L11: Read and Write Three-Digit Numbers	5	30–45
13	L12: Compare Three-Digit Numbers	5	30–45
14	L13: Add Three-Digit Numbers	5	30–45
15	L14: Subtract Three-Digit Numbers	5	30–45
16	L15: Add Several Two-Digit Numbers	5	30–45
	Unit 2 Interim Assessment	1	**30–45**
17	L16: Understand Length and Measurement Tools	5	30–45
18	L17: Measure Length	5	30–45
19	L18: Understand Measurement With Different Units	5	30–45
20	L19: Understand Estimating Length	5	30–45
21	L20: Compare Lengths	5	30–45
22	L21: Add and Subtract Lengths	5	30–45
23	L22: Understand Reading and Making Line Plots	5	30–45
24	L23: Draw and Use Bar Graphs and Picture Graphs	5	30–45
25	L24: Tell and Write Time	5	30–45
26	L25: Solve Problems Involving Money	5	30–45
	Unit 3 Interim Assessment	1	**30–45**
27	L26: Recognize and Draw Shapes	5	30–45
28	L27: Understand Tiling in Rectangles	5	30–45
29	L28: Understand Halves, Thirds, and Fourths in Shapes	5	30–45
	Unit 4 Interim Assessment	1	**30–45**
30	Practice Test 2 or *i-Ready* Year-End Diagnostic	3	60

©Curriculum Associates, LLC   Copying is not permitted.

Ready® Instruction Weekly Pacing (One Lesson a Week)

Use **Ready Common Core Instruction** as the foundation of a year-long mathematics program. The Year-Long Sample Week (below) shows a recommended schedule for teaching one lesson per week. Each day is divided into periods of direct instruction, independent work, and assessment. Use the Year-Long Pacing Guide on page A14 for a specific week-to-week schedule.

	Day 1 Introduction	Day 2 Modeled/Guided Instruction	Day 3 Modeled/Guided Instruction	Day 4 Guided Practice	Day 5 Common Core Practice
Whole Class	**Introduction**, including Vocabulary (30 minutes) **Mathematical Discourse** (10 min)	Discuss graphic and verbal representations of a problem. **Visual Support** (15 minutes)	Discuss graphic and verbal representations of a problem. **Concept Extension** (15 minutes)	Discuss a sample problem. (10 minutes)	
Small Group/ Independent	**Hands-On Activity**	Work the math with a symbolic representation and practice with **Try It** problems. (20 minutes)	Work the math with a symbolic representation and practice with **Try It** problems. (20 minutes)	Work three problems independently, then **Pair/Share**. (20 minutes)	Solve problems in test format or complete a **Performance Task**. (30 minutes)
Assessment	Discuss answer to the **Reflect** question. (5 minutes)	Discuss solutions to the **Try It** problems. (10 minutes)	Discuss solutions to the **Try It** problems. (10 minutes)	Check solutions and facilitate **Pair/ Share**. (15 minutes)	Review solutions and explanations. (15 minutes) **Assessment and Remediation** (time will vary)

Ready Instruction Weekly Pacing (Two Lessons a Week)

Target **Ready Common Core Instruction** lessons based on **Ready Common Core Practice** results to focus learning in a compressed time period. The chart below models teaching two lessons per week. The two lessons are identified as Lesson A and Lesson B in the chart below.

	Day 1	Day 2	Day 3	Day 4	Day 5
In Class	*Lesson A* Introduction (15 minutes) Modeled Instruction (30 minutes)	*Lesson A* Guided Instruction (15 minutes) Guided Practice (30 minutes)	*Lesson B* Introduction (15 minutes) Modeled Instruction (30 minutes)	*Lesson B* Guided Instruction (15 minutes) Guided Practice (30 minutes)	*Lesson A* Review concepts and skills (20 minutes) *Lesson B* Review concepts and skills (20 minutes)
Homework (optional)		*Lesson A* Common Core Practice		*Lesson B* Common Core Practice	

©Curriculum Associates, LLC   Copying is not permitted.

Content Emphasis in the Common Core Standards

Major Areas of Emphasis

Not all of the content in a given grade is emphasized equally in the Common Core Standards. Some clusters of the standards require greater emphasis than others. This greater emphasis may be based on the depth of the ideas, the time that students need to master the concepts, the content's importance to future mathematics topics, or a combination of some or all of these. A greater focus on the most critical material at each grade allows for lessons to go more in-depth and for students to have more time to master concepts and mathematical practices.

The tables on these two pages identify the Major Clusters emphasized by the Common Core Standards and assessments and those that are Supporting and Additional Clusters. In addition, the **Ready®** lessons that correspond to these clusters are also identified.

Use the tables on these pages to help inform instructional decisions regarding the amount of time spent on clusters of varying degrees of emphasis. If you are using **Ready** as a supplement with another program, you may want to spend more time with the **Ready** lessons connected to clusters with a major emphasis.

The table below indicates the clusters of Major Emphasis in the Common Core Standards.

Standard Clusters with Major Emphasis	Standards	*Ready* Lessons
OPERATIONS AND ALGEBRAIC THINKING		
Represent and solve problems involving addition and subtraction.	2.OA.1	2, 6
Add and subtract within 20.	2.OA.2	1, 3
NUMBER AND OPERATIONS IN BASE TEN		
Understand place value.	2.NBT.1, 2.NBT.2, 2.NBT.3, 2.NBT.4	10, 11, 12
Use place value understanding and properties of operations to add and subtract.	2.NBT.5, 2.NBT.6, 2.NBT.7, 2.NBT.8, 2.NBT.9	7, 8, 9, 13, 14, 15
MEASUREMENT AND DATA		
Measure and estimate lengths in standard units.	2.MD.1, 2.MD.2, 2.MD.3, 2.MD.4	16, 17, 18, 19, 20
Relate addition and subtraction to length.	2.MD.5, 2.MD.6	21, 22

©Curriculum Associates, LLC   Copying is not permitted.

Supporting and Additional Areas of Emphasis

Although some clusters have greater emphasis in the Common Core Standards, this does not mean that standards within the clusters identified as Supporting or Additional can be neglected during instruction. Neglecting material will leave gaps in students' skills and understanding and may leave students unprepared for the challenges of a later grade. Standards for topics that are not major emphases are written in such a way as to support and strengthen the areas of major emphasis. This allows for valuable connections that add coherence to the grade.

In addition, the Supporting and Additional clusters provide students with understanding that is essential for success on the Common Core assessments, though they are not a major focus of the assessments. The Common Core assessments will mirror the emphasis developed by the Common Core and highlighted here. Major clusters will represent the majority of the questions on the Common Core assessments, but it is important to note that items identified as being Supporting or Additional will also be included.

The table below indicates the clusters with Supporting or Additional Emphasis in the Common Core Standards.

Standard Clusters with Supporting or Additional Emphasis	Standards	*Ready* Lessons
OPERATIONS AND ALGEBRAIC THINKING		
Work with equal groups of objects to gain foundations for multiplication.	2.OA.3, 2.OA.4	4, 5
MEASUREMENT AND DATA		
Work with time and money.	2.MD.7, 2.MD.8	24, 25
Represent and interpret data.	2.MD.9, 2.MD.10	23
GEOMETRY		
Reason with shapes and their attributes.	2.G.1, 2.G.2, 2.G.3	26, 27, 28

Additional Resources

For more information on Content Emphases, see these helpful resources.

media.doe.in.gov/commoncore/docs/math_shifts_and_major_work_of_grade.pdf

www.parcconline.org/parcc-model-content-frameworks

www.smarterbalanced.org/wordpress/wp-content/uploads/2011/12/Math-Content-Specifications.pdf

engageny.org/resource/math-content-emphases/

©Curriculum Associates, LLC   Copying is not permitted.

Connecting with the *Ready® Teacher Toolbox*

Designed for use with the **Ready® Common Core Instruction**, the Teacher Toolbox provides a host of multilevel resources teachers can use to differentiate instruction. If you purchased the Teacher Toolbox, you should have received an insert with access codes and information. Please contact Customer Service at (800) 225-0248 if you need this information. Visit *www.teacher-toolbox.com* to get started.

The Common Core builds on skills covered in the previous year's standards. Of course, many students will not have mastered those standards, and most students could use a review. **Ready Common Core** allows you to access lessons from previous **Ready** grades through the Teacher Toolbox.

How Do I Use the Teacher Toolbox?

Lessons are conveniently organized to match your print materials, making it easy to find additional resources for teaching the skills and standards associated with each lesson. All of these resources are perfect for use with any interactive whiteboard or other computer projection screen.

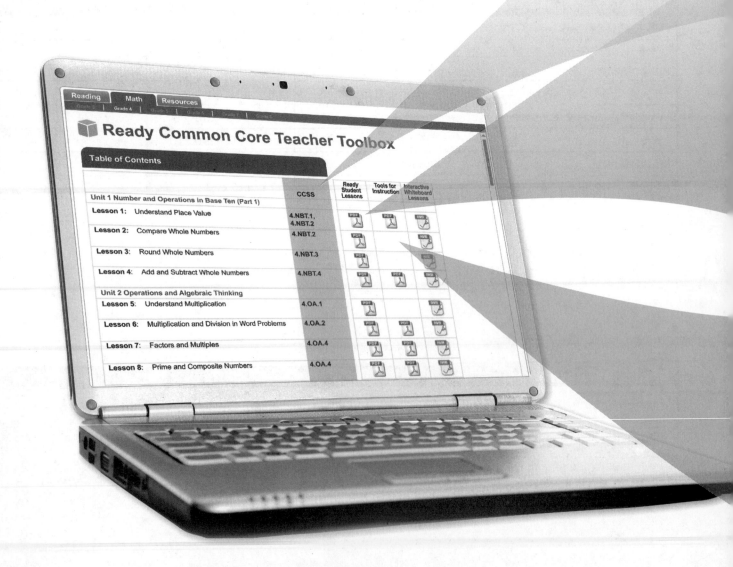

©Curriculum Associates, LLC   Copying is not permitted.

Downloadable *Ready®* Lessons

Downloadable **Ready®** lessons make it easy for teachers to focus on particular skills, or even reteach skills that students may not have mastered at earlier grade levels. What you get:

- Every lesson in this book is available online as an individual PDF file, which you can project for whole-class and small-group use and access from any internet connection.

- Prerequisite student and teacher lessons are available from prior grades to address gaps in content coverage or strengthen prerequisite skills.

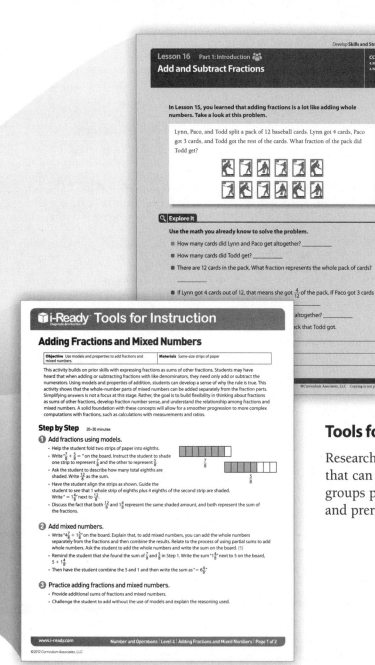

Tools for Instruction

Research-based, best-practice routines and activities that can be used with the whole class or small groups provide ways to teach or review standards and prerequisite skills.

Guided Interactive Tutorials

Guided interactive tutorials give teachers another engaging way to provide whole-class or small-group instruction. Lessons follow a consistent structure of explicit instruction and guided practice. Immediate corrective feedback continuously supports students.

©Curriculum Associates, LLC   Copying is not permitted.

Using *i-Ready® Diagnostic* with *Ready® Common Core*

If you have already purchased *i-Ready® Diagnostic*, you can use its robust reporting to monitor students' overall and domain-specific mathematics proficiency as they move through *Ready® Instruction*. Specifically, use the Student Profile report and the Instructional Grouping report to identify Next Step skills for student instruction.

i-Ready Diagnostic available for Grades K–12

Student Profile Report

The **Student Profile** report shows teachers students' performance levels for each domain and shows where they are struggling. Plus, it provides detailed recommendations and resources to support teacher-led instruction.

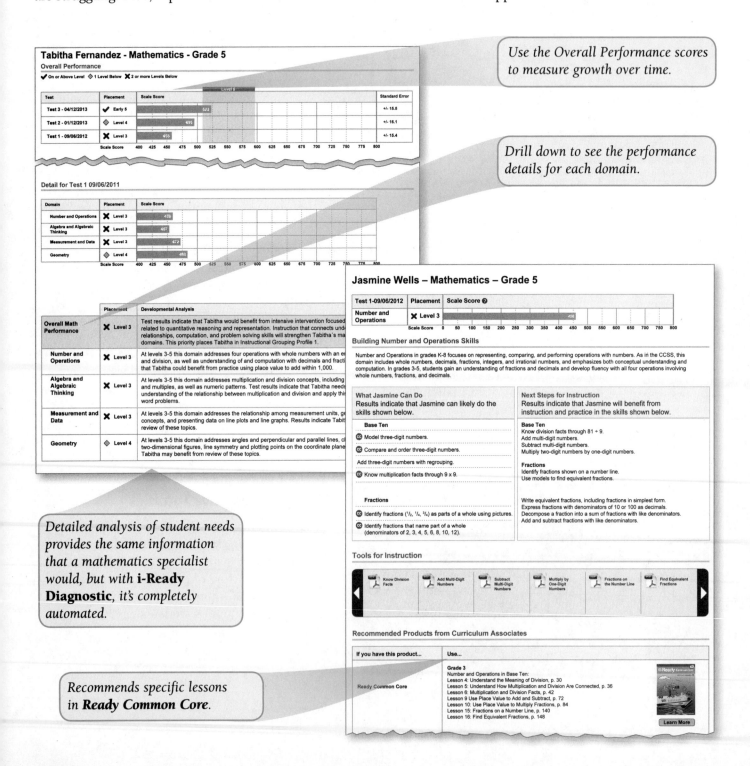

Use the Overall Performance scores to measure growth over time.

Drill down to see the performance details for each domain.

*Detailed analysis of student needs provides the same information that a mathematics specialist would, but with **i-Ready Diagnostic**, it's completely automated.*

*Recommends specific lessons in **Ready Common Core**.*

©Curriculum Associates, LLC   Copying is not permitted.

Instructional Grouping Profile

The **Instructional Grouping Profile** report shows teachers exactly how to group students so that students who are struggling with the same skills get the most out of small-group instruction. The report also gives effective instructional recommendations and resources for each group profile.

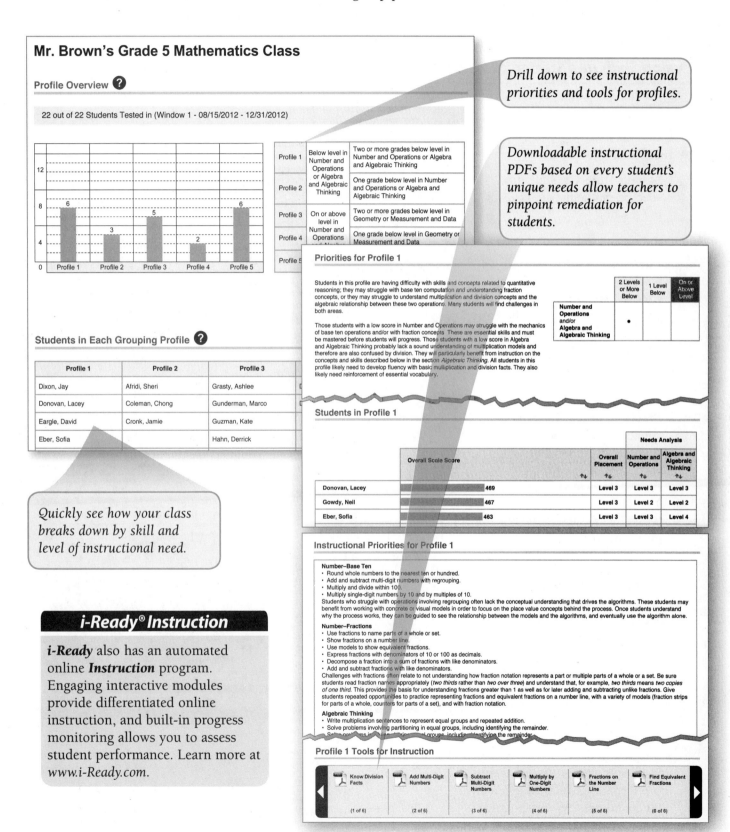

Mr. Brown's Grade 5 Mathematics Class

Profile Overview ?

22 out of 22 Students Tested in (Window 1 - 08/15/2012 - 12/31/2012)

Bar chart values: Profile 1 = 6, Profile 2 = 3, Profile 3 = 5, Profile 4 = 2, Profile 5 = 6

Profile 1	Below level in Number and Operations or Algebra and Algebraic Thinking	Two or more grades below level in Number and Operations or Algebra and Algebraic Thinking
Profile 2		One grade below level in Number and Operations or Algebra and Algebraic Thinking
Profile 3	On or above level in Number and Operations	Two or more grades below level in Geometry or Measurement and Data
Profile 4		One grade below level in Geometry or Measurement and Data
Profile 5		

Students in Each Grouping Profile ?

Profile 1	Profile 2	Profile 3
Dixon, Jay	Afridi, Sheri	Grasty, Ashlee
Donovan, Lacey	Coleman, Chong	Gunderman, Marco
Eargle, David	Cronk, Jamie	Guzman, Kate
Eber, Sofia		Hahn, Derrick

Drill down to see instructional priorities and tools for profiles.

Downloadable instructional PDFs based on every student's unique needs allow teachers to pinpoint remediation for students.

Quickly see how your class breaks down by skill and level of instructional need.

Priorities for Profile 1

Students in this profile are having difficulty with skills and concepts related to quantitative reasoning; they may struggle with base ten computation and understanding fraction concepts, or they may struggle to understand multiplication and division concepts and the algebraic relationship between these two operations. Many students will find challenges in both areas.

Those students with a low score in Number and Operations may struggle with the mechanics of base ten operations and/or with fraction concepts. These are essential skills and must be mastered before students will progress. Those students with a low score in Algebra and Algebraic Thinking probably lack a sound understanding of multiplication models and therefore are also confused by division. They will particularly benefit from instruction on the concepts and skills described below in the section *Algebraic Thinking*. All students in this profile likely need to develop fluency with basic multiplication and division facts. They also likely need reinforcement of essential vocabulary.

	2 Levels or More Below	1 Level Below	On or Above Level
Number and Operations and/or Algebra and Algebraic Thinking	•		

Students in Profile 1

Overall Scale Score		Overall Placement	Needs Analysis	
			Number and Operations	Algebra and Algebraic Thinking
Donovan, Lacey	469	Level 3	Level 3	Level 3
Gowdy, Neil	467	Level 3	Level 2	Level 2
Eber, Sofia	463	Level 3	Level 3	Level 4

Instructional Priorities for Profile 1

Number–Base Ten
- Round whole numbers to the nearest ten or hundred.
- Add and subtract multi-digit numbers with regrouping.
- Multiply and divide within 100.
- Multiply single-digit numbers by 10 and by multiples of 10.

Students who struggle with operations involving regrouping often lack the conceptual understanding that drives the algorithms. These students may benefit from working with concrete or visual models in order to focus on the place value concepts behind the process. Once students understand why the process works, they can be guided to see the relationship between the models and the algorithms, and eventually use the algorithm alone.

Number–Fractions
- Use fractions to name parts of a whole or set.
- Show fractions on a number line.
- Use models to show equivalent fractions.
- Express fractions with denominators of 10 or 100 as decimals.
- Decompose a fraction into a sum of fractions with like denominators.
- Add and subtract fractions with like denominators.

Challenges with fractions often relate to not understanding how fraction notation represents a part or multiple parts of a whole or a set. Be sure students read fraction names appropriately (*two thirds* rather than *two over three*) and understand that, for example, *two thirds* means *two copies of one third*. This provides the basis for understanding fractions greater than 1 as well as for later adding and subtracting unlike fractions. Give students repeated opportunities to practice representing fractions and equivalent fractions on a number line, with a variety of models (fraction strips for parts of a whole, counters for parts of a set), and with fraction notation.

Algebraic Thinking
- Write multiplication sentences to represent equal groups and repeated addition.
- Solve problems involving partitioning in equal groups, including identifying the remainder.

Profile 1 Tools for Instruction

Know Division Facts	Add Multi-Digit Numbers	Subtract Multi-Digit Numbers	Multiply by One-Digit Numbers	Fractions on the Number Line	Find Equivalent Fractions
(1 of 6)	(2 of 6)	(3 of 6)	(4 of 6)	(5 of 6)	(6 of 6)

i-Ready® Instruction

i-Ready also has an automated online **Instruction** program. Engaging interactive modules provide differentiated online instruction, and built-in progress monitoring allows you to assess student performance. Learn more at *www.i-Ready.com*.

©Curriculum Associates, LLC   Copying is not permitted.

Features of *Ready® Common Core Instruction*

This section guides teachers to the key features of the Student Book and Teacher Resource Book. Numbered boxes call out and describe the key features. Use this section to familiarize yourself with the overall structure of a *Ready® Instruction* lesson. There are two types of lessons in *Ready*. Pages A22–A29 show a **Develop Skills and Strategies** lesson and pages A30–A37 show a **Focus on Math Concepts** lesson.

Develop Skills and Strategies Lessons

In the Teacher Resource Book, each lesson begins with a full page of orientation on the standards addressed in that lesson.

Teacher Resource Book

1 **Lesson Objectives** identify specific mathematical goals of the lesson.

2 **The Learning Progression** helps teachers see the standard in context, how the standard builds on prior knowledge, particularly from the previous grade, and how it leads to the expectations for the next year.

3 **Prerequisite Skills** list key concepts and skills required for success with the lesson.

4 **Vocabulary** that is new as well as terms that should be reviewed are provided with clear definitions.

5 ***Ready Teacher Toolbox*** identifies on-level and prerequisite lessons, activities, and tutorials that are connected to the lesson and available online in the Teacher Toolbox.

6 **CCSS Focus** identifies the Common Core State Standards featured in the lesson, Additional Standards covered in activities in the Teacher Resource Book, and the Standards for Mathematical Practice integrated into the lesson.

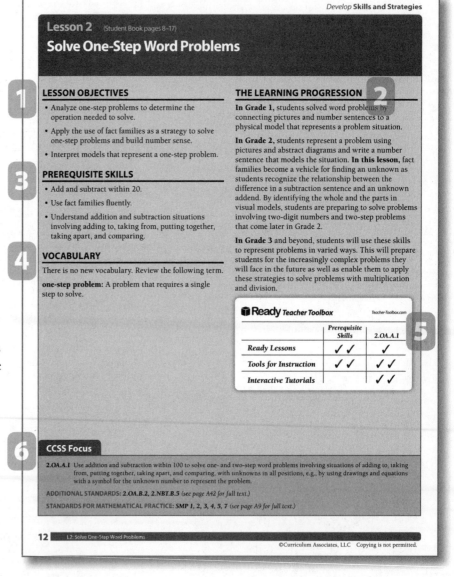

Develop **Skills and Strategies**

Lesson 2 (Student Book pages 8–17)

Solve One-Step Word Problems

1 **LESSON OBJECTIVES**
- Analyze one-step problems to determine the operation needed to solve.
- Apply the use of fact families as a strategy to solve one-step problems and build number sense.
- Interpret models that represent a one-step problem.

3 **PREREQUISITE SKILLS**
- Add and subtract within 20.
- Use fact families fluently.
- Understand addition and subtraction situations involving adding to, taking from, putting together, taking apart, and comparing.

4 **VOCABULARY**

There is no new vocabulary. Review the following term.

one-step problem: A problem that requires a single step to solve.

2 **THE LEARNING PROGRESSION**

In Grade 1, students solved word problems by connecting pictures and number sentences to a physical model that represents a problem situation.

In Grade 2, students represent a problem using pictures and abstract diagrams and write a number sentence that models the situation. **In this lesson,** fact families become a vehicle for finding an unknown as students recognize the relationship between the difference in a subtraction sentence and an unknown addend. By identifying the whole and the parts in visual models, students are preparing to solve problems involving two-digit numbers and two-step problems that come later in Grade 2.

In Grade 3 and beyond, students will use these skills to represent problems in varied ways. This will prepare students for the increasingly complex problems they will face in the future as well as enable them to apply these strategies to solve problems with multiplication and division.

5

Ready Teacher Toolbox	Prerequisite Skills	2.OA.A.1
Ready Lessons	✓ ✓	✓
Tools for Instruction	✓ ✓	✓ ✓
Interactive Tutorials		✓ ✓

Teacher-Toolbox.com

6 **CCSS Focus**

2.OA.A.1 Use addition and subtraction within 100 to solve one- and two-step word problems involving situations of adding to, taking from, putting together, taking apart, and comparing, with unknowns in all positions, e.g., by using drawings and equations with a symbol for the unknown number to represent the problem.

ADDITIONAL STANDARDS: **2.OA.B.2, 2.NBT.B.5** *(see page A42 for full text.)*

STANDARDS FOR MATHEMATICAL PRACTICE: **SMP 1, 2, 3, 4, 5, 7** *(see page A9 for full text.)*

12 L2: Solve One-Step Word Problems

©Curriculum Associates, LLC   Copying is not permitted.

©Curriculum Associates, LLC   Copying is not permitted.

Teacher Resource Book

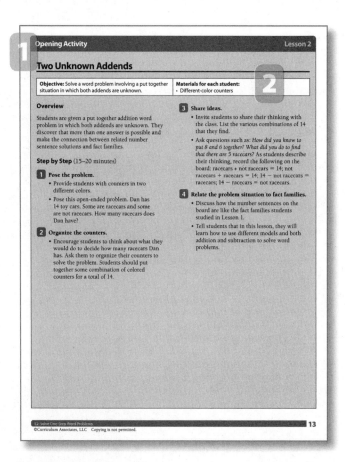

1 **Opening activities** provide a way to introduce the concepts of the lesson, often with a hands-on activity.

2 Materials suggested to complete the activity are listed, including, as needed, **Activity Sheets** found on page 307 of this Teacher Resource Book.

Differentiated Instruction in *Develop Skills and Strategies* Lessons

Each **Develop Skills and Strategies** lesson concludes with Differentiated Instruction activities, giving you opportunities to extend and reinforce learning with all types of students.

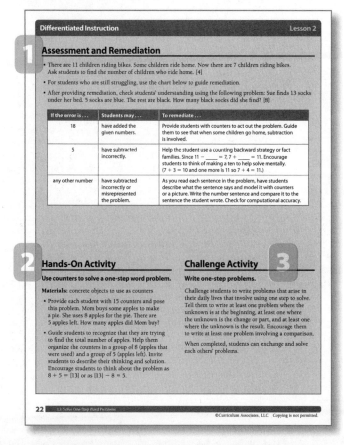

Teacher Resource Book

1 In the **Assessment and Remediation**, a closure question is given with a chart that provides teachers with a list of incorrect answers based on common errors and gives specific remediation suggestions for each incorrect answer.

2 A **Hands-On Activity** extends the concepts and skills of the standard using manipulatives and group collaboration.

3 A **Challenge Activity** gives students who have mastered the skills and concepts of the lesson a chance to apply their understanding to a more sophisticated problem-solving challenge.

©Curriculum Associates, LLC   Copying is not permitted.

Introduction in *Develop Skills and Strategies* Lessons

This section presents a problem designed to establish a connection between what students already know and what they are about to learn. Students can answer the Explore It questions individually, in pairs, or as a group.

Student Book

1 The CCSS covered in the lesson are given for easy reference.

2 This section poses a new problem that can be solved using prior knowledge, providing point-of-use review of prerequisites while working towards understanding new concepts.

3 In **Explore It**, the student is guided through finding the solution to the problem, usually with at least one question that asks students to explain their thinking.

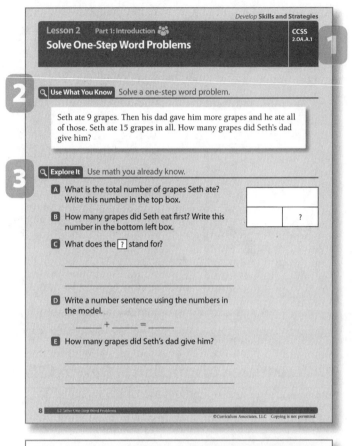

Teacher Resource Book

1 **Step by Step** guidance helps the teacher support the students in answering the questions.

2 The **Mathematical Discourse** questions help teachers lead rich classroom discussions and include answers as well as key topics to listen for in student responses.

3 **SMP Tip** highlights a particular Standard for Mathematical Practice that is one of many practice standards integrated in the lesson.

4 **Real-World Connection** prompts teachers to help students connect the math to their own experiences.

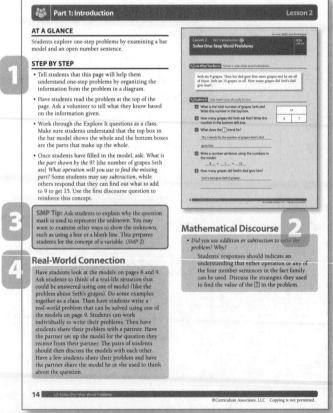

A24

©Curriculum Associates, LLC   Copying is not permitted.

Introduction in *Develop Skills and Strategies* Lessons

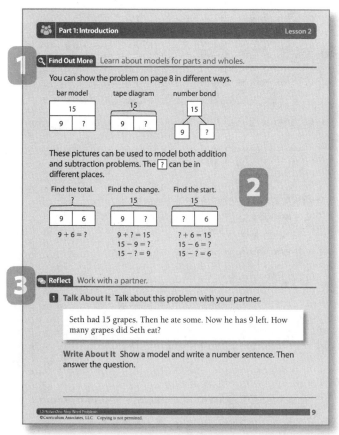

Student Book

1 The teacher can use **Find Out More** to formally introduce the key vocabulary, notation, and concepts of the lesson.

2 In student-friendly language, this section describes the formal math the student used to solve the problem, and introduces related skills to be covered in the lesson.

3 Use the **Reflect** question to assess students' understanding about what they just learned.

Teacher Resource Book

1 **Step by Step** gives page-specific teaching suggestions that build student understanding.

2 **Hands-On Activities** suggest a differentiation option involving manipulatives.

3 The **Mathematical Discourse** questions help teachers lead rich classroom discussions and include answers as well as key topics to listen for in student responses.

©Curriculum Associates, LLC   Copying is not permitted.

Modeled Instruction in *Develop Skills and Strategies* Lessons

The teacher supports students as they explore different ways of solving a real-world or mathematical problem. The direction line above the problem identifies the learning objective.

Student Book

1 A problem is posed that can be solved efficiently by using the lesson's new skills and strategies.

2 Different ways of representing the problem create multiple access points to draw on prior knowledge.

Teacher Resource Book

1 Point-of-use **ELL Support** helps the teacher recognize strategies to use to enhance learning with English Language Learners.

2 The **Mathematical Discourse** questions help teachers lead rich classroom discussions and include answers as well as key topics to listen for in student responses.

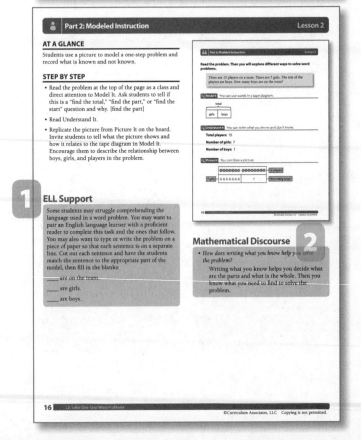

A26

©Curriculum Associates, LLC   Copying is not permitted.

Guided Instruction in *Develop Skills and Strategies* Lessons

Scaffolded questions guide students to answer and sometimes extend the problem on the previous page. Students are then given an opportunity to practice what they learned.

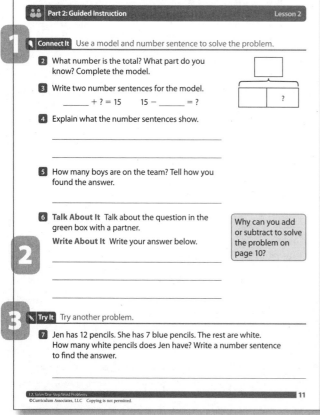

Student Book

1 In **Connect It**, students connect the representations on the previous page to a more symbolic representation of the problem and solution.

2 After working through the symbolic representation, students explain how to solve any similar problem.

3 In **Try It**, students apply what they learned to solve a similar problem.

For lessons addressing standards with multiple subskills, another two pages of Modeled and Guided Instruction are provided for each subskill.

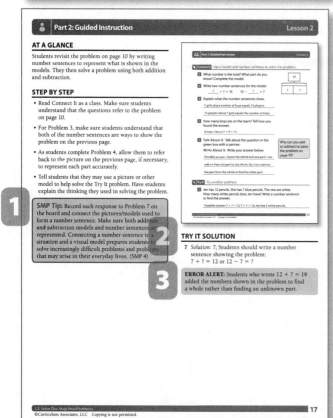

Teacher Resource Book

1 **SMP Tip** highlights a particular Standard for Mathematical Practice that is one of many practice standards integrated in the lesson.

2 **Try It Solutions** provide complete solutions and brief explanations including multiple solutions to show different approaches.

3 **Error Alerts** explain a typical computational error, the wrong answer it might produce, and explanations to help students avoid those errors in the future.

©Curriculum Associates, LLC   Copying is not permitted.

Guided Practice in *Develop Skills and Strategies* Lessons

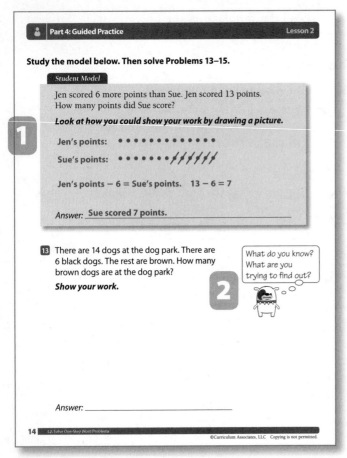

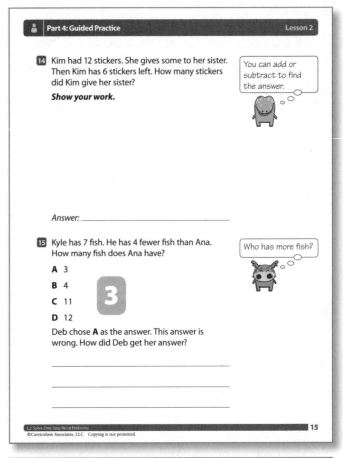

Student Book

1 The first problem is completed for students, modeling how they could show their work.

2 The Study Buddy models self-questioning and the habits of mind of proficient mathematics students.

3 The last multiple-choice question asks students to analyze and explain a student error based on common misconceptions.

Teacher Resource Book

1 **Step by Step** support provides information and useful tips the teacher can use to build students' understanding of how to think about the problems.

2 Complete solutions at point-of-use provide a correct response and an explanation of how a student might solve the problem and also note the DOK level of each question.

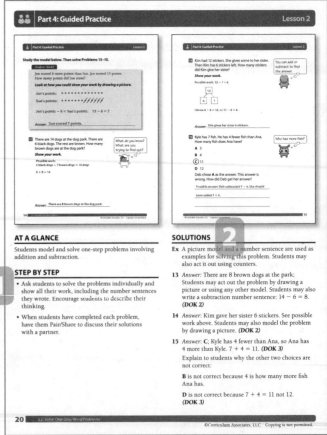

©Curriculum Associates, LLC   Copying is not permitted.

Common Core Practice in *Develop Skills and Strategies* Lessons

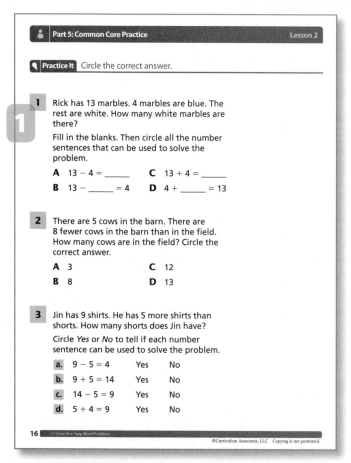

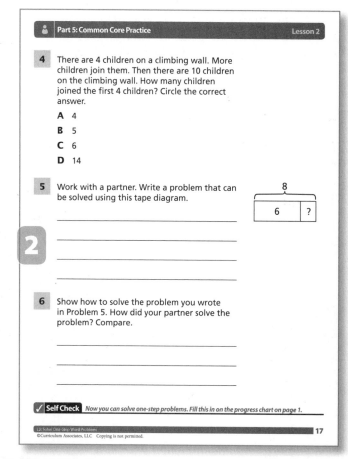

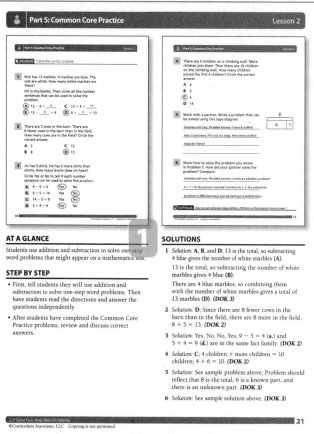

Student Book

1 **Common Core Practice** provides students with questions in a variety of Common Core assessment formats that integrate and extend concepts and skills.

2 Open-ended questions allow for multiple approaches and, when appropriate, more than one correct response.

Teacher Resource Book

1 Complete solutions at point-of-use provide a correct response and model at least one way to solve the problem in addition to providing the DOK level for each question.

©Curriculum Associates, LLC   Copying is not permitted.

Focus on Math Concepts Lessons

The Common Core State Standards demand a balance between conceptual understanding, procedural skills and fluency, and application. **Ready® Focus on Math Concepts** lessons, develop understanding through questioning, discussing, writing, and problem-solving. These lessons build a solid conceptual understanding of topics so students know why a strategy or procedure works or when it is appropriate to use it—not just how to use it. This understanding empowers students to apply what they have learned to new situations.

Intensive Teacher Support

In the Teacher Resource Book, each lesson begins with a full page of orientation on the standards addressed in that lesson.

Teacher Resource Book

1 **Lesson Objectives** identify specific mathematical goals of the lesson.

2 The **Learning Progression** helps teachers see the standard in context, how the standard build on prior knowledge, particularly from the previous grade, and how it leads to the expectations for the next year.

3 **Prerequisite Skills** list key concepts and skills required for success with the lesson.

4 **Vocabulary** that is new as well as terms that should be reviewed are provided with clear definitions.

5 *Ready Teacher Toolbox* identifies on-level and prerequisite lessons, activities, and animated videos that are connected to the lesson and available online in the Teacher Toolbox.

6 **CCSS Focus** identifies the Common Core State Standards featured in the lesson, Additional Standards covered in activities in the Teacher Resource Book, and the Standards for Mathematical Practice integrated into the lesson.

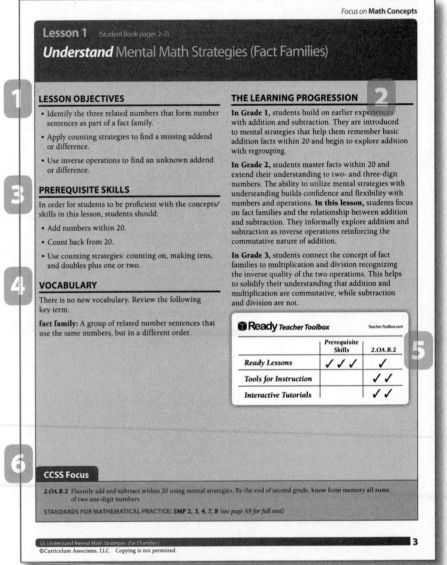

Focus on Math Concepts

Lesson 1 (Student Book pages 2–7)
Understand Mental Math Strategies (Fact Families)

LESSON OBJECTIVES

- Identify the three related numbers that form number sentences as part of a fact family.
- Apply counting strategies to find a missing addend or difference.
- Use inverse operations to find an unknown addend or difference.

PREREQUISITE SKILLS

In order for students to be proficient with the concepts/skills in this lesson, students should:

- Add numbers within 20.
- Count back from 20.
- Use counting strategies: counting on, making tens, and doubles plus one or two.

VOCABULARY

There is no new vocabulary. Review the following key term.

fact family: A group of related number sentences that use the same numbers, but in a different order.

THE LEARNING PROGRESSION

In Grade 1, students build on earlier experiences with addition and subtraction. They are introduced to mental strategies that help them remember basic addition facts within 20 and begin to explore addition with regrouping.

In Grade 2, students master facts within 20 and extend their understanding to two- and three-digit numbers. The ability to utilize mental strategies with understanding builds confidence and flexibility with numbers and operations. **In this lesson,** students focus on fact families and the relationship between addition and subtraction. They informally explore addition and subtraction as inverse operations reinforcing the commutative nature of addition.

In Grade 3, students connect the concept of fact families to multiplication and division recognizing the inverse quality of the two operations. This helps to solidify their understanding that addition and multiplication are commutative, while subtraction and division are not.

Ready Teacher Toolbox — Teacher-Toolbox.com

	Prerequisite Skills	2.OA.B.2
Ready Lessons	✓ ✓ ✓	✓
Tools for Instruction		✓ ✓
Interactive Tutorials		✓ ✓

CCSS Focus

2.OA.B.2 Fluently add and subtract within 20 using mental strategies. By the end of second grade, know from memory all sums of two one-digit numbers

STANDARDS FOR MATHEMATICAL PRACTICE: SMP 2, 3, 4, 7, 8 *(see page A9 for full text)*

L1: Understand Mental Math Strategies (Fact Families)
©Curriculum Associates, LLC   Copying is not permitted. — 3

©Curriculum Associates, LLC   Copying is not permitted.

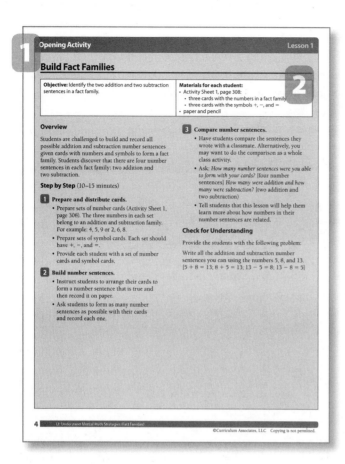

Teacher Resource Book

1 **Opening Activities** provide a way to introduce the concepts of the lesson, often with a hands-on activity.

2 Materials suggested to complete the activity are listed, including, as needed, **Activity Sheets** found on page 307 of this Teacher Resource Book.

Differentiated Instruction in *Focus on Math Concepts* Lessons

Each concept lesson concludes with Differentiated Instruction activities, giving you opportunities to extend and reinforce learning with all types of students.

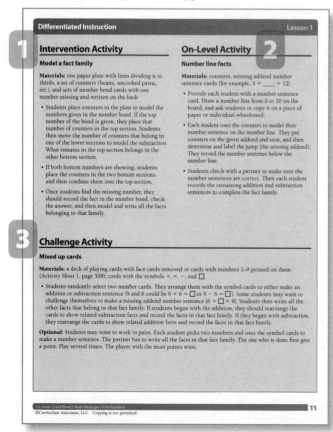

Teacher Resource Book

1 **Intervention Activity** provides an opportunity to reteach the concepts and skills of the current lesson.

2 **On-Level Activity** has students apply the concepts of the lesson to new situations.

3 **Challenge Activity** gives students who have mastered the skills and concepts of the lesson a chance to extend their learning.

©Curriculum Associates, LLC   Copying is not permitted.

Introduction in *Focus on Math Concepts* Lessons

The introduction makes connections between what students already know and what they are about to learn. By making these connections, students develop a deeper understanding and see the relationship between mathematical concepts, rather than seeing everything as a separate, unrelated idea.

Student Book

1 Each **Focus on Math Concepts** lesson begins with a key question that gets students thinking about the new concept.

2 Students develop deeper understanding by connecting new concepts to prior knowledge and skills.

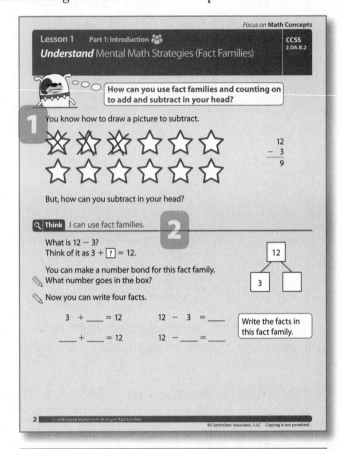

Teacher Resource Book

1 **Step by Step** gives suggestions for leading class discussions for each section of the lesson.

2 **SMP Tips** help teachers recognize a specific opportunity to reinforce one of the Standards for Mathematical Practice.

3 **Mathematical Discourse** questions promote thoughtful dialogue and exchange of ideas and are specific to each page.

4 **Misconception Alert** describes common habits of thinking that may interfere with proper understanding of the underlying concepts, and provides handy ways of overcoming them.

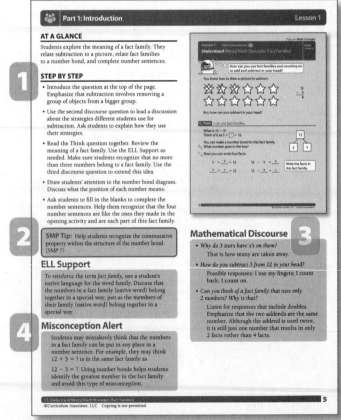

A32

©Curriculum Associates, LLC   Copying is not permitted.

Introduction in *Focus on Math Concepts* Lessons

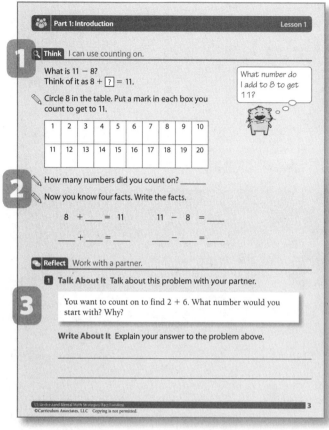

Student Book

1 The **Think** sections of the introduction ask students to think about new concepts and connections.

2 Pencil icons in the **Think** section indicate where students are asked to respond to questions embedded in the text.

3 **Talk About It** encourages proper habits of mathematical discourse, and **Write About It** allows students to reflect on their learning and deepen their understanding.

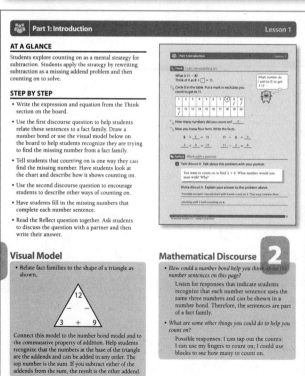

Teacher Resource Book

1 Use the **Visual Model** to encourage interactivity, engage visual learners, and give ELL students a new perspective on the concept.

2 The **Mathematical Discourse** questions help teachers lead rich classroom discussions and include answers as well as key topics to listen for in student responses.

©Curriculum Associates, LLC   Copying is not permitted.

Guided Instruction in *Focus on Math Concepts* Lessons

Student Book

1 In **Explore It**, students build understanding by answering thought-provoking questions about new problem-solving strategies and models.

2 Students apply what they have learned to new problems, explaining their solutions and often the reasons for using the strategies they choose.

Teacher Resource Book

1 **Step by Step** gives teaching suggestions and questions for leading class discussions for each page.

2 **SMP Tips** help teachers recognize a specific opportunity to reinforce one of the Standards for Mathematical Practice.

3 **Hands-On Activities** can be used to reinforce concepts or provide another, often more concrete, approach for students who need remediation.

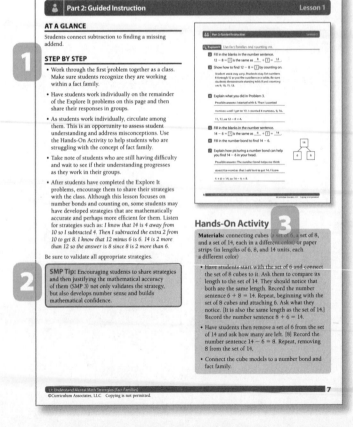

©Curriculum Associates, LLC   Copying is not permitted.

Guided Instruction in *Focus on Math Concepts* Lessons

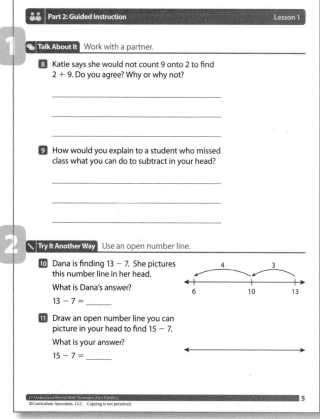

Student Book

1 In **Talk About It**, students work in pairs or small groups to answer questions about a specific problem using the concepts of the lesson.

2 In **Try It Another Way**, students look at other ways to do the problem they just discussed, giving them exposure to multiple ways of thinking about a problem and building flexibility in their ability to solve problems.

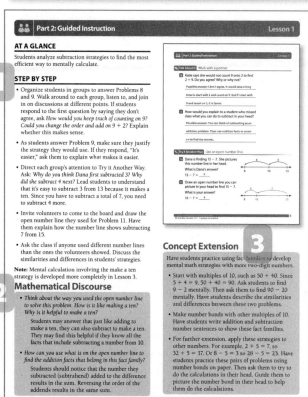

Teacher Resource Book

1 **Step by Step** gives teaching suggestions and questions for leading class discussions for each page.

2 The **Mathematical Discourse** questions help teachers lead rich classroom discussions and include answers as well as key topics to listen for in student responses.

3 Each **Concept Extension** suggests an optional strategy for going deeper into the concept behind the skill, or for connecting that concept to related understandings.

Guided Practice in *Focus on Math Concepts* Lessons

Student Book

1 In **Connect It**, students apply higher-order thinking skills and engage in meaningful class discussions.

2 Students develop deeper understanding by connecting to prior knowledge and skills. Students use the Standards for Mathematical Practice to solve problems designed to promote higher-order thinking.

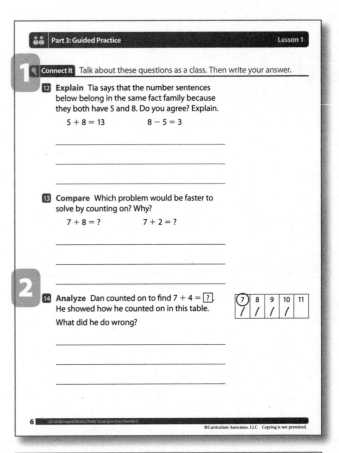

Teacher Resource Book

1 **Step by Step** gives teacher support and suggestions for leading class discussions for each page.

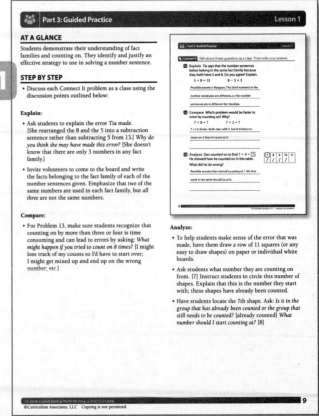

©Curriculum Associates, LLC   Copying is not permitted.

Common Core Performance Task in *Focus on Math Concepts* Lessons

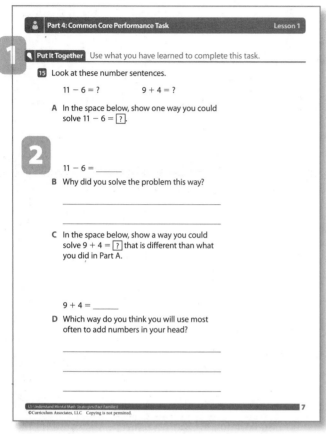

Student Book

1 In **Put It Together**, students are asked to think through a critical-thinking problem that often has multiple points of entry and/or more than one correct answer.

2 The tasks are scaffolded, with each step building on previous steps.

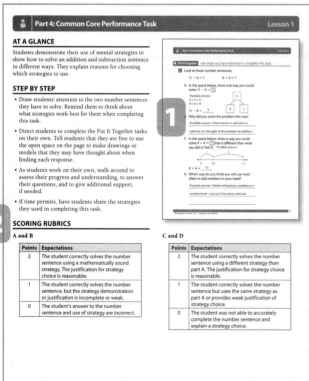

Teacher Resource Book

1 Sample responses and worked-out solutions are provided for the performance task.

2 **Scoring Rubrics** offer guidance for evaluating students' responses.

©Curriculum Associates, LLC   Copying is not permitted.

Overview

Ready® Common Core Mathematics is founded on research from a variety of federal initiatives, national literacy organizations, and literacy experts. As a result, this program may be used in support of several instructional models.

Ready® Uses . . .	Examples	Research Says . . .
Instructional Strategies		
Scaffolded Instruction is the gradual withdrawal of support through modeled, guided, and independent instruction.	*Ready* lessons follow the pattern of modeled and guided instruction, modeled and guided practice, and independent practice.	"Successful teachers help to create independent learners . . . . Contingent scaffolded instruction . . . is a powerful tool for achieving this goal." (Beed et al., 1991)
Mathematical Discourse in instruction uses questioning, listening, writing, and reflection to encourage conversation about mathematics.	*Ready* lessons include regular verbal exchange of ideas and sharing of understanding in whole group, small group, and pair settings. **Talk About It** leads students through discussions of key ideas. **Pair/Share** prompts students to compare answers and reasoning to identify misconceptions. **Mathematical Discourse** in the Teacher Resource Book suggests thoughtful question prompts.	"The process of encouraging students to verbalize their thinking—by talking, writing, or drawing the steps they used in solving a problem—was consistently effective." (NCTM, 2007)
Applying Prior Knowledge These are experiences and knowledge that a student brings with himself or herself to learn about a topic.	In each lesson, **Explore It** introduces a new skill by guiding students to solve a new problem by applying prior knowledge.	"What and how students are taught should reflect not only the topics that fall within a certain academic discipline, but also the key ideas that determine how knowledge is organized and generated within that discipline." (Schmidt, Houang, & Cogan, 2002)
Collaborative Learning Students work together in pairs or small groups to attain their individual goals.	**Talk About It** leads students through discussions of key ideas. **Pair/Share** prompts students to compare answers and reasoning to identify misconceptions.	Collaborative learning improves computational skills. Use of cooperative or collaborative learning has been advocated in various mathematics education reports and in state curricular frameworks, policies, and instructional guidelines. (National Math Advisory Panel, 2008)
Visual Representation is using an image to help describe or define a mathematical problem or relationship, or to depict a real-life problem situation.	*Ready* routinely uses pictorial (**Picture It**) and other visual models such as number lines (**Model It**) to illustrate mathematical concepts. **Visual Support** in the Teacher Resource Books suggests additional visual representations.	"Graphic representations of mathematical concepts and problems . . . are crucial components of programs used in nations that perform well on international comparisons, such as Singapore, Korea, or the Netherlands." (NCTM, 2007)

©Curriculum Associates, LLC   Copying is not permitted.

Ready® Uses . . .	Examples	Research Says . . .
Instructional Strategies (continued)		
Multiple Representations are the ways in which a teacher or student represents a math idea, including spoken, written, symbolic, and concrete formats.	*Ready* routinely uses pictorial (**Picture It**) and visual models (**Model It**) to illustrate mathematical concepts. **Connect It** develops the symbolic representation. **Hands-On Activities** and **Visual Support** in the Teacher Resource Book offer suggestions for additional representations.	"The usefulness of numerical ideas is enhanced when students encounter and use multiple representations for the same concept." (National Research Council, 2001)
Formative Assessment (or **Progress Monitoring**) is a strategy that involves frequent, in-classroom progress checks of students' understanding and mastery of math concepts and skills.	**Solutions and Explanations** with **Error Alerts** in the Teacher Resource Books create ongoing formative assessment opportunities, with support for correcting misconceptions throughout each lesson. **Assessment and Remediation** charts at the end of the lesson help the teacher assess mastery of the skill, identify specific misconceptions, and remediate on the spot as necessary.	Teachers' regular use of formative assessment improves their students' learning, especially if teachers have additional guidance on using the assessment to design and to individualize instruction. (National Mathematics Advisory Panel, 2008)
Differentiated Instruction is an approach to teaching that gives students multiple ways to access and make sense of mathematical ideas.	*Ready* student books provide verbal, visual, and symbolic representations of each new skill and concept. **Hands-On Activities**, **Visual Support**, **Concept Extension**, and **Challenge Activities** in the Teacher Resource Books provide additional differentiation options.	Many teachers and teacher educators have recently identified differentiated instruction as a method of helping more students in diverse classroom settings experience success. (Hall et al., 2003)
Hands-On Activities are any activities in which the student is handling manipulatives used to explore mathematical quantities, relationships, or operations.	Found throughout the Teacher Resource Book.	"The benefit of this [hands-on, manipulative] approach may be that its intensity and concreteness help students maintain a framework in their working memory for solving problems of this type." (NCTM, 2007)
ELL Support consists of tips to provide teachers the content knowledge and pedagogy to minimize obstacles to learning math due to language or cultural issues.	The *Ready* student book uses pictorial and visual representations combined with direct simple text to clearly present concepts. Point-of-use **ELL Support** tips for teachers are found throughout the Teacher Resource Book as appropriate.	Expanded opportunities should be available to English language learners (ELL students) who need them to develop mathematical understanding and proficiency. (NCTM, 2008)

©Curriculum Associates, LLC   Copying is not permitted.

Ready® Uses . . .	Examples	Research Says . . .
Instructional Features		
Standards for Mathematical Practice (SMPs) identify habits of mind and everyday ways of approaching math that are hallmarks of successful math students.	Throughout **Ready** Student Book, SMPs are built into the instruction and problems. Teacher Resource Books feature **SMP Tips** in every lesson to alert teachers to particular instances of each SMP.	"These practices rest on important 'processes and proficiencies' with longstanding importance in mathematics education." (CCSS, 2010)
Computational Fluency is having quick recall of number facts and knowledge and ability to apply multiple computational methods involving whole numbers, decimals, fractions, and other numbers as appropriate to the grade level.	**Ready** lessons all directly address computation skills, develop the conceptual understanding to support computation, or provide applications of computation skills.	"Basic skills with numbers continue to be vitally important for a variety of everyday uses. They also provide a crucial foundation for the higher-level mathematics essential for success in the workplace, which must now also be part of a basic education." (Ball et al., 2005)
Conceptual Understanding is the knowledge of why math processes and rules work.	All **Ready** lessons begin by laying a foundation of conceptual understanding of the mathematical principles underlying the skill being addressed. Special **Focus on Math Concepts** lessons put a special emphasis on these principles. **Concept Extension** features in the Teacher's Resource Book further support conceptual understanding.	"To prepare students for Algebra, the curriculum must simultaneously develop conceptual understanding, computational fluency, and problem-solving skills." (National Mathematics Advisory Panel, 2008)
Problem Solving (or **Application**) is the process of formulating a real-life problem as a mathematical problem, then performing the calculations necessary, and interpreting the result to find the solution to the problem.	**Ready** presents new math problems in real-world contexts and models finding the solution. (**Explore It, Picture It, Model It, Connect It**) Students then practice with similar problems in **Try It**. Practice problems always include real-world problems.	". . . An important part of our conception of mathematical proficiency involves the ability to formulate and solve problems coming from daily life or other domains, including mathematics itself." (National Research Council, 2001)
Answer Explanations for Students As a part of scaffolded instruction, students receive immediate feedback on their answer choices and the reasoning behind correct and incorrect answers.	In the **Guided Instruction**, **Guided Practice**, **Common Core Practice**, and **Interim Assessments** sections of the Teacher Resource Book, answer explanations are given for each question.	When students receive direct instruction about the reasons why an answer choice is correct or incorrect, they demonstrate long-term retention and understanding of newly learned content. (Pashler et al., 2007)

©Curriculum Associates, LLC   Copying is not permitted.

References

Ball, D. L., Ferrini-Mundy, J., Kilpatrick, J., Milgram, R. J., Schmid, W., & Schaar, R. (2005). Reaching for common ground in K–12 mathematics education. *Notices of the American Mathematical Society*, 52(9).

Beed, P. L., Hawkins, E. M., & Roller, C. M. (1991). Moving learners toward independence: The power of scaffolded instruction. *The Reading Teacher*, 44(9), 648–655.

Eastburn, J. A. (2011). The effects of a concrete, representational, abstract (CRA) instructional model on tier 2 first-grade math students in a response to intervention model: Educational implications for number sense and computational fluency. Dissertation. *ProQuest Information & Learning*, AAI3408708.

Furner, J. M., Yahya, N., & Duffy, M. L. (2005). 20 Ways to teach mathematics: strategies to reach all students. *Intervention in School and Clinic*, 41(1).

Hall, T., Strangman, N., & Meyer, A. (2003). Differentiated instruction and implications for UDL implementation. National Center on Accessing the General Curriculum. Accessed at: *http://aim.cast.org/learn/historyarchive/backgroundpapers/differentiated*

Hess, K. K., Carlock, D., Jones, B., & Walkup, J. R. (2009). *What exactly do "fewer, clearer, and higher standards" really look like in the classroom? Using a cognitive rigor matrix to analyze curriculum, plan lessons, and implement assessments.* Accessed at: *http://www.nciea.org/cgi-bin/pubspage.cgi?sortby=pub_date.*

National Council of Teachers of Mathematics. (2007). Effective strategies for teaching students with difficulties in mathematics. Accessed at: *http://www.nctm.org/news/content.aspx?id=8452.*

———. (2008). Teaching mathematics to English language learners. Accessed at: *http://www.nctm.org/about/content.aspx?id=16135*

National Governors Association Center for Best Practices and Council of Chief State School Officers. (2010). *Common Core State Standards for Mathematics.* Accessed at: *http://www.corestandards.org/the-standards.*

———. (2012). *Publisher's Criteria for the Common Core State Standards in Mathematics, K–8.* Accessed at: *http://www.corestandards.org/resources.*

National Mathematics Advisory Panel. (2008). Foundations for success: The final report of the National Mathematics Advisory Panel. Accessed at: *http://www2.ed.gov/about/bdscomm/list/mathpanel/index.html.*

National Research Council. (2001). *Adding it Up: Helping Children Learn Mathematics.* Mathematics Learning Study Committee: Kilpatrick, J., Swafford, J., & Findell, B. (eds.). Washington, D.C.: National Academy Press.

Partnership for Assessment of Readiness for College and Careers. (2011). *PARCC model content frameworks: English language arts/literacy grades 3–11.* Accessed at: *http://www.parcconline.org/parcc-model-content-frameworks.*

Pashler, H., Bain, P., Bottge, B., Graesser, A., Koedinger, K., McDaniel, M., & Metcalfe, J. (2007). *Organizing instruction and study to improve student learning* (NCER 2007–2004). Washington, D.C.: National Center for Education Research, Institute of Education Sciences, U.S. Department of Education. Retrieved from *http://ncer.ed.gov.*

Robertson, K. (2009). Math instruction for English language learners. *Colorín Colorado!* Accessed at: *http://www.colorincolorado.org/article/30570/.*

Schmidt, W., Houang, R., & Cogan, L. (2002). A coherent curriculum, *American Educator*, Summer, 2002.

Seethaler, P. M., Fuchs, L. S., Fuchs, D., & Compton, D. L. (2012). Predicting first graders' development of calculation versus word-problem performance: the role of dynamic assessment. *Journal of Educational Psychology* 104(1), 224–234.

Smarter Balanced Assessment Consortium. (2012). *General Item Specifications.* Accessed at: *http://www.smarterbalanced.org/wordpress/wp-content/uploads/2012/05/TaskItemSpecifications/ItemSpecifications/GeneralItemSpecifications.pdf.*

©Curriculum Associates, LLC   Copying is not permitted.

Correlation Charts

Common Core State Standards Coverage by *Ready® Instruction*

The table below correlates each Common Core State Standard to the **Ready® Common Core Instruction** lesson(s) that offer(s) comprehensive instruction on that standard. Use this table to determine which lessons your students should complete based on their mastery of each standard.

Common Core State Standards for Grade 2 — Mathematics Standards		Content Emphasis	Ready® Common Core Instruction Lesson(s)
Operations and Algebraic Thinking			
Represent and solve problems involving addition and subtraction.			
2.OA.A.1	Use addition and subtraction within 100 to solve one- and two-step word problems involving situations of adding to, taking from, putting together, taking apart, and comparing, with unknowns in all positions, e.g., by using drawings and equations with a symbol for the unknown number to represent the problem.	Major	2, 6, 9, 21
Add and subtract within 20.			
2.OA.B.2	Fluently add and subtract within 20 using mental strategies. By end of Grade 2, know from memory all sums of two one-digit numbers.	Major	1, 3
Work with equal groups of objects to gain foundations for multiplication.			
2.OA.C.3	Determine whether a group of objects (up to 20) has an odd or even number of members, e.g., by pairing objects or counting them by 2s; write an equation to express an even number as a sum of two equal addends.	Supporting/ Additional	4
2.OA.C.4	Use addition to find the total number of objects arranged in rectangular arrays with up to 5 rows and up to 5 columns; write an equation to express the total as a sum of equal addends.	Supporting/ Additional	5
Number and Operations in Base Ten			
Understand place value.			
2.NBT.A.1	Understand that the three digits of a three-digit number represent amounts of hundreds, tens, and ones; e.g., 706 equals 7 hundreds, 0 tens, and 6 ones. Understand the following as special cases:	Major	–
2.NBT.A.1a	100 can be thought of as a bundle of ten tens — called a "hundred."	Major	10
2.NBT.A.1b	The numbers 100, 200, 300, 400, 500, 600, 700, 800, 900 refer to one, two, three, four, five, six, seven, eight, or nine hundreds (and 0 tens and 0 ones).	Major	10
2.NBT.A.2	Count within 1000; skip-count by 5s, 10s, and 100s.	Major	5, 10, 24, 25
2.NBT.A.3	Read and write numbers to 1000 using base-ten numerals, number names, and expanded form.	Major	11
2.NBT.A.4	Compare two three-digit numbers based on meanings of the hundreds, tens, and ones digits, using >, =, and < symbols to record the results of comparisons.	Major	12
2.NBT.B.5	Fluently add and subtract within 100 using strategies based on place value, properties of operations, and/or the relationship between addition and subtraction.	Major	7, 8, 9
2.NBT.B.6	Add up to four two-digit numbers using strategies based on place value and properties of operations.	Major	15
2.NBT.B.7	Add and subtract within 1000, using concrete models or drawings and strategies based on place value, properties of operations, and/or the relationship between addition and subtraction; relate the strategy to a written method. Understand that in adding or subtracting three-digit numbers, one adds or subtracts hundreds and hundreds, tens and tens, ones and ones; and sometimes it is necessary to compose or decompose tens or hundreds.	Major	13, 14

The Standards for Mathematical Practice are integrated throughout the instructional lessons.

Common Core State Standards © 2010. National Governors Association Center for Best Practices and Council of Chief State School Officers. All rights reserved.

©Curriculum Associates, LLC   Copying is not permitted.

Common Core State Standards for Grade 2 — Mathematics Standards	Content Emphasis	*Ready*® *Common Core Instruction* Lesson(s)
Number and Operations in Base Ten (*continued*)		
Use place value understanding and properties of operations to add and subtract.		
2.NBT.B.8 Mentally add 10 or 100 to a given number 100–900, and mentally subtract 10 or 100 from a given number 100–900.	Major	7, 8
2.NBT.B.9 Explain why addition and subtraction strategies work, using place value and the properties of operations.	Major	13, 14
Measurement and Data		
Measure and estimate lengths in standard units.		
2.MD.A.1 Measure the length of an object by selecting and using appropriate tools such as rulers, yardsticks, meter sticks, and measuring tapes.	Major	16, 17
2.MD.A.2 Measure the length of an object twice, using length units of different lengths for the two measurements; describe how the two measurements relate to the size of the unit chosen.	Major	18
2.MD.A.3 Estimate lengths using units of inches, feet, centimeters, and meters.	Major	19
2.MD.A.4 Measure to determine how much longer one object is than another, expressing the length difference in terms of a standard length unit.	Major	20
Relate addition and subtraction to length.		
2.MD.B.5 Use addition and subtraction within 100 to solve word problems involving lengths that are given in the same units, e.g., by using drawings (such as drawings of rulers) and equations with a symbol for the unknown number to represent the problem.	Major	21
2.MD.B.6 Represent whole numbers as lengths from 0 on a number line diagram with equally spaced points corresponding to the numbers 0, 1, 2, ..., and represent whole-number sums and differences within 100 on a number line diagram.	Major	21, 22
Work with time and money.		
2.MD.C.7 Tell and write time from analog and digital clocks to the nearest five minutes, using A.M. and P.M.	Supporting/ Additional	24
2.MD.C.8 Solve word problems involving dollar bills, quarters, dimes, nickels, and pennies, using $ and ¢ symbols appropriately. *Example: If you have 2 dimes and 3 pennies, how many cents do you have?*	Supporting/ Additional	25
Represent and interpret data.		
2.MD.D.9 Generate measurement data by measuring lengths of several objects to the nearest whole unit, or by making repeated measurements of the same object. Show the measurements by making a line plot, where the horizontal scale is marked off in whole-number units.	Supporting/ Additional	22
2.MD.D.10 Draw a picture graph and a bar graph (with single-unit scale) to represent a data set with up to four categories. Solve simple put-together, take-apart, and compare problems using information presented in a bar graph.	Supporting/ Additional	23
Geometry		
Reason with shapes and their attributes.		
2.G.A.1 Recognize and draw shapes having specified attributes, such as a given number of angles or a given number of equal faces. Identify triangles, quadrilaterals, pentagons, hexagons, and cubes.	Supporting/ Additional	26
2.G.A.2 Partition a rectangle into rows and columns of same-size squares and count to find the total number of them.	Supporting/ Additional	27
2.G.A.3 Partition circles and rectangles into two, three, or four equal shares, describe the shares using the words halves, thirds, half of, a third of, etc., and describe the whole as two halves, three thirds, four fourths. Recognize that equal shares of identical wholes need not have the same shape.	Supporting/ Additional	28

©Curriculum Associates, LLC   Copying is not permitted.

Interim Assessment Correlations

The tables below show the depth-of-knowledge (DOK) level for the items in the Interim Assessments, as well as the standard(s) addressed, and the corresponding *Ready® Instruction* lesson(s) being assessed by each item. Use this information to adjust lesson plans and focus remediation.

Ready® Common Core Interim Assessment Correlations			
Unit 1: Operations and Algebraic Thinking			
Question	**DOK[1]**	**Standard(s)**	***Ready® Common Core* Student Lesson(s)**
1	2	2.OA.C.4	5
2	2	2.OA.A.1	2
3	2	2.OA.A.1	6
4	2	2.OA.B.2	3
5	1	2.OA.C.3	4
6	3	2.OA.A.1, 2.OA.B.2, 2.OA.C.3, 2.OA.C.4, 2.NBT.B.5	1–9
Unit 2: Number and Operations in Base Ten			
Question	**DOK**	**Standard(s)**	***Ready® Common Core* Student Lesson(s)**
1	1	2.NBT.A.4	12
2	2	2.NBT.B.7	13
3	2	2.NBT.B.7	14
4	2	2.NBT.B.7	14
5	2	2.NBT.A.1a, 2.NBT.A.1b, 2.NBT.A.2, 2.NBT.A.3	10, 11
6	3	2.OA.1, 2.NBT.1.a, 2.NBT.1.b, 2.NBT.3, 2.NBT.4, 2.NBT.5, 2.NBT.6, 2.NBT.7	10–15

[1]Depth of Knowledge levels:
1. The item requires superficial knowledge of the standard.
2. The item requires processing beyond recall and observation.
3. The item requires explanation, generalization, and connection to other ideas.

©Curriculum Associates, LLC   Copying is not permitted.

Ready® Common Core Interim Assessment Correlations (continued)

Unit 3: Measurement and Data

Question	DOK	Standard(s)	Ready® Common Core Student Lesson(s)
1	2	2.MD.C.8, 2.NBT.A.2	25
2	2	2.MD.D.10	23
3	2	2.MD.B.5, 2.MD.B.6, 2.OA.A.1	21
4	1	2.MD.A.3	19
5	2	2.MD.C.7, 2.NBT.A.2	24
6	3	2.OA.A.1, 2.MD.A.1, 2.MD.A.2, 2.MD.A.4, 2.MD.D.9	16–18, 20–22

Unit 4: Geometry

Question	DOK	Standard(s)	Ready® Common Core Student Lesson(s)
1	2	2.G.A.2	27
2	2	2.G.A.3	28
3	1	2.G.A.1	26
4	2	2.G.2	27
5	3	2.G.A.3	28

©Curriculum Associates, LLC   Copying is not permitted.

Which lessons are students building upon?

Grade 1, Lesson 6
Doubles and Doubles Plus 1
1.OA.C.6

Grade 1, Lesson 9
Number Partners for 10
1.OA.C.6

Grade 1, Lesson 11
Facts I Know
1.OA.C.6

Grade 1, Lesson 3
Add and Subtract in Word Problems
1.OA.A.1

Grade 1, Lesson 5
Subtract to Compare in Word Problems
1.OA.A.1

Grade 1, Lesson 13
Understand Sums Greater than 10
1.OA.C.6

Grade 1, Lesson 15
Add Three Numbers
1.OA.A.2

Grade 1, Lesson 16
Make a 10 to Subtract
1.OA.C.6

Grade 1, Lesson 30
Compare Data
1.MD.C.4

Grade 1, Lesson 13
Understand Sums Greater than 10
1.OA.C.6

Grade 1, Lesson 15
Add Three Numbers
1.OA.A.2

Grade 1, Lesson 3
Add and Subtract in Word Problems
1.OA.A.1

Grade 1, Lesson 5
Subtract to Compare in Word Problems
1.OA.A.1

©Curriculum Associates, LLC   Copying is not permitted.

Unit 1

Which lessons are students preparing for?

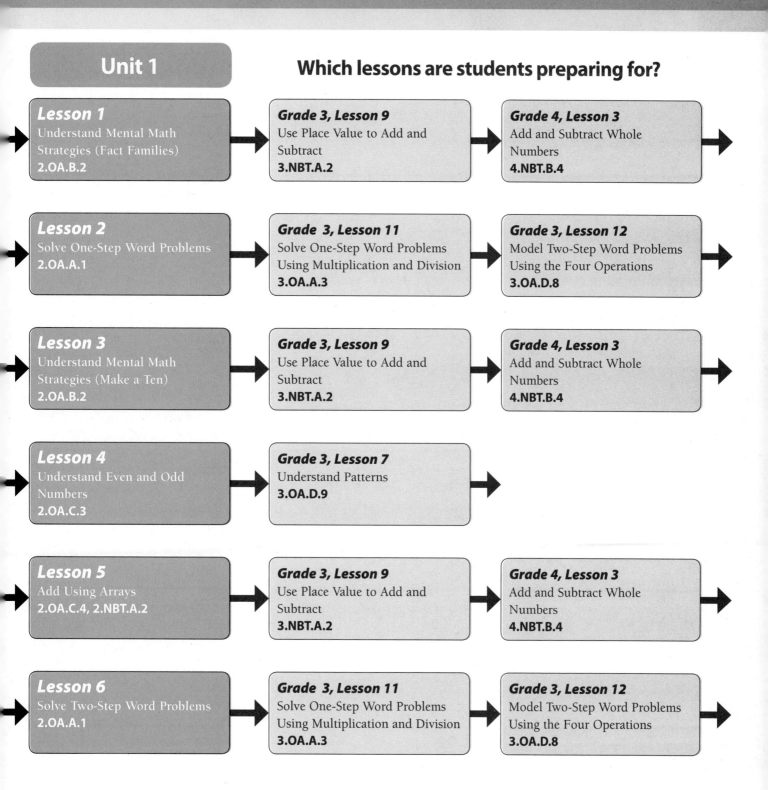

Lesson 1
Understand Mental Math Strategies (Fact Families)
2.OA.B.2

→ **Grade 3, Lesson 9**
Use Place Value to Add and Subtract
3.NBT.A.2

→ **Grade 4, Lesson 3**
Add and Subtract Whole Numbers
4.NBT.B.4

Lesson 2
Solve One-Step Word Problems
2.OA.A.1

→ **Grade 3, Lesson 11**
Solve One-Step Word Problems Using Multiplication and Division
3.OA.A.3

→ **Grade 3, Lesson 12**
Model Two-Step Word Problems Using the Four Operations
3.OA.D.8

Lesson 3
Understand Mental Math Strategies (Make a Ten)
2.OA.B.2

→ **Grade 3, Lesson 9**
Use Place Value to Add and Subtract
3.NBT.A.2

→ **Grade 4, Lesson 3**
Add and Subtract Whole Numbers
4.NBT.B.4

Lesson 4
Understand Even and Odd Numbers
2.OA.C.3

→ **Grade 3, Lesson 7**
Understand Patterns
3.OA.D.9

Lesson 5
Add Using Arrays
2.OA.C.4, 2.NBT.A.2

→ **Grade 3, Lesson 9**
Use Place Value to Add and Subtract
3.NBT.A.2

→ **Grade 4, Lesson 3**
Add and Subtract Whole Numbers
4.NBT.B.4

Lesson 6
Solve Two-Step Word Problems
2.OA.A.1

→ **Grade 3, Lesson 11**
Solve One-Step Word Problems Using Multiplication and Division
3.OA.A.3

→ **Grade 3, Lesson 12**
Model Two-Step Word Problems Using the Four Operations
3.OA.D.8

©Curriculum Associates, LLC   Copying is not permitted.

Lesson 1 (Student Book pages 2–7)

Understand Mental Math Strategies (Fact Families)

LESSON OBJECTIVES

- Identify the three related numbers that form number sentences as part of a fact family.

- Apply counting strategies to find a missing addend or difference.

- Use inverse operations to find an unknown addend or difference.

PREREQUISITE SKILLS

In order for students to be proficient with the concepts/skills in this lesson, students should:

- Add numbers within 20.

- Count back from 20.

- Use counting strategies: counting on, making tens, and doubles plus one or two.

VOCABULARY

There is no new vocabulary. Review the following key term.

fact family: A group of related number sentences that use the same numbers, but in a different order.

THE LEARNING PROGRESSION

In Grade 1, students build on earlier experiences with addition and subtraction. They are introduced to mental strategies that help them remember basic addition facts within 20 and begin to explore addition with regrouping.

In Grade 2, students master facts within 20 and extend their understanding to two- and three-digit numbers. The ability to utilize mental strategies with understanding builds confidence and flexibility with numbers and operations. **In this lesson,** students focus on fact families and the relationship between addition and subtraction. They informally explore addition and subtraction as inverse operations reinforcing the commutative nature of addition.

In Grade 3, students connect the concept of fact families to multiplication and division recognizing the inverse quality of the two operations. This helps to solidify their understanding that addition and multiplication are commutative, while subtraction and division are not.

▣ **Ready** *Teacher Toolbox*		*Teacher-Toolbox.com*
	Prerequisite Skills	**2.OA.B.2**
Ready Lessons	✓ ✓ ✓	✓
Tools for Instruction		✓ ✓
Interactive Tutorials		✓ ✓

CCSS Focus

2.OA.B.2 Fluently add and subtract within 20 using mental strategies. By the end of second grade, know from memory all sums of two one-digit numbers

STANDARDS FOR MATHEMATICAL PRACTICE: SMP 2, 3, 4, 7, 8 (see page A9 for full text)

©Curriculum Associates, LLC   Copying is not permitted.

Build Fact Families

Objective: Identify the two addition and two subtraction sentences in a fact family.

Materials for each student:
- Activity Sheet 1, page 308:
  - three cards with the numbers in a fact family
  - three cards with the symbols +, −, and =
- paper and pencil

Overview

Students are challenged to build and record all possible addition and subtraction number sentences given cards with numbers and symbols to form a fact family. Students discover that there are four number sentences in each fact family: two addition and two subtraction.

Step by Step (10–15 minutes)

1 **Prepare and distribute cards.**

- Prepare sets of number cards (Activity Sheet 1, page 308). The three numbers in each set belong to an addition and subtraction family. For example: 4, 5, 9 or 2, 6, 8.
- Prepare sets of symbol cards. Each set should have +, −, and =.
- Provide each student with a set of number cards and symbol cards.

2 **Build number sentences.**

- Instruct students to arrange their cards to form a number sentence that is true and then record it on paper.
- Ask students to form as many number sentences as possible with their cards and record each one.

3 **Compare number sentences.**

- Have students compare the sentences they wrote with a classmate. Alternatively, you may want to do the comparison as a whole class activity.
- Ask: *How many number sentences were you able to form with your cards?* [four number sentences] *How many were addition and how many were subtraction?* [two addition and two subtraction]
- Tell students that this lesson will help them learn more about how numbers in their number sentences are related.

Check for Understanding

Provide the students with the following problem:

Write all the addition and subtraction number sentences you can using the numbers 5, 8, and 13. [$5 + 8 = 13$; $8 + 5 = 13$; $13 − 5 = 8$; $13 − 8 = 5$]

©Curriculum Associates, LLC   Copying is not permitted.

AT A GLANCE

Students explore the meaning of a fact family. They relate subtraction to a picture, relate fact families to a number bond, and complete number sentences.

STEP BY STEP

- Introduce the question at the top of the page. Emphasize that subtraction involves removing a group of objects from a bigger group.

- Use the second discourse question to lead a discussion about the strategies different students use for subtraction. Ask students to explain how they use their strategies.

- Read the Think question together. Review the meaning of a fact family. Use the ELL Support as needed. Make sure students recognize that no more than three numbers belong to a fact family. Use the third discourse question to extend this idea.

- Draw students' attention to the number bond diagram. Discuss what the position of each number means.

- Ask students to fill in the blanks to complete the number sentences. Help them recognize that the four number sentences are like the ones they made in the opening activity and are each part of this fact family.

SMP Tip: Help students recognize the commutative property within the structure of the number bond. (SMP 7)

ELL Support

To reinforce the term *fact family,* use a student's native language for the word family. Discuss that the numbers in a fact family (native word) belong together in a special way, just as the members of their family (native word) belong together in a special way.

Misconception Alert

Students may mistakenly think that the numbers in a fact family can be put in any place in a number sentence. For example, they may think 12 + 3 = ? is in the same fact family as

12 − 3 = ?. Using number bonds helps students identify the greatest number in the fact family and avoid this type of misconception.

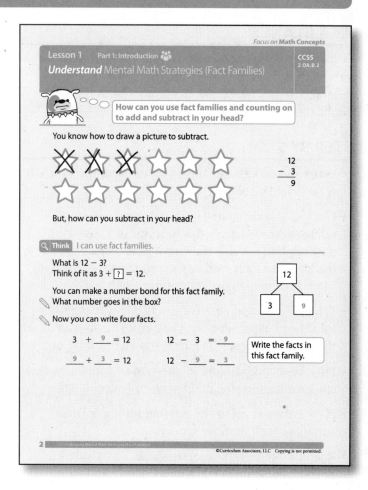

Mathematical Discourse

- *Why do 3 stars have x's on them?*

  That is how many are taken away.

- *How do you subtract 3 from 12 in your head?*

  Possible responses: I use my fingers; I count back; I count on.

- *Can you think of a fact family that uses only 2 numbers? Why is that?*

  Listen for responses that include doubles. Emphasize that the two addends are the same number. Although the addend is used twice, it is still just one number that results in only 2 facts rather than 4 facts.

AT A GLANCE

Students explore counting on as a mental strategy for subtraction. Students apply the strategy by rewriting subtraction as a missing addend problem and then counting on to solve.

STEP BY STEP

- Write the expression and equation from the Think section on the board.

- Use the first discourse question to help students relate these sentences to a fact family. Draw a number bond or use the visual model below on the board to help students recognize they are trying to find the missing number from a fact family.

- Tell students that counting on is one way they can find the missing number. Have students look at the chart and describe how it shows counting on.

- Use the second discourse question to encourage students to describe other ways of counting on.

- Have students fill in the missing numbers that complete each number sentence.

- Read the Reflect question together. Ask students to discuss the question with a partner and then write their answer.

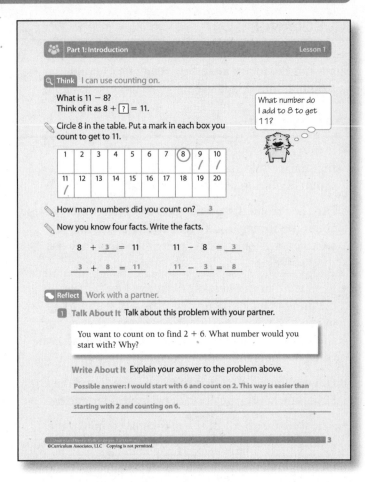

Visual Model

- Relate fact families to the shape of a triangle as shown.

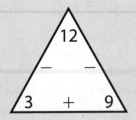

Connect this model to the number bond model and to the commutative property of addition. Help students recognize that the numbers at the base of the triangle are the addends and can be added in any order. The top number is the sum. If you subtract either of the addends from the sum, the result is the other addend.

Mathematical Discourse

- *How could a number bond help you think about the number sentences on this page?*

  Listen for responses that indicate students recognize that each number sentence uses the same three numbers and can be shown in a number bond. Therefore, the sentences are part of a fact family.

- *What are some other things you could do to help you count on?*

  Possible responses: I can tap out the counts; I can use my fingers to count on; I could use blocks to see how many to count on.

©Curriculum Associates, LLC   Copying is not permitted.

AT A GLANCE

Students connect subtraction to finding a missing addend.

STEP BY STEP

- Work through the first problem together as a class. Make sure students recognize they are working within a fact family.

- Have students work individually on the remainder of the Explore It problems on this page and then share their responses in groups.

- As students work individually, circulate among them. This is an opportunity to assess student understanding and address misconceptions. Use the Hands-On Activity to help students who are struggling with the concept of fact family.

- Take note of students who are still having difficulty and wait to see if their understanding progresses as they work in their groups.

- After students have completed the Explore It problems, encourage them to share their strategies with the class. Although this lesson focuses on number bonds and counting on, some students may have developed strategies that are mathematically accurate and perhaps more efficient for them. Listen for strategies such as: *I know that 14 is 4 away from 10 so I subtracted 4. Then I subtracted the extra 2 from 10 to get 8. I know that 12 minus 6 is 6. 14 is 2 more than 12 so the answer is 8 since 8 is 2 more than 6.*

Be sure to validate all appropriate strategies.

> **SMP Tip:** Encouraging students to share strategies and then justifying the mathematical accuracy of them (*SMP 3*) not only validates the strategy, but also develops number sense and builds mathematical confidence.

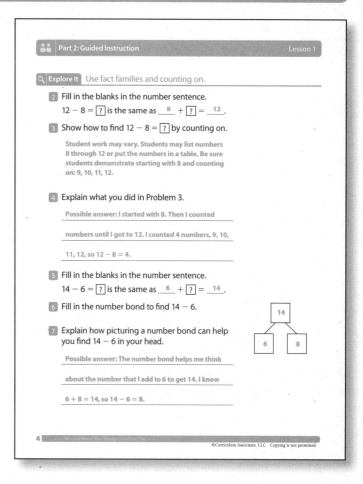

Hands-On Activity

Materials: connecting cubes (a set of 6, a set of 8, and a set of 14, each in a different color) or paper strips (in lengths of 6, 8, and 14 units, each a different color)

- Have students start with the set of 6 and connect the set of 8 cubes to it. Ask them to compare its length to the set of 14. They should notice that both are the same length. Record the number sentence $6 + 8 = 14$. Repeat, beginning with the set of 8 cubes and attaching 6. Ask what they notice. [It is also the same length as the set of 14.] Record the number sentence $8 + 6 = 14$.

- Have students then remove a set of 6 from the set of 14 and ask how many are left. [8] Record the number sentence $14 - 6 = 8$. Repeat, removing 8 from the set of 14.

- Connect the cube models to a number bond and fact family.

AT A GLANCE

Students analyze subtraction strategies to find the most efficient way to mentally calculate.

STEP BY STEP

• Organize students in groups to answer Problems 8 and 9. Walk around to each group, listen to, and join in on discussions at different points. If students respond to the first question by saying they don't agree, ask *How would you keep track of counting on 9? Could you change the order and add on 9 + 2?* Explain whether this makes sense.

• As students answer Problem 9, make sure they justify the strategy they would use. If they respond, "It's easier," ask them to explain what makes it easier.

• Direct each group's attention to Try it Another Way. Ask: *Why do you think Dana first subtracted 3? Why did she subtract 4 next?* Lead students to understand that it's easy to subtract 3 from 13 because it makes a ten. Since you have to subtract a total of 7, you need to subtract 4 more.

• Invite volunteers to come to the board and draw the open number line they used for Problem 11. Have them explain how the number line shows subtracting 7 from 15.

• Ask the class if anyone used different number lines than the ones the volunteers showed. Discuss the similarities and differences in students' strategies.

Note: Mental calculation involving the make a ten strategy is developed more completely in Lesson 3.

Mathematical Discourse

• *Think about the way you used the open number line to solve this problem. How is it like making a ten? Why is it helpful to make a ten?*

   Students may answer that just like adding to make a ten, they can also subtract to make a ten. They may find this helpful if they know all the facts that include subtracting a number from 10.

• *How can you use what is on the open number line to find the addition facts that belong in this fact family?*

   Students should notice that the number they subtracted (subtrahend) added to the difference results in the sum. Reversing the order of the addends results in the same sum.

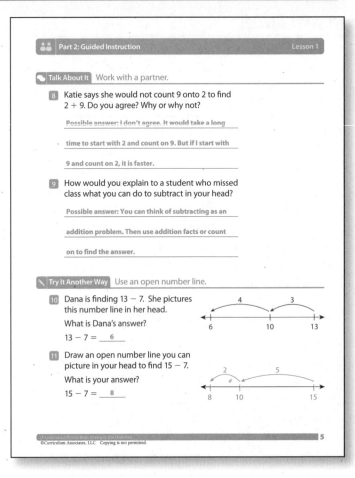

Concept Extension

Have students practice using fact families to develop mental math strategies with more two-digit numbers.

• Start with multiples of 10, such as 50 + 40. Since 5 + 4 = 9, 50 + 40 = 90. Ask students to find 9 − 2 mentally. Then ask them to find 90 − 20 mentally. Have students describe the similarities and differences between these two problems.

• Make number bonds with other multiples of 10. Have students write addition and subtraction number sentences to show these fact families.

• For further extension, apply these strategies to other numbers. For example, 2 + 5 = 7, so 32 + 5 = 37. Or 8 − 5 = 3 so 28 − 5 = 23. Have students practice these pairs of problems using number bonds on paper. Then ask them to try to do the calculations in their head. Guide them to picture the number bond in their head to help them do the calculations.

©Curriculum Associates, LLC   Copying is not permitted.

AT A GLANCE

Students demonstrate their understanding of fact families and counting on. They identify and justify an effective strategy to use in solving a number sentence.

STEP BY STEP

- Discuss each Connect It problem as a class using the discussion points outlined below:

Explain:

- Ask students to explain the error Tia made. [She rearranged the 8 and the 5 into a subtraction sentence rather than subtracting 5 from 13.] *Why do you think she may have made this error?* [She doesn't know that there are only 3 numbers in any fact family.]

- Invite volunteers to come to the board and write the facts belonging to the fact family of each of the number sentences given. Emphasize that *two* of the same numbers are used in each fact family, but *all three* are not the same numbers.

Compare:

- For Problem 13, make sure students recognize that counting on by more than three or four is time consuming and can lead to errors by asking: *What might happen if you tried to count on 8 times?* [I might lose track of my counts so I'd have to start over; I might get mixed up and end up on the wrong number; etc.]

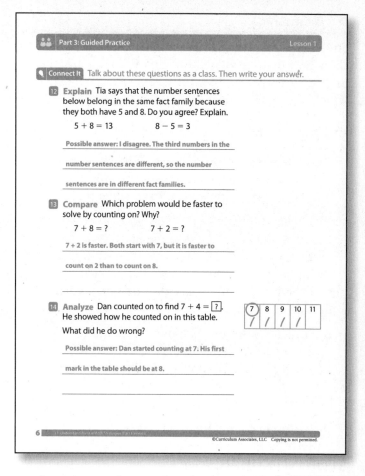

Analyze:

- To help students make sense of the error that was made, have them draw a row of 11 squares (or any easy to draw shapes) on paper or individual white boards.

- Ask students what number they are counting on from. [7] Instruct students to circle this number of shapes. Explain that this is the number they start with; these shapes have already been counted.

- Have students locate the 7th shape. Ask: *Is it in the group that has already been counted or the group that still needs to be counted?* [already counted] *What number should I start counting at?* [8]

AT A GLANCE

Students demonstrate their use of mental strategies to show how to solve an addition and subtraction sentence in different ways. They explain reasons for choosing which strategies to use.

STEP BY STEP

- Draw students' attention to the two number sentences they have to solve. Remind them to think about what strategies work best for them when completing this task.

- Direct students to complete the Put It Together tasks on their own. Tell students that they are free to use the open space on the page to make drawings or models that they may have thought about when finding each response.

- As students work on their own, walk around to assess their progress and understanding, to answer their questions, and to give additional support, if needed.

- If time permits, have students share the strategies they used in completing this task.

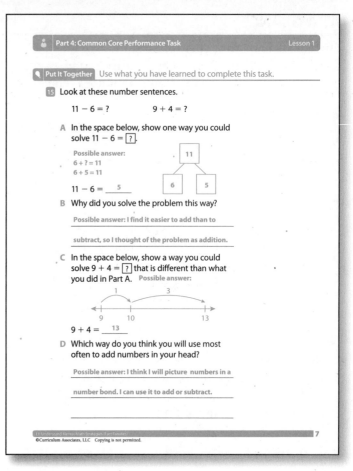

SCORING RUBRICS

A and B

Points	Expectations
2	The student correctly solves the number sentence using a mathematically sound strategy. The justification for strategy choice is reasonable.
1	The student correctly solves the number sentence, but the strategy demonstration or justification is incomplete or weak.
0	The student's answer to the number sentence and use of strategy are incorrect.

C and D

Points	Expectations
2	The student correctly solves the number sentence using a different strategy than part A. The justification for strategy choice is reasonable.
1	The student correctly solves the number sentence but uses the same strategy as part A or provides weak justification of strategy choice.
0	The student was not able to accurately complete the number sentence and explain a strategy choice.

©Curriculum Associates, LLC   Copying is not permitted.

Intervention Activity

Model a fact family

Materials: one paper plate with lines dividing it in thirds, a set of counters (beans, uncooked pasta, etc.), and sets of number bond cards with one number missing and written on the back

- Students place counters in the plate to model the numbers given in the number bond. If the top number of the bond is given, they place that number of counters in the top section. Students then move the number of counters that belong in one of the lower sections to model the subtraction. What remains in the top section belongs in the other bottom section.

- If both bottom numbers are showing, students place the counters in the two bottom sections and then combine them into the top section.

- Once students find the missing number, they should record the fact in the number bond, check the answer, and then model and write all the facts belonging to that family.

On-Level Activity

Number line facts

Materials: counters, missing addend number sentence cards (for example, $3 +$ _____ $= 12$)

- Provide each student with a number sentence card. Draw a number line from 0 to 20 on the board, and ask students to copy it on a piece of paper or individual whiteboard.

- Each student uses the counters to model their number sentence on the number line. They put counters on the given addend and sum, and then determine and label the jump (the missing addend). They record the number sentence below the number line.

- Students check with a partner to make sure the number sentences are correct. Then each student records the remaining addition and subtraction sentences to complete the fact family.

Challenge Activity

Mixed up cards

Materials: a deck of playing cards with face cards removed or cards with numbers 1–9 printed on them (Activity Sheet 1, page 308); cards with the symbols $+$, $=$, $-$, and $\square$

- Students randomly select two number cards. They arrange them with the symbol cards to either make an addition or subtraction sentence (9 and 6 could be $9 + 6 = \square$ or $9 - 6 = \square$). Some students may want to challenge themselves to make a missing addend number sentence ($6 + \square = 9$). Students then write all the other facts that belong in that fact family. If students began with the addition, they should rearrange the cards to show related subtraction facts and record the facts in that fact family. If they began with subtraction, they rearrange the cards to show related addition facts and record the facts in that fact family.

Optional: Students may want to work in pairs. Each student picks two numbers and uses the symbol cards to make a number sentence. The partner has to write all the facts in that fact family. The one who is done first gets a point. Play several times. The player with the most points wins.

©Curriculum Associates, LLC   Copying is not permitted.

Solve One-Step Word Problems

LESSON OBJECTIVES

- Analyze one-step problems to determine the operation needed to solve.
- Apply the use of fact families as a strategy to solve one-step problems and build number sense.
- Interpret models that represent a one-step problem.

PREREQUISITE SKILLS

- Add and subtract within 20.
- Use fact families fluently.
- Understand addition and subtraction situations involving adding to, taking from, putting together, taking apart, and comparing.

VOCABULARY

There is no new vocabulary. Review the following term.

one-step problem: A problem that requires a single step to solve.

THE LEARNING PROGRESSION

In Grade 1, students solved word problems by connecting pictures and number sentences to a physical model that represents a problem situation.

In Grade 2, students represent a problem using pictures and abstract diagrams and write a number sentence that models the situation. **In this lesson,** fact families become a vehicle for finding an unknown as students recognize the relationship between the difference in a subtraction sentence and an unknown addend. By identifying the whole and the parts in visual models, students are preparing to solve problems involving two-digit numbers and two-step problems that come later in Grade 2.

In Grade 3 and beyond, students will use these skills to represent problems in varied ways. This will prepare students for the increasingly complex problems they will face in the future as well as enable them to apply these strategies to solve problems with multiplication and division.

Ready *Teacher Toolbox*   *Teacher-Toolbox.com*

	Prerequisite Skills	2.OA.A.1
Ready Lessons	✓ ✓	✓
Tools for Instruction	✓ ✓	✓ ✓
Interactive Tutorials		✓ ✓

CCSS Focus

2.OA.A.1 Use addition and subtraction within 100 to solve one- and two-step word problems involving situations of adding to, taking from, putting together, taking apart, and comparing, with unknowns in all positions, e.g., by using drawings and equations with a symbol for the unknown number to represent the problem.

ADDITIONAL STANDARDS: **2.OA.B.2, 2.NBT.B.5** *(see page A42 for full text.)*

STANDARDS FOR MATHEMATICAL PRACTICE: **SMP 1, 2, 3, 4, 5, 7** *(see page A9 for full text.)*

©Curriculum Associates, LLC   Copying is not permitted.

Two Unknown Addends

Objective: Solve a word problem involving a put together situation in which both addends are unknown.

Materials for each student:
- Different-color counters

Overview

Students are given a put together addition word problem in which both addends are unknown. They discover that more than one answer is possible and make the connection between related number sentence solutions and fact families.

Step by Step (15–20 minutes)

1 Pose the problem.

- Provide students with counters in two different colors.

- Pose this open-ended problem. Dan has 14 toy cars. Some are racecars and some are not racecars. How many racecars does Dan have?

2 Organize the counters.

- Encourage students to think about what they would do to decide how many racecars Dan has. Ask them to organize their counters to solve the problem. Students should put together some combination of colored counters for a total of 14.

3 Share ideas.

- Invite students to share their thinking with the class. List the various combinations of 14 that they find.

- Ask questions such as: *How did you know to put 8 and 6 together? What did you do to find that there are 5 racecars?* As students describe their thinking, record the following on the board: racecars + not racecars = 14; not racecars + racecars = 14; 14 − not racecars = racecars; 14 − racecars = not racecars.

4 Relate the problem situation to fact families.

- Discuss how the number sentences on the board are like the fact families students studied in Lesson 1.

- Tell students that in this lesson, they will learn how to use different models and both addition and subtraction to solve word problems.

AT A GLANCE

Students explore one-step problems by examining a bar model and an open number sentence.

STEP BY STEP

- Tell students that this page will help them understand one-step problems by organizing the information from the problem in a diagram.

- Have students read the problem at the top of the page. Ask a volunteer to tell what they know based on the information given.

- Work through the Explore It questions as a class. Make sure students understand that the top box in the bar model shows the whole and the bottom boxes are the parts that make up the whole.

- Once students have filled in the model, ask: *What is the part shown by the 9?* [the number of grapes Seth ate] *What operation will you use to find the missing part?* Some students may say *subtraction*, while others respond that they can find out what to add to 9 to get 15. Use the first discourse question to reinforce this concept.

> **SMP Tip:** Ask students to explain why the question mark is used to represent the unknown. You may want to examine other ways to show the unknown, such as using a box or a blank line. This prepares students for the concept of a variable. (*SMP 2*)

Real-World Connection

Have students look at the models on pages 8 and 9. Ask students to think of a real-life situation that could be answered using one of model (like the problem about Seth's grapes). Do some examples together as a class. Then have students write a real-world problem that can be solved using one of the models on page 9. Students can work individually to write their problems. Then have students share their problem with a partner. Have the partner set up the model for the question they receive from their partner. The pairs of students should then discuss the models with each other. Have a few students share their problem and have the partner share the model he or she used to think about the question.

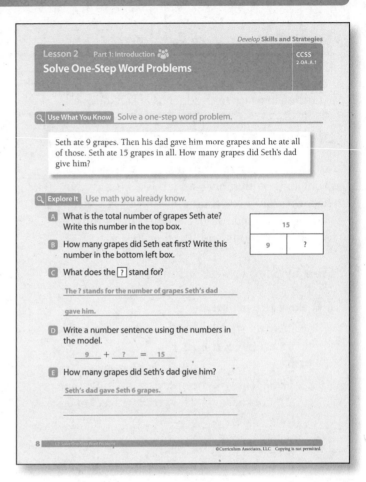

Mathematical Discourse

- *Did you use addition or subtraction to solve the problem? Why?*

  Students' responses should indicate an understanding that either operation or any of the four number sentences in the fact family can be used. Discuss the strategies they used to find the value of the ? in the problem.

©Curriculum Associates, LLC   Copying is not permitted.

AT A GLANCE

Students use varied models to represent a word problem and analyze the three possible positions of an unknown.

STEP BY STEP

- Ask students to look at the models in Find Out More. Ask: *Where are the parts in each model?* [the two boxes at the bottom] *Where is the whole?* [the box or number at the top] Encourage students to describe how each model shows addition and how it shows subtraction. Use the Hands-On Activity to reinforce the concept of part and whole.

- Read and discuss the possible positions for the question mark. You may want to use the Hands-On Activity to physically model each of these situations.

- Ask students to work in pairs and think of a simple problem for each position of the unknown. Encourage students to share their problems. Analyze each one as a class to ensure it is asking for the part stated.

- Have student pairs read and solve the Reflect problem. Discuss how this problem is the same and how it is different from the problem on the previous page.

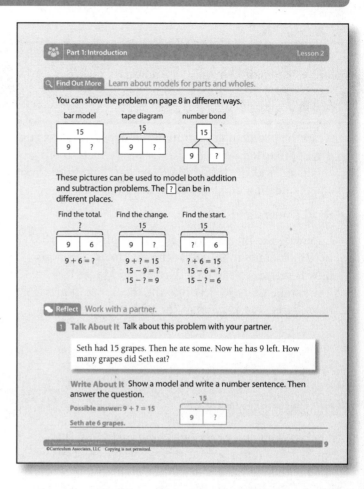

Hands-On Activity

Use physical models to understand visual models.

Materials: 1 set of 3 rectangles (one 9" × 3", and two 4½" × 3") cut from construction paper for each student; 15 counters per student

- Place the two small rectangles below the large one to show the bar model. Remove the large rectangle to show the tape diagram. Fold the large rectangle in half to show the number bond.

- Use the counters to model each situation, moving them as needed to show or find the unknown.

Mathematical Discourse

- *How are the models on this page alike? How are they different?*

   Listen for responses such as: They are the same because the whole is at the top and the two parts are under it. They are different because some are put together next to each other and one is spread apart.

- *How is finding the unknown part like using fact families?*

   You can either add the parts to get the whole or subtract the known part from the whole to get the unknown part.

AT A GLANCE

Students use a picture to model a one-step problem and record what is known and not known.

STEP BY STEP

- Read the problem at the top of the page as a class and direct attention to Model It. Ask students to tell if this is a "find the total," "find the part," or "find the start" question and why. [find the part]

- Read Understand It.

- Replicate the picture from Picture It on the board. Invite students to tell what the picture shows and how it relates to the tape diagram in Model It. Encourage them to describe the relationship between boys, girls, and players in the problem.

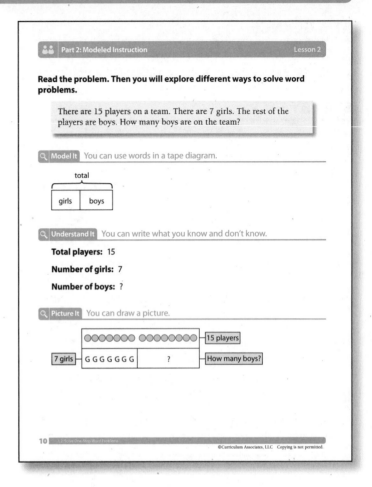

ELL Support

Some students may struggle comprehending the language used in a word problem. You may want to pair an English language learner with a proficient reader to complete this task and the ones that follow. You may also want to type or write the problem on a piece of paper so that each sentence is on a separate line. Cut out each sentence and have the students match the sentence to the appropriate part of the model, then fill in the blanks:

_____ are on the team.

_____ are girls.

_____ are boys.

Mathematical Discourse

- *How does writing what you know help you solve the problem?*

  Writing what you know helps you decide what are the parts and what is the whole. Then you know what you need to find to solve the problem.

©Curriculum Associates, LLC   Copying is not permitted.

AT A GLANCE

Students revisit the problem on page 10 by writing number sentences to represent what is shown in the models. They then solve a problem using both addition and subtraction.

STEP BY STEP

- Read Connect It as a class. Make sure students understand that the questions refer to the problem on page 10.

- For Problem 3, make sure students understand that both of the number sentences are ways to show the problem on the previous page.

- As students complete Problem 4, allow them to refer back to the picture on the previous page, if necessary, to represent each part accurately.

- Tell students that they may use a picture or other model to help solve the Try It problem. Have students explain the thinking they used in solving the problem.

SMP Tip: Record each response to Problem 7 on the board and connect the pictures/models used to form a number sentence. Make sure both addition and subtraction models and number sentences are represented. Connecting a number sentence to a situation and a visual model prepares students to solve increasingly difficult problems and problems that may arise in their everyday lives. *(SMP 4)*

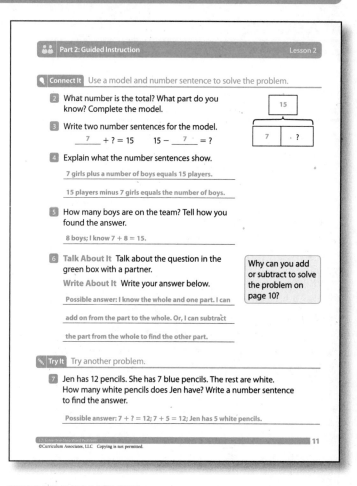

TRY IT SOLUTION

7 *Solution*: 7; Students should write a number sentence showing the problem:
$7 + ? = 12$ or $12 - 7 = ?$

ERROR ALERT: Students who wrote $12 + 7 = 19$ added the numbers shown in the problem to find a whole rather than finding an unknown part.

AT A GLANCE

Students solve a word problem using a picture model and record what is known and not known.

STEP BY STEP

- Read the problem at the top of the page as a class. Help students connect the information in the problem to the abbreviated version in Understand It. Discuss that this is a comparison problem. The small and big bags are both wholes. Explain that students are not trying to find one of two parts of a single whole, but the part of the whole big bag that makes it a different number of balls than the small bag.

- Examine and ask students to explain Picture It. Make sure students understand that in the picture, the 3 "fewer" circles shown are not soccer balls. These are only images (or your thinking) of the number that would need to be added to the small bag to make it equal to the number in the big bag.

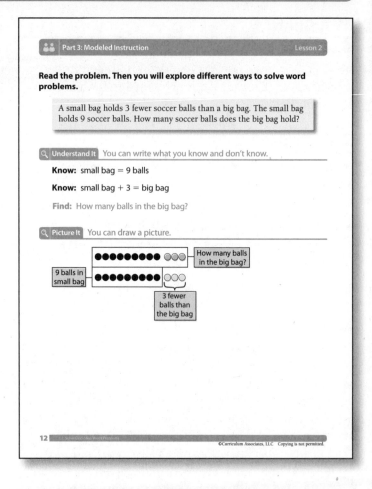

Visual Model

A picture graph can be used to model the concept of more and fewer.

- Replicate the graph below on the board, oriented either horizontally or vertically.

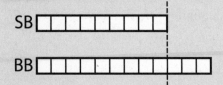

- Compare by asking questions that use the words more and fewer, such as: *How many more are in BB than SB?* [3]

- Use a ruler to indicate where the SB and BB are equal as shown. Discuss that since they don't have the same amount, one must have *more* and one must have *fewer* items.

Mathematical Discourse

- *How does the picture help you compare the balls in the big and small bags?*

  Students should recognize that the picture shows 9 balls in the small bag lined up with the 9 balls in the big bag and that "3 fewer" in small bag means "3 more" in the big bag.

©Curriculum Associates, LLC Copying is not permitted.

AT A GLANCE

Students revisit the problem on page 12, writing a number sentence to model the situation. Then students solve a one-step word problem involving an unknown.

STEP BY STEP

- Tell students that Connect It will help them learn how to write number sentences for the problem on page 12.

- Help students understand the logic involved in Problem 8. You may wish to use a picture or physical model to emphasize how the antonyms *fewer* and *more* are used in each sentence to describe the same model or situation.

- Refer to Visual Model on the previous page to reinforce the concepts *fewer* and *more*. Discuss that if BB had the same number as SB they would each have 9 so BB has *more* than SB. Then move the ruler to the right to line up with the number in BB. Explain that if they both had the *same* number as BB, they would each have 12, so SB has *fewer* than BB.

- Have students discuss their answers to Problem 10. Make sure they connect the number sentence to the logic described in Problem 8.

- Have students discuss Talk About It in pairs and then write an answer using their own words. Suggest that they think about how a fact family can help answer the question.

- Remind students that for the Try It problem, they can use a picture or physical model to help them make sense of the problem, but they should also write a number sentence and show work.

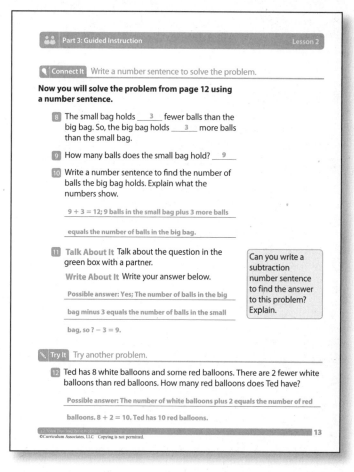

TRY IT SOLUTION

12 *Solution:* The number of white balloons plus 2 equals the number of red balloons. $8 + 2 = 10$.

ERROR ALERT: Students who answer 6 subtracted 2 from 8.

Mathematical Discourse

- *Meg said that there were 6 soccer balls in the big bin. What do you think she did wrong?*

  Students should note that $9 - 3 = 6$. They should realize that the word *fewer* refers to subtraction and that Meg just subtracted the two numbers shown.

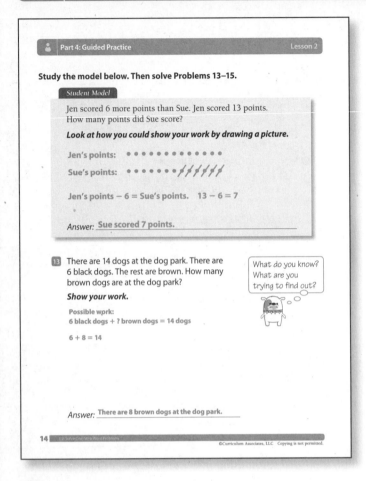

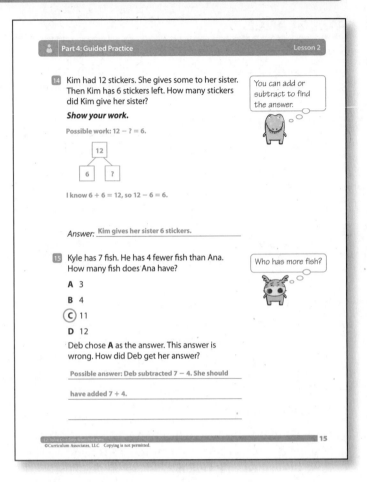

AT A GLANCE

Students model and solve one-step problems involving addition and subtraction.

STEP BY STEP

- Ask students to solve the problems individually and show all their work, including the number sentences they wrote. Encourage students to describe their thinking.

- When students have completed each problem, have them Pair/Share to discuss their solutions with a partner.

SOLUTIONS

Ex A picture model and a number sentence are used as examples for solving this problem. Students may also act it out using counters.

13 *Answer:* There are 8 brown dogs at the park; Students may act out the problem by drawing a picture or using any other model. Students may also write a subtraction number sentence: $14 - 6 = 8$. **(DOK 2)**

14 *Answer:* Kim gave her sister 6 stickers. See possible work above. Students may also model the problem by drawing a picture. **(DOK 2)**

15 *Answer:* **C**; Kyle has 4 fewer than Ana, so Ana has 4 more than Kyle. $7 + 4 = 11$. **(DOK 3)**

Explain to students why the other two choices are not correct:

B is not correct because 4 is how many more fish Ana has.

D is not correct because $7 + 4 = 11$ not 12. **(DOK 3)**

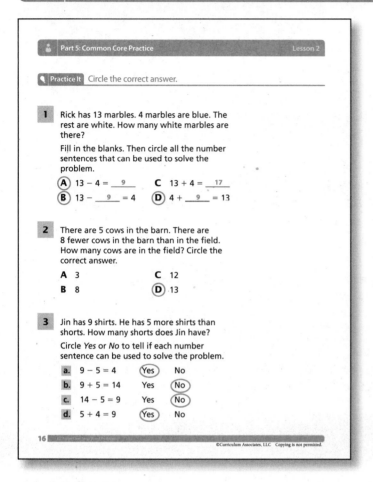

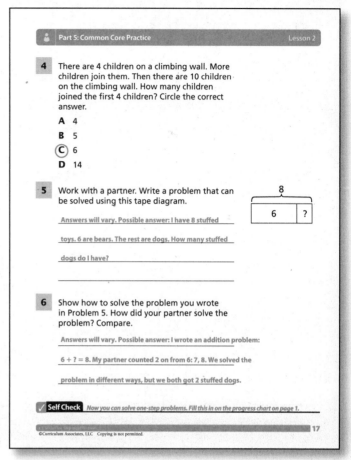

AT A GLANCE

Students use addition and subtraction to solve one-step word problems that might appear on a mathematics test.

STEP BY STEP

- First, tell students they will use addition and subtraction to solve one-step word problems. Then have students read the directions and answer the questions independently.

- After students have completed the Common Core Practice problems, review and discuss correct answers.

SOLUTIONS

1 *Solution:* **A**, **B**, and **D**; 13 is the total, so subtracting 4 blue gives the number of white marbles (**A**).

13 is the total, so subtracting the number of white marbles gives 4 blue (**B**).

There are 4 blue marbles, so combining them with the number of white marbles gives a total of 13 marbles (**D**). (*DOK 3*)

2 *Solution:* **D**; Since there are 8 fewer cows in the barn than in the field, there are 8 more in the field. $8 + 5 = 13$. (*DOK 2*)

3 *Solution:* Yes, No, No, Yes; $9 - 5 = 4$ (**a.**) and $5 + 4 = 9$ (**d.**) are in the same fact family. (*DOK 2*)

4 *Solution:* **C**; 4 children + more children = 10 children; $4 + 6 = 10$. (*DOK 2*)

5 *Solution:* See sample problem above; Problem should reflect that 8 is the total, 6 is a known part, and there is an unknown part. (*DOK 3*)

6 *Solution:* See sample solution above. (*DOK 3*)

Assessment and Remediation

- There are 11 children riding bikes. Some children ride home. Now there are 7 children riding bikes. Ask students to find the number of children who ride home. [4]

- For students who are still struggling, use the chart below to guide remediation.

- After providing remediation, check students' understanding using the following problem: Sue finds 13 socks under her bed. 5 socks are blue. The rest are black. How many black socks did she find? [8]

If the error is . . .	Students may . . .	To remediate . . .
18	have added the given numbers.	Provide students with counters to act out the problem. Guide them to see that when some children go home, subtraction is involved.
5	have subtracted incorrectly.	Help the student use a counting backward strategy or fact families. Since $11 - \rule{1cm}{0.15mm} = 7, 7 + \rule{1cm}{0.15mm} = 11$. Encourage students to think of making a ten to help solve mentally. ($7 + 3 = 10$ and one more is 11 so $7 + 4 = 11$.)
any other number	have subtracted incorrectly or misrepresented the problem.	As you read each sentence in the problem, have students describe what the sentence says and model it with counters or a picture. Write the number sentence and compare it to the sentence the student wrote. Check for computational accuracy.

Hands-On Activity

Use counters to solve a one-step word problem.

Materials: concrete objects to use as counters

- Provide each student with 15 counters and pose this problem. Mom buys some apples to make a pie. She uses 8 apples for the pie. There are 5 apples left. How many apples did Mom buy?

- Guide students to recognize that they are trying to find the total number of apples. Help them organize the counters in a group of 8 (apples that were used) and a group of 5 (apples left). Invite students to describe their thinking and solution. Encourage students to think about the problem as $8 + 5 = [13]$ or as $[13] - 8 = 5$.

Challenge Activity

Write one-step problems.

Challenge students to write problems that arise in their daily lives that involve using one step to solve. Tell them to write at least one problem where the unknown is at the beginning, at least one where the unknown is the change or part, and at least one where the unknown is the result. Encourage them to write at least one problem involving a comparison.

When completed, students can exchange and solve each others' problems.

©Curriculum Associates, LLC   Copying is not permitted.

Lesson 3 (Student Book pages 18–23)

Understand Mental Math Strategies (Make a Ten)

LESSON OBJECTIVES

- Demonstrate the mental process involved in the make a 10 strategy when adding and subtracting numbers within 20.

- Interpret models that represent the reasoning behind the make a 10 strategy.

PREREQUISITE SKILLS

In order to be proficient with the concept/skills in this lesson, students should:

- Compose and decompose tens and ones in two-digit numbers less than 20.

- Add numbers within 20.

- Break apart numbers as the sum of two other numbers.

- Understand how a model represents a numerical situation.

VOCABULARY

There is no new vocabulary.

THE LEARNING PROGRESSION

In Grade 1, students model the make a 10 strategy using physical models such as connecting cubes and tiles.

In Grade 2, students extend those models to more abstract visual representations, such as an open number line and a ladder model. **In this lesson,** students build on the foundations laid in Grade 1 for applying mental strategies to addition and subtraction within 20. Students refine their understanding of the commutative and associative properties. For example, they realize that when solving the addition 4 + 9, they can start with the 9 since it is closer to 10 and then add 4. This mental flexibility will assist students later in grade 2 as they work with 2- and 3-digit numbers.

In Grade 3, students gain fluency with addition and subtraction of numbers within 1,000. They use the make a 10 strategy with number lines as a way to help attain this fluency. Students also apply what they have learned about the commutative property of addition to multiplication.

⬛ Ready *Teacher Toolbox*   Teacher-Toolbox.com

	Prerequisite Skills	2.OA.B.2
Ready Lessons	✓ ✓ ✓	✓
Tools for Instruction		✓
Interactive Tutorials	✓ ✓	

CCSS Focus

2.OA.B.2 Fluently add and subtract within 20 using mental strategies. By end of Grade 2, know from memory all sums of two one-digit numbers.

STANDARDS FOR MATHEMATICAL PRACTICE: *SMP 1, 3, 4, 5, 7, 8* (*see page A9 for full text*)

©Curriculum Associates, LLC   Copying is not permitted.

Partners of Ten

Objective: Find all the combinations of 1-digit whole numbers that have a sum of 10.

Materials for each student:
• Pencil and paper or whiteboards and markers

Overview

Students record all the possible combinations of one-digit whole numbers that have a sum of 10. They organize the number sentences to check that they have found all possible combinations and to discuss the patterns they see.

Step by Step (20–30 minutes)

1 **Write all the partners of ten.**

• Ask students to write all the ways that two numbers can be combined to make ten.

2 **Organize the number sentences.**

• Invite volunteers to name one or two of the number sentences they wrote. Record the number sentences on the board in the order shown below.

0 + 10 = 10	10 + 0 = 10
1 + 9 = 10	9 + 1 = 10
2 + 8 = 10	8 + 2 = 10
3 + 7 = 10	7 + 3 = 10
4 + 6 = 10	6 + 4 = 10
5 + 5 = 10	5 + 5 = 10

• Discuss how organizing the number sentences like this can help to check that all possible number sentences are included.

3 **Talk about patterns.**

• Talk about the patterns students see in the list of tens facts on the left. Ask: *How does the first addend change as you go down the list? How does the second addend change?* Each first addend is 1 more than the one before it. Each second addend is 1 less than the one before it.

• Now ask the same questions about the list on the right. It's the opposite. Each first addend is 1 less than the one before it. Each second addend is 1 more than the one before it.

• Ask: *How can finding a pattern help you remember the tens facts? Give an example.* If you know that 5 + 5 is 10, then just take 1 away from one 5 and add it to the other 5 to get 4 + 6.

• You may want students to use cubes to model this thinking. They should notice that the initial number of cubes does not change. No cubes are added or subtracted; they are just rearranged.

©Curriculum Associates, LLC   Copying is not permitted.

AT A GLANCE

Students explore breaking an addend apart in order to make a 10 to add.

STEP BY STEP

- Introduce the question at the top of the page. Allow students to generate ideas of the ways in which they mentally compute.

- Draw attention to the number bonds at the top of the page. Encourage students to describe what they know about number bonds.

- Read the first addition sentence of the Think section together. Make sure to emphasize that the 10 frames show a way to organize 9 + 7. Use the Hands-On Activity to help students solidify the concept.

  Note: The process shown here is an application of the associative property of addition. That property will be explored in more depth later in the lesson.

- Use the Mathematical Discourse questions to promote flexible thinking and the use of the commutative property of addition.

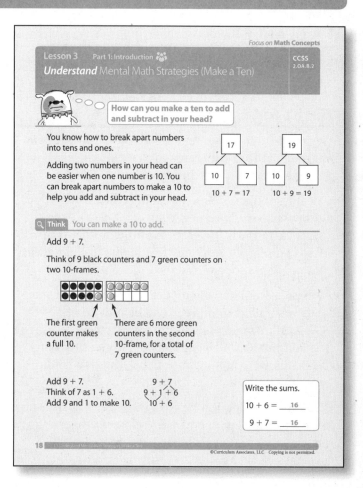

Hands-On Activity

Use connecting cubes to understand making tens.

Materials: connecting cubes

- Distribute 20 cubes to each student. Ask students to make a bar of 9 and a bar of 7 cubes. Ask: *How can you make the 9 a 10?* [Add 1 cube.] *Where can we get the 1 cube?* [from the bar of 7 cubes] Once again, emphasize that students are reorganizing the cubes, not adding to or taking from the total number of cubes they had at the beginning.

- Instruct students to take 1 cube from the bar of 7 and add it to the bar of 9 and ask how many are in each bar now. Connect the process and outcome to the model and diagram on the page in the student book.

Mathematical Discourse

- *Why is it easy to add numbers when one of them is a ten?*

  Students may respond that you can think of the number that is not the ten as a teen number, like $10 + 6 = $ six*teen*. They might also find it easy to add 10 plus a one-digit number because they know how to break the numbers 11–19 into tens and ones.

- *When adding 9 + 7, why does it make sense to start with the 9 instead of the 7?*

  Nine is closer to 10 and you only have to add 1 to it to get 10.

- *Could we start with the 7 first? Why? What would it look like?*

  Yes, because the order of the addends does not change the sum; $7 + 6 + 3 = 16$.

AT A GLANCE

Students explore the make a 10 strategy as it applies to subtraction.

STEP BY STEP

- Write the number sentence from the Think section on the board. Ask students to share strategies they know to calculate the difference.

- Put the subtraction into a real life context with the following: Sam has a new pack of 10 baseball cards and 4 extra cards. He gives his little brother 6 cards. How could he do this? Allow students to share ideas and strategies they would use.

- Complete the 10-frame model as a class. Make sure students understand that 6 can be broken into $4 + 2$, allowing them to subtract 4 from 14 and then the additional 2. Relate the model to the situation posed above. You may want to use the Hands-On activity to reinforce this concept.

- Read the Reflect question with the class. Ask students to discuss ideas with a partner before writing an answer. Invite students to share responses with the class, using a model to justify their reasoning.

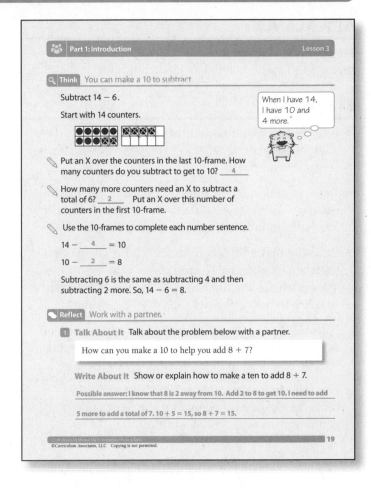

Hands-On Activity

Use connecting cubes to understand subtraction.

Materials: connecting cubes

- Distribute 10 each of two different-color cubes. Have students make a bar of 10 with one color and connect 4 of the other color onto the bar of 10.

- Ask students to use the cubes to show the thinking involved in making a 10 to subtract 6 from 14 and explain to a partner what was done.

ELL Support

During whole group discussions or when giving oral directions, assist students by either writing the given numbers on the board or repeating the numbers in the students' native language.

Mathematical Discourse

- *How is the make a 10 strategy for subtraction like counting back?*

  You count back from the number you start with until you get to ten and then count back some more until you have subtracted the entire number.

- *Think about the Reflect question. What are two ways you can make a 10 to find the sum?*

  $8 + 7 = 8 + 2 + 5$; or $7 + 8 = 7 + 3 + 5$

- *Which way do you think is easier?*

  Answers will vary. Listen for accurate mathematical reasoning.

©Curriculum Associates, LLC   Copying is not permitted.

AT A GLANCE

Students model the make a 10 strategy for addition and subtraction on an open number line.

STEP BY STEP

- Work through Problem 2 with the class. Ask students how the numbers in $8 + 8 = 16$ were broken out to get the two number sentences in Problem 2. Use the Concept Extension to reinforce the properties of operations.

- Tell students they will have time to work individually on the remainder of the Explore It problems on this page and then share their responses in groups.

- As students work individually, circulate among them. This is an opportunity to assess student understanding and address student misconceptions. Use the Mathematical Discourse questions to stimulate thinking. Relate the third question to the Hands-On activity in the previous lesson.

- Take note of students who are still having difficulty and wait to see if their understanding progresses as they work in their groups during the next part of the lesson.

> **SMP Tip:** Formal exploration of the associative property validates the structure informally used by students and provides a foundation for future applications of the property. (*SMP 7*)

Mathematical Discourse

- *When subtracting 7 from 13, how do you know where to begin on the number line?*

    Start at the 13 because it is the largest number. When you subtract you have to move backward.

- *How did you choose the first number you subtracted from 13? Where did you get it?*

    I subtracted 3 first since $13 - 3 = 10$. I took 3 from the 7 that I need to subtract.

- *How do you know how many more to subtract?*

    Since $3 + 4 = 7$, I have to subtract 4 more after subtracting 3 so that I subtract a total of 7.

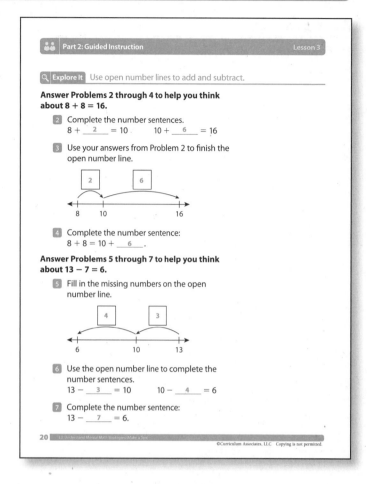

Concept Extension

Explore an application of the associative property of addition.

- Write the expression $7 + 5$ on the board. Instruct students to model the addition with cubes or 10 frames using the make a 10 strategy.

- Invite a volunteer to explain his or her thinking and record it on the board. Example: Student says, "I broke the 5 into 3 and 2 to add to 7." Write: $7 + 5 = 7 + (3 + 2)$. Student says, "I added the 3 to the 7 to make 10 and then added the other 2." Write: $(7 + 3) + 2$.

- Discuss the function of the parentheses and the way the addends didn't change, just the way they are grouped.

AT A GLANCE

Students analyze the make a 10 strategy and then represent it using a ladder model.

STEP BY STEP

- Instruct students to work in groups to complete Problems 8–10. Walk around to each group, listen to, and join in on discussions at different points.

- As students work on Problem 10, encourage them to use number sentences to show what they did, but allow them to draw a picture or 10 frames to help them articulate their mental process.

- Direct the group's attention to Try it Another Way. Have them discuss the model with a partner. As students share their interpretations, ask them to write + 2 and + 4 next to the arrows on the left and − 4 and − 2 next to the arrows on the right. Connect this model to the open number line. Use the Mathematical Discourse question to expand students' reasoning.

- Replicate the ladder model on the board and ask students to complete it for number sentences such as 7 + 8 and 9 + 5 and then model each inverse.

> **SMP Tip:** Encourage students to compare consistencies in patterns by following the structure of the Concept Extension, but beginning with a different set of numbers like 8 + 8 = 10 + ____ . (SMP 8)

Mathematical Discourse

- *How are the two ladder models the same? How are they different? Explain.*

  The numbers you add or subtract are the same but are in a different order (+ 2 is first in the addition, − 4 is first in the subtraction). Students should notice that since the two number sentences are related (fact families) one adds 6 while the other subtracts 6. In both cases, 6 is broken into 2 and 4. In the addition 8 is 2 away from 10 and in the subtraction 14 is 4 away from 10. Some students may notice that since 14 is 4 away from 10, after adding 2 in the first problem, you then add the 4. The process is reversed for subtraction.

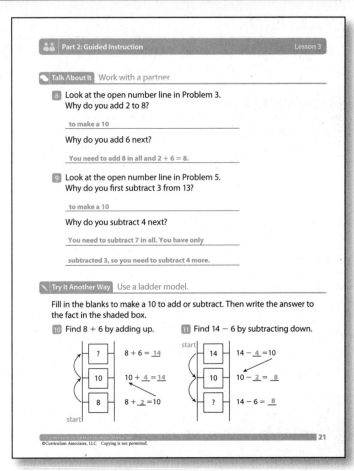

Concept Extension

Help students recognize patterns in addition and subtraction.

- Write the following on the board:

9 + 9 = 10 + ____	17 − 8 = 10 − ____
9 + 8 = 10 + ____	16 − 8 = 10 − ____
9 + 7 = 10 + ____	15 − 8 = 10 − ____
9 + 6 = 10 + ____	14 − 8 = 10 − ____

- Ask students to fill in the blanks and describe the patterns they notice. Accept all responses, but then lead students to connect a pattern to the make a 10 strategy. Help them notice that the number they write is what is left over after making a 10. Relate the decreasing pattern of the second addend in the additions, the decreasing pattern of the minuend in the subtractions, and the pattern found among the number in the blanks.

©Curriculum Associates, LLC   Copying is not permitted.

AT A GLANCE

Students demonstrate their understanding of the make a 10 strategy. They compare and analyze applications of the strategy.

STEP BY STEP

- Discuss each Connect It problem as a class using the discussion points outlined below.

Demonstrate:

- Allow students to work with a partner to share strategies. Encourage them to explain their thinking using words, numbers, and/or pictures. Have students work together to make their explanation clear.

- As students share their strategies with the class, ask questions like: *Why did you begin with the 6? Why did you begin with the 9? Why did you break the number up the way you did? How is adding 6 + 4 + 5 the same as adding 6 + 9? How is it like adding 10 + 5?* Listen for responses that demonstrate students' understanding of the commutative and associative properties of addition. Help students refine their responses to clearly articulate the math concepts.

Compare:

- Ask two volunteers (one male and one female) to come to the front of the class. Ask the female student to explain to the class Greta's strategy in words and/or pictures. Then ask the male student to explain Chuck's strategy in words and/or pictures.

- As students are sharing the strategies, ask questions such as: *Why doesn't it matter that Greta and Chuck broke apart the numbers differently?* [The order and grouping in addition doesn't matter.] *Why do you think they chose to break apart the numbers the way they did?* [People have their own way of thinking. They use the strategy that makes sense to them.]

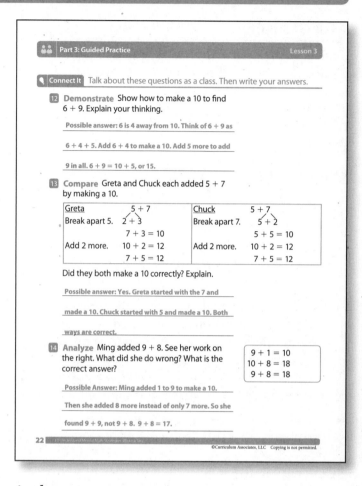

Analyze:

- If students are unable to identify the error, model the situation with 10 frames.

- Ask: *Why do you think Ming made the error she did?* Make sure students realize that when making a 10, the amount added to the first number to make it a 10 must be taken away from the second number. You may want to model with connecting cubes by adding 1 to make a 10 and then adding the additional 8. Ming actually adds 9 to 9.

AT A GLANCE

Students demonstrate their understanding of the make a 10 strategy by selecting numbers for which the strategy can be applied for addition. Students are then asked to model the strategy for the addition, write a related subtraction sentence, and model making a 10 to subtract.

STEP BY STEP

- Direct students to complete the Put It Together task on their own.

- Read the directions with students and make sure they understand each part of the task before proceeding.

- As students work on their own, walk around to assess their progress and understanding, to answer their questions, and to give additional support, if needed. Some students may choose numbers with a sum greater than 20. You may want to allow this if you feel students are capable of completing the task.

- If time permits, ask students to share the numbers they chose and justify their choices.

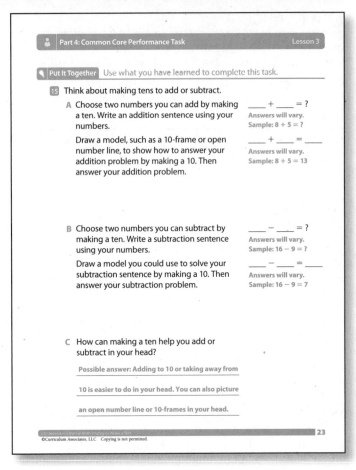

SCORING RUBRICS

A

Points	Expectations
2	The student selects two numbers with a sum greater than 10 and uses a model to accurately represent the make a 10 strategy.
1	Either the number selection or modeling is correct, but not both.
0	Both the number selection and modeling are inaccurate.

B

Points	Expectations
2	The student accurately writes and models the related subtraction.
1	Either the number selection or modeling is correct, but not both.
0	The student was not able to complete the number sentence correctly, and the modeling was inaccurate.

C

Points	Expectations
2	The student's response shows a clear understanding of the make a 10 strategy.
1	The student's response shows some understanding of the strategy.
0	The student was not able to articulate proper use of the strategy.

©Curriculum Associates, LLC   Copying is not permitted.

Intervention Activity

Model making a 10 on a chart.

Materials: 1–20 charts (the first two rows of a hundreds chart; Activity Sheet 2, page 309), counters in two different colors, paper and pencil

- Provide each student with a chart and counters.

- Write the problem 8 + 3 = ? on the board. Tell students to use the chart and counters to solve by using one color for the first addend and the other color for the second addend. Make sure students place counters correctly starting at 1 when modeling the first addend and do not skip any numbers as they continue with the second addend. Remind them that they are free to start with either addend.

- Have students write the number sentences that show how to make a 10 to find the sum. For example: 8 + 3 = 8 + 2 + 1 and 10 + 1 = 11.

- Repeat with other addition and subtraction problems.

On-Level Activity

Play a make-a-10 game.

Materials: counters, 3 sets of number cards (1–9; Activity Sheet 1, page 308) for each group

- Put students in pairs or groups of 3 and give them counters and number cards.

- Place the number cards face-down and turn the top card face-up next to the pile. This number is the first addend. A player picks a card from the pile and mentally adds it to the first addend. If the sum is less than 10, place the card at the bottom of the pile and move to the next player. If the sum is greater than 10, the student describes how to make a 10 to find the sum.

- Students check the sum. They may choose to use counters for this. If the group agrees that the sum is correct, the player keeps the card and play continues. Use the same first addend until each player has had an opportunity to make a 10 with it. After that, draw a new card for the first addend. Continue until all cards are gone.

- Adapt for subtraction by using 2 stacks of cards, one with numbers greater than 10 and the other less than 10.

Challenge Activity

Materials: hundreds charts (Activity Sheet 2, page 309), small objects to use as counters, paper and pencil

- Write the number sentence 26 + 7 = ? on the board or on an individual card for each student. Instruct students to work in pairs or small groups. Ask them to use the hundreds chart and counters to show how the make a 10 strategy can be applied to numbers greater than 20.

- Tell students to show their thinking and explain what they did using words and/or pictures. Repeat with other problems, such as 27 + 8 = ? and 39 + 6 = ?.

- You may want to have students make up similar problems that they can exchange among themselves and solve.

©Curriculum Associates, LLC   Copying is not permitted.

Lesson 4 (Student Book pages 24–29)

Understand Even and Odd Numbers

LESSON OBJECTIVES

- Identify odd and even numbers.
- Relate doubles and doubles + 1 facts to odd and even numbers.
- Use skip counting by 2s to identify even numbers.

PREREQUISITE SKILLS

In order to be proficient with the concept/skills in this lesson, students should:

- Know doubles facts to 20
- Count by 2s
- Understand the meaning of equal groups

VOCABULARY

There is no new vocabulary. During the lesson you will review the key terms:

even number: a whole number that can be divided into 2 equal groups

odd number: a whole number that cannot be divided evenly into 2 equal groups

THE LEARNING PROGRESSION

In Grade 1, students to skip count by 2s and learn doubles and doubles + 1 facts. They also examine the concept of equality and equal shares.

In Grade 2, students continue to develop skip-counting abilities and deepen understanding of equality. **In this lesson,** students connect skip counting by 2s to the concept of odd and even numbers. They learn that even numbers can be seen as equal groups of 2 or as 2 equal groups of any number. Students relate the concept of 2 equal groups to doubles, examine doubles + 1 facts, and relate both to the structure of even and odd numbers. They examine odd and even numbers in a hundreds chart and study patterns.

In Grade 3, students continue the exploration of patterns in a hundreds chart. They examine patterns in addition and observe the structure found in multiplication tables.

Ready *Teacher Toolbox*

Teacher-Toolbox.com

	Prerequisite Skills	2.OA.C.3
Ready Lessons		✓
Tools for Instruction	✓	
Interactive Tutorials	✓	✓

CCSS Focus

2.OA.C.3 Determine whether a group of objects (up to 20) has an odd or even number of members, e.g., by pairing objects or counting them by 2s; write an equation to express an even number as a sum of 2 equal addends.

ADDITIONAL STANDARDS: 2.NBT.A.2 *(see page A42 for full text)*

STANDARDS FOR MATHEMATICAL PRACTICE: SMP 2, 3, 4, 7 *(see page A9 for full text)*

©Curriculum Associates, LLC   Copying is not permitted.

Equal and Unequal Groups

Objective: Examine equal and unequal groups of objects to explore the concept of odd and even numbers.	**Materials for each student:** • a set of 20 connecting cubes • pencil and paper or whiteboards

Overview

Students explore the concept of odd and even numbers by breaking cube trains into equal groups. Students will develop the understanding that not all numbers can be divided in half.

Step by Step (20–30 minutes)

1. **Prepare students for the activity.**

   • Give each student or student group a set of connecting cubes.

   • Ask students to follow along as you give instructions and model the activity.

2. **Work with an even number of cubes.**

   • Instruct students to connect 6 cubes to make a train. Model this with your set of cubes.

   • Tell students to break the train into 2 equal parts. Ask them how they know the parts are the same. Listen for ideas such as counting the cubes in each part or matching them up to see that they are the same.

   • Repeat with a train of 10 cubes.

3. **Work with an odd number of cubes.**

   • Tell students to make a train of 13 cubes. Have them try to break the train into 2 equal groups. Tell students to get the groups as even as possible. Ask what they notice about the groups. They are not equal.

   • Repeat with a train of 7 blocks.

4. **Work independently with different numbers of cubes.**

   • Give students about 5 minutes to make trains with different numbers of cubes and try to break them into 2 equal parts. Have them record the numbers of cubes that can and cannot divide equally into 2 parts.

5. **Discuss the results.**

   • Have students take turns giving you a number and telling if it did or did not divide equally. Write the numbers on the board in a vertical column in order from least to greatest. Write yes or no next to each number. For incorrect responses, ask students to justify with the cubes and correct the error.

   • Discuss any observations students make about the numbers. Listen for reference to counting by 2s other patterns.

   • Ask: *What did you notice about the leftovers every time there were not 2 equal parts?* [There was 1 extra cube.] *What do you think it means when we say a number is even?* [The numbers can be divided *evenly* into 2 groups.]

©Curriculum Associates, LLC   Copying is not permitted.

AT A GLANCE

Students explore the concept of odd and even numbers by breaking numbers of items into groups of 2.

STEP BY STEP

- Introduce the question at the top of the page. Remind students of what they discovered in the opening activity.

- Draw attention to the socks that are circled. Guide students to see that there are 4 groups of 2 socks each with no leftovers.

- Read the Think section together. Instruct students to circle groups of 2 shoes and answer the question in the box.

- Use the Mathematical Discourse questions to reinforce the relationship between odd and even numbers.

Hands-On Activity

Use models to understand odd and even numbers.

Materials: connecting cubes

- Ask each student to take a handful of cubes. Make sure there is variation in how many they end up with. Have students organize the cubes into groups of 2.

- Invite students to tell whether their cubes divided evenly or if there was a leftover. Help them recognize that students started with different numbers of cubes but there are only two possible outcomes: equal groups of 2 or 1 leftover.

- Ask students if they think this would happen if they combined cubes with a partner or if they grouped all the cubes in the classroom. Help them generalize that no matter how many cubes are used, they can either be grouped evenly into groups of 2 or there will be 1 leftover.

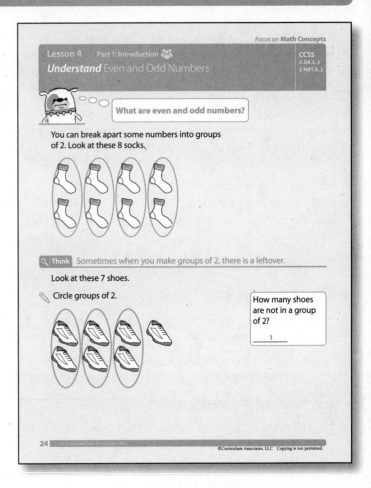

Mathematical Discourse

- *How are the leftover shoes you found on this page like the leftover blocks in the opening activity?*

  Students should notice that in both cases there is 1 left over.

- *What would happen if you added 1 more shoe to the group of 8? Why?*

  If you added 1 more shoe, you could make another group of 2.

- *What would happen if you took away 1 shoe from the group of 8? Explain.*

  If you took away 1 shoe, you could make 3 groups of 2 with 1 leftover.

©Curriculum Associates, LLC   Copying is not permitted.

AT A GLANCE

Students explore two ways of thinking about odd and even numbers. They think about even numbers in terms of groups of 2 or 2 equal groups and odd numbers as having 1 leftover.

STEP BY STEP

- Read the first Think section together. Ask students how this relates to what they discovered on the previous page.

- Read the second Think section together. Make sure that students understand the difference between groups of 2 and 2 equal groups.

- Have students read the Reflect question with their partner and write their reply in the space provided.

> **SMP Tip:** Have students consider the scenarios described in the Real-World Connection and ask whether it is possible for there to be more than one person left over. Have students explain their thinking, using a model to justify. *(SMP 4)*

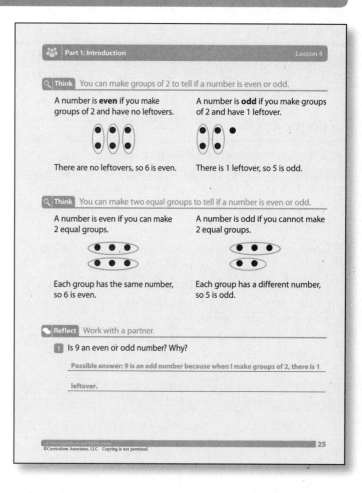

Concept Extension

Examine unequal groups of cubes.

Materials: connecting cubes

- Put students in pairs. Have partners make a train of 12 cubes, then break it into a group of 7 and a group of 5. Ask partners to discuss why this would or would not be a good way to show if 12 is odd or even.

- Call on volunteers to share their ideas with the class. Help students recognize that by moving 1 cube from the group of 7 to the group of 5, you can make 2 groups of 6.

- Repeat the activity using 11 cubes in 4 groups of 2 and 1 group of 3. Ask students to rearrange the cubes to show whether 11 is odd or even.

Real-World Connection

Relate the concept of odd and even numbers to a familiar situation. Ask students what happens when they are picking two teams for an outdoor game or a game in gym class and there is an even number of students in the class. What happens when there are an odd number of students?

Encourage students to think of other real-world situations that involve odd and even numbers. They may think of pairing up for math activities or pairing up with a "buddy" on a field trip. Discuss what happens when there is an even or odd number of students.

©Curriculum Associates, LLC   Copying is not permitted.

AT A GLANCE

Students model the concept of odd and even numbers by dividing groups of items into groups of 2 or into 2 equal groups.

STEP BY STEP

- Tell students that they will have time to work individually on the Explore It problems on their page and then share their responses in groups. Use the Mathematical Discourse questions to engage student thinking.

- Remind students that in Problems 2 and 3 they are circling groups of two. In Problems 4 and 5 they are circling 2 equal groups, if possible. Since each picture has 2 rows, suggest that students circle each row to try to find 2 equal groups.

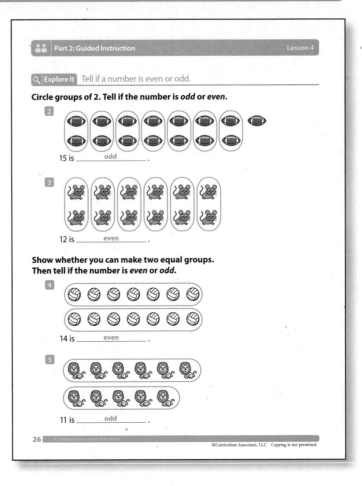

Visual Model

Analyze odd/even structure in dominoes.

- Project a domino block or draw a large domino with 6 dots. Ask students if they can tell without counting whether the number of dots is an odd or even number. They should recognize that the way the dots are lined up, you can see equal groups of 2 or 2 equal groups.

- Repeat the activity, showing dominoes with a variety of odd and even number of dots. Ask students to determine whether the number shown is odd or even and justify their responses.

- This activity builds visual/spatial skills as well as reinforces the concept of the structure of even and odd numbers.

Mathematical Discourse

- *How can you tell if a number is odd or even?*

    If there are no leftovers after making groups of 2, the number is even. If there is a leftover, the number is odd.

- *In Problem 5 how did you know the number of lions to circle?*

    Students might recognize that 5 lions match up in each row, but the top row has 1 more lion.

ELL Support

Help ELL students connect an everyday meaning of *even* and *odd* to the mathematical use of the word. *Odd* can mean *different*. The leftover means that the groups are not the same (they are different). The word *even* relates to equality, for example, *evenly* dividing some cookies.

©Curriculum Associates, LLC   Copying is not permitted.

AT A GLANCE

Students use doubles and doubles + 1 facts to identify odd and even numbers. They skip count by 2s to identify even numbers.

STEP BY STEP

- Organize students in pairs to complete the Talk About It section. You may choose to work through Problem 6 with the class.

- As students work in pairs, walk around to each group, listen to, and join in on discussions at different points. Use the Mathematical Discourse questions to help support or extend student thinking.

- Direct the groups' attention to Try It Another Way. Have volunteers come to the board and share their solutions on the number line used in the Visual Model.

> **SMP Tip:** Emphasize the structure of odd and even numbers on the number line, leading students to recognize the AB pattern that is formed. *(SMP 7)*

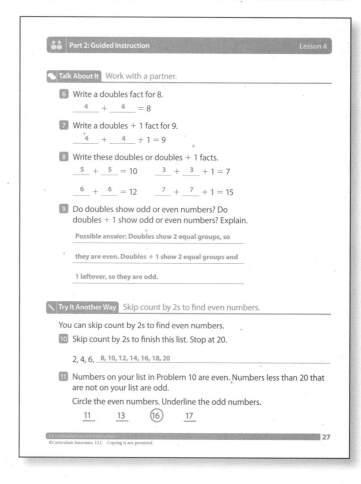

Mathematical Discourse

- *How is using doubles and doubles + 1 like using the models on page 26?*

  Doubles are like finding two equal groups. When you add them the sum is always even. The 1 in a doubles + 1 fact is the leftover.

- *What would happen if you subtracted 1 from a doubles fact?*

  It would also be an odd number. If you take 1 away, one of the equal groups will have 1 less than the other.

Visual Model

See odd and even numbers on a number line.

- Draw a 0–20 number line on the board.

- Point to 0 and ask students to tell you where your first "jump" will land if you skip count by 2s. Make an arc from 0 to 2 on the number line. Draw attention to the 2 *intervals* you skipped over.

- Continue to model skip counting on the number line as students identify each number you land on.

- Lead students to notice that the numbers you landed on are even and the odd numbers are in between.

- On the same number line, make two arcs below the line, from 0 to 3 and from 3 to 6. Point to 6 and ask if you landed on an even or odd number. [even] Have students add 1 more, tell where you will land, and identify this number as odd or even. [7; odd]. Repeat the activity using the other doubles and doubles + 1 facts from the student page.

AT A GLANCE

Students analyze pictures and real-world situations to determine whether numbers are odd or even.

STEP BY STEP

- Discuss each Connect It problem as a class using the discussion points outlined below.

Evaluate:

- Replicate the arrangement of apples on the board and ask students if Pat is correct that this is an odd number. [Pat is not correct.] To engage student thinking, attempt to justify Pat's strategy. Use a statement like the following: *But he made 2 equal groups of 6 with some leftover. Why can't it be an odd number?*

- Ask: *How can you help Pat organize his apples differently? When there are two apples leftover, what does that tell you?* Students should realize that Pat can put 1 leftover in each of the 2 groups to make 2 equal groups.

Analyze:

- If students struggle to make sense of the scenario presented, lead them to choose an appropriate tool to help visualize the problem. Allow each student to select the representation that he or she finds most meaningful and then share it with the class.

- Some students may solve by displaying 9 groups of 2 and 1 extra, while others may show 2 groups of 9 with 1 extra. Display models for both and discuss why they show the same total number.

- Show a third model by drawing a row of 9 dots below a row of 10 dots on the board. Ask volunteers to show how to find the total using all three models, then write the corresponding number sentences. This investigation sets the stage for arrays that are presented in the next lesson.

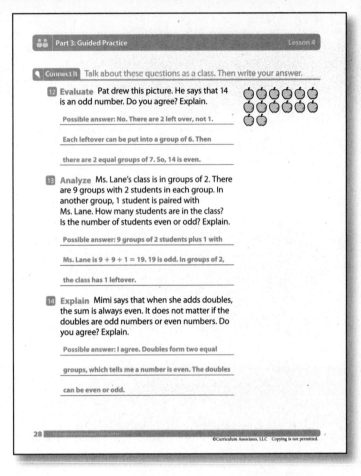

Explain:

- Encourage students to model the conjecture Mimi made. A number line may be the most efficient representation, but allow students to self-select.

- Draw two rows of 4 circles or squares on the board. Ask: *How many are in each row?* [4] *Is this number odd or even?* [even] *What is the total? Is it odd or even?* [8; even]

- Invite a volunteer to come to the board and draw one more in each row. Ask the same questions as above. Students should realize that there is an odd number of items in each row, but the total is an even number.

- Ask: *How many in all were added when (student's name) put 1 more in each row?* [2 were added to the total.]

©Curriculum Associates, LLC   Copying is not permitted.

AT A GLANCE

Students demonstrate their understanding of odd and even numbers by identifying and generalizing a pattern on a 1–20 chart.

STEP BY STEP

- Direct students to complete the Put It Together task on their own. Make sure they have red and blue crayons, markers, or colored pencils.

- Read the directions with students and make sure they understand each part of the task before proceeding.

- As students work on their own, walk around to assess their progress and understanding, to answer their questions, and to give additional support, if needed. Encourage students to list all the patterns they see in the chart. Some may notice that every other column contains odd numbers and every other column contains even numbers. Allow them to also explore other odd/even patterns, such as the pattern found in the diagonals.

- If time permits, ask students to share their observations and ideas about Amy's conjecture with the class.

Part 4: Common Core Performance Task   Lesson 4

Put It Together   Use what you have learned to complete this task.

15   Use this table to answer the questions.

1	2	3	4	5	6	7	8	9	10
11	12	13	14	15	16	17	18	19	20

Odd numbers should be colored red. Even numbers should be colored blue.

A   Color squares with odd numbers red. Color squares with even numbers blue. What patterns do you see in the numbers?

Possible answer: Every other number is odd. Every other number is even.

B   Look at 15. Is the ones digit odd or even? Is 15 odd or even?

The ones digit, 5, is odd. 15 is odd.

C   Look at 16. Is the ones digit odd or even? Is 16 odd or even?

The ones digit, 6, is even. 16 is even.

D   Amy says that if a two-digit number has an even number in the ones place, the number is also even. Is she correct? Why?

Possible answer: Amy is correct. When you skip count by 2, you get even numbers and all of those numbers have an even number in the ones place.

L4: Understand Even and Odd Numbers   29
©Curriculum Associates, LLC   Copying is not permitted.

SCORING RUBRICS

A

Points	Expectations
2	The student completes the color pattern accurately and describes at least one pattern, clearly articulating the odd/even structure.
1	The student completes most of the color pattern accurately and describes some kind of an odd/even pattern, although not clearly.
0	The student does not follow the color pattern accurately and does not describe an odd/even pattern.

B and C

Points	Expectations
2	The student identifies 5 and 15 as odd and 6 and 16 as even.
1	The student identifies either 5 and 15 as odd or 6 and 15 as even, but does not answer both questions correctly.
0	The student is not able to identify the digits or numbers as odd or even.

D

Points	Expectations
2	The student justifies the conjecture by generalizing it to the numbers shown on the chart and by using logical reasoning or models.
1	The student may agree with the conjecture, but the justification is not clear or lacks logical reasoning.
0	The student's response indicates a lack of understanding of the conjecture.

©Curriculum Associates, LLC   Copying is not permitted.

Intervention Activity

Model odd and even numbers with rectangles.

Materials: 20 counters per student, 1-inch grid paper cut into varied sizes of rectangles, each containing 2 rows (Activity Sheet 3, page 310)

- Instruct students to select a rectangle and place a counter in each box. Ask if the number of counters is an odd or even number and why. Direct students to write a number sentence to show how many counters are in the rectangle.

- Discuss why one more counter cannot be placed inside the rectangle. Then have students place 1 counter outside the rectangle and write a number sentence that shows the total number of counters inside and outside of the rectangle. (Example: $4 + 4 + 1 = 9$) Talk about how this shows doubles $+ 1$, which is an odd number.

- Repeat the above activities using different rectangles, asking students to write the related number sentences and identify the number of counters as odd or even.

On-Level Activity

Describe doubles and doubles + 1 strips.

Materials: grid paper cut into strips of different lengths (1×6 up to 1×20; Activity Sheet 3, page 310), crayons or colored pencils

- Ask each student to fold a 1×8 strip of grid paper in half. Model how to fold the strip so the grid lines are visible. Have students color each group of 4 squares with a different color. Discuss how this relates to doubles. Then ask students to refold the same strip in 4 groups of 2 squares. Emphasize that the entire strip is divided into groups of 2 with no leftovers. Ask students to describe how the model shows an odd or even number.

- Tell students to fold a 1×11 strip so the fold is on a line, coming as close as possible to dividing the strip in half. Have them color only the squares that are part of the double, leaving one square blank. Then ask students to refold in groups of 2 squares starting at the colored end. Discuss how this relates to doubles $+ 1$. Compare the odd and even strips they made.

- Repeat using different strips.

Challenge Activity

Materials: poster board or large paper

- Remind students of the conjecture made in the Performance Task: *If a number has an even number in the ones place, the number is even.* Challenge students to determine if this statement generalizes to all numbers no matter how many digits they have. Tell them that to prove the statement wrong, they must find an example of a number that doesn't follow the conjecture.

- Allow students to use whatever tools they need to try to prove or disprove the statement. They should create a poster displaying their findings and be prepared to present it to the class.

- You may want to challenge some students to think about 0, tell whether it is an even or odd number, and explain their reasoning.

©Curriculum Associates, LLC   Copying is not permitted.

Lesson 5 (Student Book pages 30–37)
Add Using Arrays

LESSON OBJECTIVES

- Interpret an array up to 5 rows and 5 columns.
- Calculate the number of items in an array using repeated addition and skip-counting.
- Write an equation to express the sum of items in an array.

PREREQUISITE SKILLS

- Add 3 one-digit numbers.
- Visually recognize groups of 2 to 6.
- Skip count by numbers up to ten.
- Write an addition equation.

VOCABULARY

array: a set of objects arranged in equal rows and equal columns

row: the horizontal groups of objects in an array

column: the vertical groups of objects in an array

THE LEARNING PROGRESSION

In Grade 1, students add up to 3 one-digit numbers. They use number sentences to express a variety of situations that involve addition. Students also apply counting skills to add, including skip-counting.

In Grade 2, students work toward fluency with sums to 20. They continue to use addition number sentences and skip-counting to model addition. **In this lesson,** students apply their knowledge of addition and skip-counting to an array. They analyze arrays, recognizing them as a set of objects organized in equal rows and columns. They recognize that adding 3 groups of 4 or adding 4 groups of 3 results in the same sum. This structure lays the foundation for the extension of the commutative property to multiplication.

In Grade 3, arrays are used as a tool to help students understand the structure of multiplication and division of whole numbers. The array is used to model the commutative and associative properties and as an introduction to area concepts.

Ready *Teacher Toolbox*

Teacher-Toolbox.com

	Prerequisite Skills	2.OA.C.4 2.NBT.A.2
Ready Lessons	✓ ✓	✓
Tools for Instruction	✓ ✓	✓
Interactive Tutorials	✓ ✓	✓

CCSS Focus

2.OA.C.4 Use addition to find the total number of objects arranged in rectangular arrays with up to 5 rows and up to 5 columns; write an equation to express the total as a sum of equal addends.

2.NBT.A.2 Count within 1000; skip count by 5s, 10s, and 100s.

STANDARDS FOR MATHEMATICAL PRACTICE: *SMP 1, 3, 4, 5, 7, 8* (*see page A9 for full text*)

©Curriculum Associates, LLC   Copying is not permitted.

Build Arrays

Objective: Introduce *row* and *column* and arrange a set of objects in equal rows and columns.	**Materials for each student:** • Square tiles (Activity Sheet 3, page 310)

Overview

Students arrange square tiles in equal rows and columns. They discover that there can be more than one way to do this.

Step by Step (15–20 minutes)

1 **Model equal rows and columns.**

- Model an array with 2 rows and 3 columns of tiles. Ask students how many tiles there are going across and down. Then have students find the total number of tiles. [3 across; 2 down; 6 total]

- Move tiles to make an array with 3 rows and 2 columns. Encourage students to compare this array with the previous one. Help them recognize that the total number of tiles is the same in both arrays, but the number going across and down is different.

2 **Introduce *row* and *column*.**

- Explain that the tiles are arranged in rows (going across) and columns (going down).

- Ask students what they notice about the number of tiles in each row and in each column. [The number in each row is the same and the number in each column is the same.]

3 **Make equal rows and columns with 8 tiles.**

- Give each student 8 tiles, and ask them to arrange the tiles in equal rows and columns.

- Once students have finished making their arrays, invite volunteers to describe what the arrays look like by telling the number of tiles in each row and column.

- Draw pictures of the arrays on the board. Guide students to understand that there is more than one way to arrange objects to make an array. Encourage them to find all possible ways to arrange the 8 tiles. [$1 \times 8, 8 \times 1, 2 \times 4, 4 \times 2$]

- You may want to challenge students to think of an easy way of finding the total number of tiles in the array.

©Curriculum Associates, LLC   Copying is not permitted.

AT A GLANCE

Students analyze an array and write a number sentence with equal addends to find the total number of objects in the array.

STEP BY STEP

- Instruct students to look at the picture of hats on a shelf. Ask students what they notice about the way the hats are arranged.

- Have students read the problem at the top of the page. Answer the Explore It questions together.

- If necessary, instruct students to circle each group of 4 hats on the shelf for visual reinforcement.

- Make sure students write the equation as a sum of the addend 4 repeated 3 times.

Note: Repeated addition is an underlying concept of multiplication and division. Recognizing 12 in terms of 3 groups of 4 leads to the understanding of multiplication as the process of combining equal-sized groups and division as the process of subdividing equal-sized groups.

> **SMP Tip:** Help students recognize that writing an equation or number sentence is a way to represent the addition found in the visual model (SMP 4) by asking them to explain how the equation relates to the picture of the hats.

Lesson 5 Part 1: Introduction 👥 | CCSS 2.OA.C.4 2.NBT.A.2

Develop **Skills and Strategies**

Add Using Arrays

🔍 **Use What You Know** | Review adding 3 one-digit numbers.

Rob's team has shelves for their hats. How many hats are there in all?

🔍 **Explore It** | Use math you already know.

A Does each shelf have the same number of hats? ___yes___

B How many hats are on each shelf? __4__

C How many shelves are there? __3__

D Look at the lines on the right. Each line shows one shelf. Use numbers to write how many hats are on each shelf.
___4___
___4___
___4___

E Use your answer to Problem D. Write a number sentence to show the total number of hats.
$4 + 4 + 4 = 12$

30 · L5: Add Using Arrays

©Curriculum Associates, LLC Copying is not permitted.

Mathematical Discourse

> - *Why is it helpful to add 4 three times rather than just count all the hats on the shelf?*
>
>   Listen for responses that indicate students recognize that the repeated addition is a faster way to calculate.

Concept Extension

Develop the concept of an array as a rectangular shape.

- Ask students: *How would the hats be arranged if there were 4 shelves? Why?* Provide students with small counters to explore this idea. You may want to provide lined paper for them to use as shelves.

- Watch to make sure students arrange the counters on their paper to form 3 columns and then point out the rectangular shape of the hats on the shelf.

- Challenge students to arrange the 12 counters in different numbers of rows and columns. Students can make the following arrays: 1×12, 12×1, 2×6, 6×2.

AT A GLANCE

Students examine a different representation of the array on page 30, using dots instead of pictures of hats. They learn array vocabulary and analyze an array.

STEP BY STEP

- Read and discuss the Find Out More as a class.

- Draw attention to the vocabulary words *array, row,* and *column.* Discuss each term, ensuring students understand their meanings.

- To reinforce the fact that the dots on the page represent any object, use the "Hands On" activity below.

- Instruct students to complete the Reflect question with a partner. Allow students to use tiles or counters, if necessary, to make sense of the problem.

- Encourage students to share their solutions using the vocabulary words they learned. If no one mentions it, point out that the number of rows is the same as the number in each column. Also, the number of columns is the same as the number in each row.

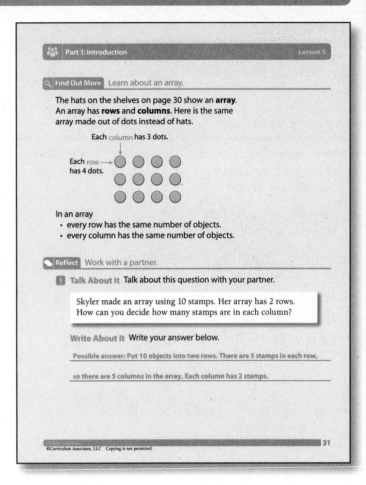

ELL Support

- Support the vocabulary by replicating the array of 12 dots on the board. Write the word array above it and label the rows and columns. Keep on display throughout the lesson.

Hands-On Activity

Using a variety of classroom objects, ask students to replicate the array of 12 dots. Students might use connecting cubes, counters, tiles, and so on. Discuss how all of these arrays are alike. [They all have 3 rows with 4 objects in each row and 4 columns with 3 objects in each column.] Tell students that the array of dots can be used as a picture to stand for any of the arrays of real objects they made.

Real-World Connection

Arrays are used in the real-world as an organizational structure. Encourage students to generate ideas of places where they have seen arrays. Responses may include: desks in a classroom, seats in a theater, eggs in a carton, stamps on a sheet, boxed items such as ornaments, glassware, tea candles, etc. You may want to have some array examples available for students to examine.

©Curriculum Associates, LLC   Copying is not permitted.

AT A GLANCE

Students use an array as a representation for solving an addition problem. Then students write a number sentence and use skip-counting to model the number of objects in the array.

STEP BY STEP

- Read the problem at the top of the page together as a class. Make sure the students understand the situation posed.

- Instruct students to look at the array and tell how many rows and how many columns they see. If necessary, project or draw the array on the board and ask students to come to the board and point to and count each row and column.

- Use the discourse question to reinforce the concept of an array.

- Direct students to look at the number sentence. Ask how many 5s are added together. [4] Connect this to the 4 groups of 5 or 4 columns of 5 in the array.

- Ask students to relate the skip-counting to both the array and the number sentence. It is important that they understand the relationship among all representations.

SMP Tip: Students should begin to look for regularity in repeated reasoning. *(SMP 8)* The models on the page reinforce that repeated addition and skip-counting by a number are ways to find the total items of an array.

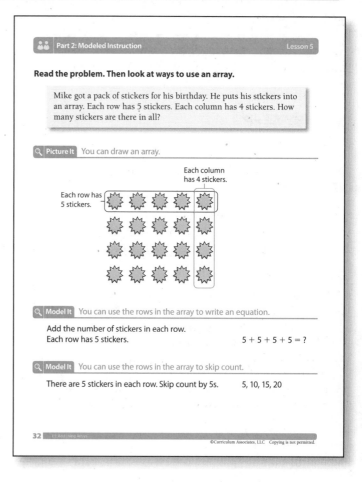

Mathematical Discourse

- *If Mike had 3 more stickers, could he make another row or column in this array? Why?*

  Students should respond that he could not make another row or column because there aren't enough extra stickers to fill up an entire row or an entire column.

©Curriculum Associates, LLC   Copying is not permitted.

AT A GLANCE

Students revisit the problem on page 32 and use a number sentence and skip-counting to find the total number of items in the array.

STEP BY STEP

- Organize students in pairs to complete the questions.

- Remind students that the questions in the Connect it section refer to the problem on the previous page.

- Tell students that Problem 3 asks them to think about the array in a different way. Make sure they understand that they are now adding the number in each column.

- Use the discourse question to help students recognize the commutative nature of an array. *(SMP 7)* Then ask what would happen to the number of columns if these stickers were organized into 4 rows. Students should notice that there would be 5 columns.

- Relate the different arrangements of rows and columns to skip-counting by 5s and by 4s.

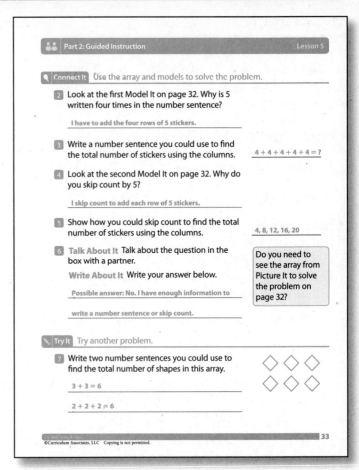

TRY IT SOLUTION

If students have difficulty writing a second number sentence, ask whether they used the number in each row or column to write the first number sentence. Use the response to guide them to the rows or columns to write the second number sentence.

Mathematical Discourse

- *Why do you think adding the stickers in the columns gives you the same answer as adding the stickers in the rows?*

  Listen for responses that indicate students recognize that the total number of stickers remains the same no matter how they are added.

©Curriculum Associates, LLC   Copying is not permitted.

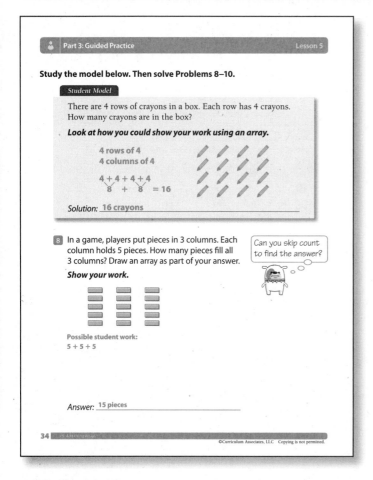

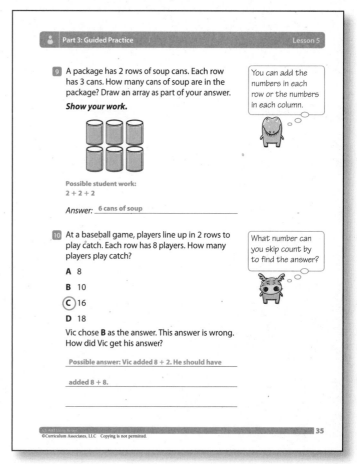

AT A GLANCE

Students practice what they know about repeated addition and skip-counting to solve array problems.

STEP BY STEP

- Draw students' attention to the sample problem. Lead them to recognize that when there is an even number of rows or columns, grouping doubles can make mental calculation easier.

- Instruct students to solve the problems individually. Direct their attention to the hints given to help them think about and solve the problems. For Problem 10, encourage students to use the open space to draw the array and check the given response for reasonableness. Then they can look back at the original problem to see why Vic may have chosen B.

- As students complete the problems, have them Pair/Share with a partner to discuss solutions.

SOLUTIONS

8 *Answer:* 15 pieces; Students should add 5 together 3 times to represent the 5 pieces in 3 columns. **(DOK 2)**

9 *Answer:* 6 cans; Encourage students to describe the strategy they used to solve. **(DOK 2)**

10 *Answer:* **C;** Add 8 (the number of players in a row) 2 times (the number of rows).

Explain to students why the other two answer choices are not correct:

A is not correct because 8 is the number in only 1 row.

D is not correct because $8 + 8 = 16$, not 18.

(DOK 3)

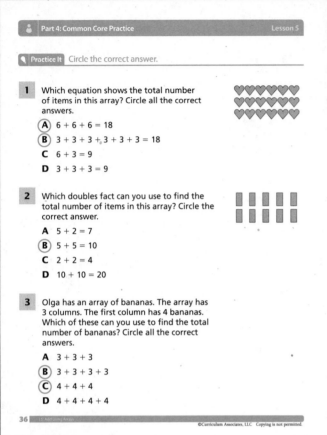

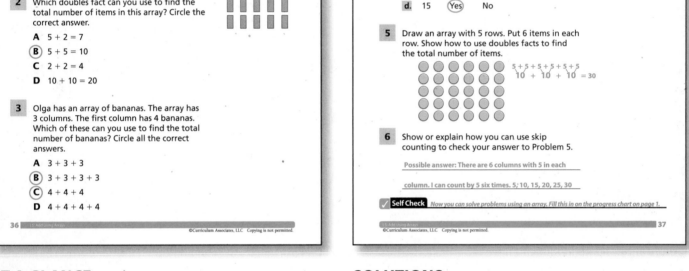

AT A GLANCE

Students solve problems involving arrays that may appear on a mathematics test.

STEP BY STEP

- Tell students that they will be finding the answers to array problems. Then have students read the directions and answer the questions independently.

- After students have completed the Common Core Practice problems, review and discuss correct answers.

SOLUTIONS

1   *Solutions:* **A** and **B**; Adding the number in each row or column will result in the correct response. **(DOK 2)**

2   *Solution:* **B**; The array is organized in 2 rows of 5. **(DOK 1)**

3   *Solutions:* **B** and **C**; Adding the number in each row or column will result in the correct response. **(DOK 3)**

4   *Solution:* Yes, No, No, Yes; 6 objects (**a.**) can be arranged in an array with three rows of two; 15 objects (**d.**) can be arranged in five rows of three objects. **(DOK 3)**

5   *Solution:* The arrays should be in a rectangular shape with 5 rows, 6 in each row. Students might add the number in each column since there is an even number of columns. **(DOK 2)**

6   *Solution:* Students may count by 5s or by 6s. **(DOK 3)**

©Curriculum Associates, LLC   Copying is not permitted.

Assessment and Remediation

- Jeremy makes an array of marbles. He makes 4 rows and 5 columns. How many marbles does he have? [20]

- For students who are still struggling, use the chart below to guide remediation.

- After providing remediation, check students' understanding by posing the following problem: There are 8 juice boxes in a package. There are 2 rows of boxes. How many are in each row? [4] Ask students to explain how they found the total number in each row. Help students recognize that the number in each row is the same as the number of columns.

If the error is . . .	Students may . . .	To remediate . . .
9	have added the given numbers.	Ask students to draw the array, ensuring they are making equal-sized rows and columns. Help them understand how to use addition to find the answer.
10	have added two 5s instead of four 5s.	Have the students reread the problem. Ask how many rows there are and how many are in each row. Lead them to see that 5 is added 4 times, or 10 is added 2 times.
any other number	have drawn the array incorrectly.	Remind students that an array has the same number of items in each row and the same number in each column. Help students correct their drawings and try to solve the problem again.

Hands-On Activity

Create and record arrays.

Materials: counters

- Give each student 18 counters and have them arrange the counters in 2 equal rows. Check to make sure the counters are arranged in 2 rows of 9 counters each. Discuss how many counters are in each row and column and how many there are in all. Challenge students to work with a partner to find as many arrays as possible for the number 18. Possible arrays: $1 \times 18, 18 \times 1, 2 \times 9, 9 \times 2, 3 \times 6, 6 \times 3$.

Challenge Activity

Search for prime numbers.

Materials: counters

- Provide students with 20 counters. Ask them to arrange groups of 2, 3, and 5 counters in separate arrays. Ask what all these arrays have in common. [Each array has only 1 row or 1 column.]

- Challenge students to find other numbers (to 20) that can only be arranged in either 1 row or 1 column.

- Discuss students' findings.

©Curriculum Associates, LLC   Copying is not permitted.

Lesson 6 (Student Book pages 38–47)

Solve Two-Step Word Problems

LESSON OBJECTIVES

- Analyze two-step problems to determine the series of operations needed to solve.
- Apply the commutative property of addition as a strategy to solve two-step problems and build number sense.
- Interpret models that represent a two-step problem.

PREREQUISITE SKILLS

- Solve one-step problems.
- Interpret a number line.

VOCABULARY

two-step problem: a word problem that requires a series of two distinct steps to solve

THE LEARNING PROGRESSION

In Grade 1, students represent a simple one-step word problem and identify the unknown in all three positions.

In Grade 2, students expand on what they have learned about solving one-step problems by seeing a two-step problem as a sequence of one-step problems. **In this lesson,** students use the terms "change" and "result" to describe the unknown. They model the problem in a diagram and open number line and then describe the situation as a number sentence. The concept of variable is explored in more depth, preparing students for its formal use in future grades.

In Grade 3, students use problem-solving strategies to solve multi-step problems involving all four operations, fractions, and measurement. They represent problems in an equation and use a letter as the variable for the unknown quantity.

Ready *Teacher Toolbox* — Teacher-Toolbox.com

	Prerequisite Skills	2.OA.A.1
Ready Lessons	✓ ✓	✓
Tools for Instruction	✓ ✓	
Interactive Tutorials	✓	✓

CCSS Focus

2.OA.A.1 Use addition and subtraction within 100 to solve one- and two-step word problems involving situations of adding to, taking from, putting together, taking apart, and comparing, with unknowns in all positions, e.g., by using drawings and equations with a symbol for the unknown number to represent the problem.

ADDITIONAL STANDARDS: *2.OA.B.2, 2.NBT.5* (see page A42 for full text)

STANDARDS FOR MATHEMATICAL PRACTICE: *SMP 1, 2, 4, 7, 8* (see page A9 for full text)

©Curriculum Associates, LLC   Copying is not permitted.

Model a Two-Step Word Problem

Objective: Model a two-step addition problem and write a corresponding number sentence.

Materials for each student:
- counters
- paper
- crayons or colored paper

Overview

Students use counters to model a two-step addition problem and then draw a picture to represent the same problem. They examine number sentences for the problem that break out and order the addends in different ways, illustrating the properties of operations.

Step by Step (10–15 minutes)

1 Pose the problem.
- Manny is going to the zoo with his family. There are 2 parents and 4 children in the van. They stop at Robby's house to pick up Robby and his sister. How many people are in the van now?

2 Model the problem.
- Instruct students to use counters to model the problem. You may want to repeat the problem slowly so students have time to count and gather the appropriate number of counters. Then ask students to draw a picture of the problem on their paper.

3 Write number sentences for the problem.
- Ask volunteers to share their pictures with the class and describe the action in the problem. You may want to suggest that students name the people who are in the van in different orders. Write a number sentence on the board that follows the progression of each description. [2 + 4 + 2 = 8; 2 + 4 + 1 + 1 = 8; 4 + 2 + 2 = 8, etc.]

4 Talk about the number sentences.
- Have students compare the different number sentences on the board. Ask what they notice about the sentences. [They are all different, but they all equal 8.] Reinforce the concept that the number 8 can be broken apart in many different ways.

©Curriculum Associates, LLC   Copying is not permitted.

AT A GLANCE

Students explore two-step problems by examining a series of one-step problems.

STEP BY STEP

- Tell students that this page will help them understand two-step problems by solving one-step problems. You may want to remind them that one-step problems are simple, such as: Joe has 3 toy cars. He gets 2 more for his birthday. How many does he have now?

- Have students read the problem at the top of the page. Ask a volunteer to tell what they know based on the information given.

- Work through the Explore It questions as a class.

- Ask students to work in pairs to think about how they could model this problem using only one tape diagram and one number sentence. [(4 + 4 + 6 = 14)] Have student pairs share their ideas with the class, justifying the number sentences they used.

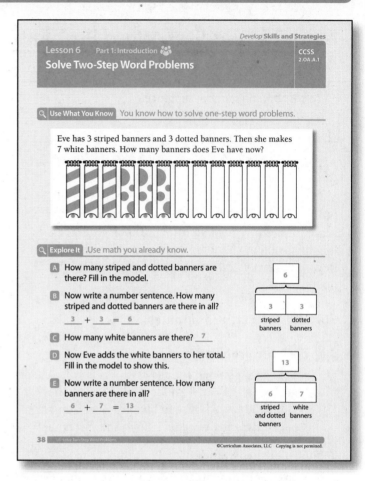

Mathematical Discourse

- *Why does it make sense to add 4 + 4 first?*

  In the problem Eve has 4 striped and 4 dotted banners before she makes more.

- *Would the answer be different if you started with 6 and then added the fours? Why?*

  No, it would not. The order of adding doesn't matter. The answer is always the same.

©Curriculum Associates, LLC   Copying is not permitted.

AT A GLANCE

Students analyze the process of solving a two-step problem and apply it to solving problems with both addition and subtraction.

STEP BY STEP

- Introduce the vocabulary word, emphasizing that in a **two-step** problem there are always two parts that must be solved before arriving at the final answer.

- Read and discuss the steps involved in solving the two-step problem on page 38. You may want to refer to the model on the previous page to clarify each step.

- Remind students that they must read carefully to decide what numbers to add and what numbers to subtract.

- Read the problem together. Ask students to tell what operations they will use and why.

- Help students connect the tape diagram to the number sentences below it. Use the discourse question to allow students to share individual strategies for finding the unknown. You may want to use connecting cubes to model the strategies they describe.

- Have student pairs read and reply to the Reflect question. Encourage students to draw a picture or use a tape diagram, if necessary, to make sense of the problem. Expect students to recognize that subtraction is used twice in this problem.

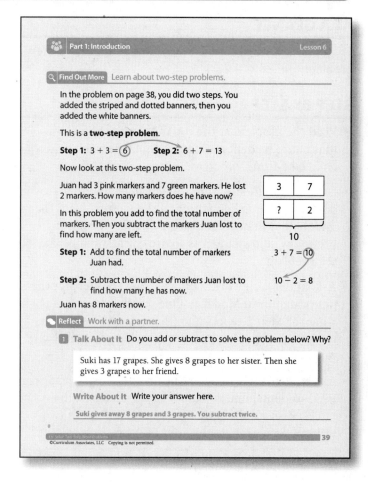

Mathematical Discourse

- *How do you know what number belongs in place of the question mark?*

  Students may respond that $10 - 2 = 8$ or since $8 + 2 = 10$, the missing number is 8.

Concept Extension

Ask students: *Do you think it matters if we subtract 2 from 3 first and then add the 7?* Have students work together in pairs to try this. Tell one student to solve $3 + 7 - 2$ and the other $3 - 2 + 7$. Remind them to add or subtract in order from left to right. Compare results.

AT A GLANCE

Students explore different ways of modeling a two-step problem.

STEP BY STEP

- Read the problem at the top of the page as a class. Make sure students recognize that this is an "add to" and "take from" problem.

- Draw students' attention to Picture It. Ask them to describe what is happening in the picture. Help them understand that in each step a change occurs. If necessary, allow students to use counters to model the problem.

- Ask students to work with a partner to interpret the tape diagram in Model It. One partner describes what the Step 1 represents [the students who sit at the table]. The other partner describes what Step 2 represents [how many students leave the table].

- Ask students what the unknown is in Step 1 [the total students] and in Step 2 [students left at the table]. Remind them that 8 + 6 and 5 + 9 are two ways of representing the sum 14.

> **SMP Tip:** As students describe each step in the solution process, they are recognizing the relationships among number sentences and developing number sense and the ability to reason about quantities and the varied ways to represent them. (SMP 2)

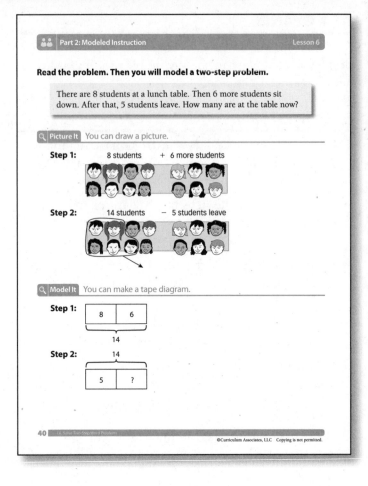

ELL Support

Some students may struggle comprehending the language used in a word problem. You may want to pair an English language learner with a proficient reader to complete this task and the ones that follow. Another option is to write each sentence of the problem on a separate line followed by a picture that represents it. Then underline the important words.

Mathematical Discourse

- *How might fact families help you find the unknown in Step 2 on the tape diagram?*

  Since $5 + 9 = 14$, $14 - 5$ must equal 9.

©Curriculum Associates, LLC   Copying is not permitted.

AT A GLANCE

Students revisit the problem on page 40 by writing number sentences to represent what is shown in the models. They then solve a problem involving addition and subtraction.

STEP BY STEP

- Read Connect It as a class. Make sure students understand that the questions refer to the problem on page 40.

- Ask students to work with a partner to write the two steps in this problem as a single number sentence [8 + 6 − 5 = 9]. Work with students to analyze any number sentence that is different from 8 + 6 − 5 = 9. Check for mathematical accuracy by asking pairs to justify their number sentence.

- Instruct students to work in pairs to discuss the question in Problem 7. Invite them to share ideas with the class before completing Write About It.

- For Try It, tell students to write a number sentence to represent the problem. Use the visual model to assist students in making sense of the problem.

Visual Model

- Tell students that drawing a picture can help them solve Problem 8.

- Show students how stick figures or tally marks can be used to quickly represent the 12 children in the pool.

- As you read each part of the problem, ask students to tell you what should be done to the picture. Complete the drawing or ask a student volunteer to do this and explain what is being done and why.

- Guide students to make the connection between the drawing and the number sentence used to solve the problem.

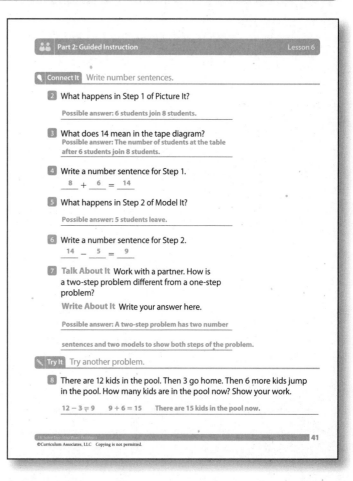

TRY IT SOLUTION

8 *Solution:* 15; Students should write number sentences showing each step of the problem: 12 − 3 = 9, 9 + 6 = 15. Some students might write a single number sentence: 12 − 3 + 6 = 15.

ERROR ALERT: Students who wrote 12 + 6 = 18 missed the step of subtracting the 3 children who went home.

AT A GLANCE

Students solve a two-step word problem using pictures and a number line.

STEP BY STEP

- Read the problem at the top of the page as a class. Make sure students recognize that this is a "take from" and "add to" problem.

- Ask students what they need to find out. Use the first discourse question to emphasize that in this problem, the result is known but the change is unknown.

- Draw students' attention to Step 1 of the picture model. Ask how many quarters are left after Russ takes 6 out. [10] Explain that this is the result. In Step 2 ask: *What do the counters that are shown tell you?* [How many quarters are in the jar after Dad added some.] Ask students what they need to find out to answer the question in the problem. Emphasize that this is the change.

> **SMP Tip:** Have students circle the number of quarters they think Dad put in the jar and then explain their thinking to a partner. Analyzing a model to find a solution and then justifying it builds perseverance in making sense of a mathematical situation. *(SMP 1)*

- Direct students to look at the number line model. Discuss that the arrow in Step 1 is moving "backward" to indicate that subtraction is involved. Move to Step 2 and ask how the number line is used to find the number of quarters Dad put in the jar.

- Ask students to work in pairs to model the problem on a single number line. Have volunteers share their ideas and discuss whether their model shows the problem accurately.

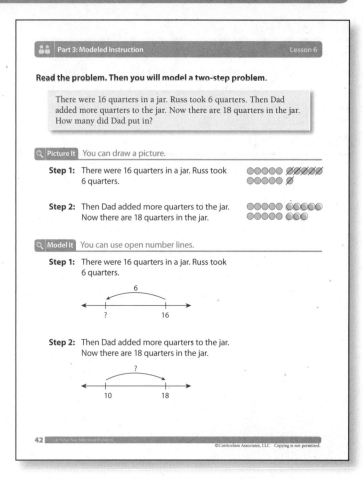

Mathematical Discourse

- *How is this two-step problem different from the other two-step problems you solved so far?*

  Students should respond that in the previous problems they were finding how many are left after adding and/or subtracting occurs. In this problem, they already know how many are in the jar and need to find out how many were put in it.

- *Do you think it is easier to use a picture or a number line model for this problem? Why?*

  Accept responses that relate to solving the problem.

- *When might it be easier to use a number line model? Why?*

  Students might recognize that when larger numbers are involved, a number line is more efficient than a picture. The number line also helps show the computation that is necessary.

©Curriculum Associates, LLC Copying is not permitted.

AT A GLANCE

Students revisit the problem on page 42, modeling it using equations. Then students solve a problem where the change is unknown.

STEP BY STEP

- Tell students that Connect It will help them learn how to write number sentences for the problem on page 42.

- After students complete Problem 10, invite them to explain how both models show that 6 quarters are taken away. Then ask: *How do the words in the problem tell you that 6 quarters are taken away?* [The word "took" refers to take away.]

- After students complete Problem 12, lead a discussion about how both models show Step 2 of the problem. Then draw students' attention to the box indicating the unknown in Problem 12. Compare the placement of the unknown in this number sentence to the placement of the unknown in Problem 9.

- Have students discuss Talk About It in pairs and then write an answer using their own words.

- Remind students that for the Try It problem, they can use a picture or number line to help them make sense of the problem, but they should try to write number sentences also.

Concept Extension

Explore the use of a variable.

- In the problem $10 + ? = 18$, the unknown is shown by using a ?. A variable or unknown can be shown in many ways.

- Write the problem from above on the board using ? as the variable. Ask students if a circle or a blank line could be used to show what is missing. Discuss whether a "q" could be used to show that you need to find the number of quarters. Challenge students to suggest what else might be used as a variable.

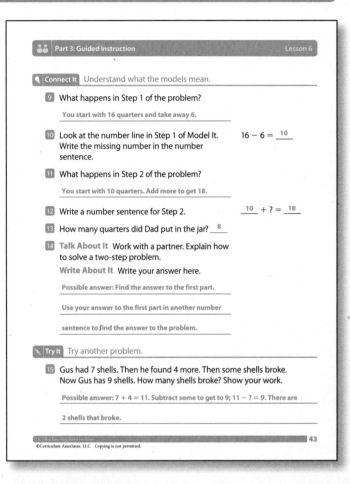

> **Part 3: Guided Instruction** Lesson 6
>
> **Connect It** Understand what the models mean.
>
> 9 What happens in Step 1 of the problem?
>
> You start with 16 quarters and take away 6.
>
> 10 Look at the number line in Step 1 of Model It. Write the missing number in the number sentence. $16 - 6 = \underline{10}$
>
> 11 What happens in Step 2 of the problem?
>
> You start with 10 quarters. Add more to get 18.
>
> 12 Write a number sentence for Step 2. $\underline{10} + ? = \underline{18}$
>
> 13 How many quarters did Dad put in the jar? 8
>
> 14 **Talk About It** Work with a partner. Explain how to solve a two-step problem.
>
> **Write About It** Write your answer here.
>
> Possible answer: Find the answer to the first part.
>
> Use your answer to the first part in another number
>
> sentence to find the answer to the problem.
>
> **Try It** Try another problem.
>
> 15 Gus had 7 shells. Then he found 4 more. Then some shells broke. Now Gus has 9 shells. How many shells broke? Show your work.
>
> Possible answer: $7 + 4 = 11$. Subtract some to get to 9; $11 - ? = 9$. There are
>
> 2 shells that broke.
>
> L6: Solve Two-Step Word Problems 43
> ©Curriculum Associates, LLC Copying is not permitted.

TRY IT SOLUTION

15 *Solution:* 2 shells; $7 + 4$ more $= 11$. Break some to get 9, so $11 - ? = 9$. Gus broke 2 shells.

ERROR ALERT: Students who answer 20 added all the numbers rather than using subtraction.

©Curriculum Associates, LLC Copying is not permitted.

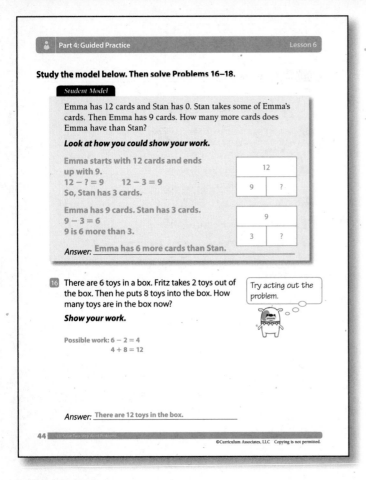

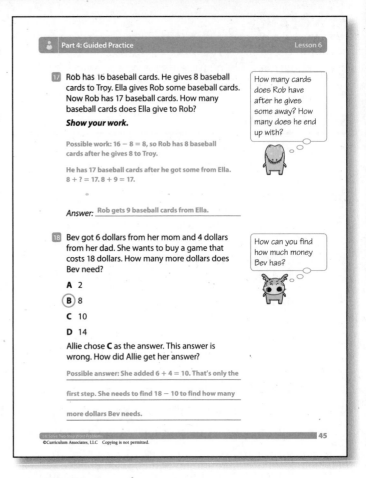

AT A GLANCE

Students model and solve two-step problems involving addition and subtraction.

STEP BY STEP

- Ask students to solve the problems individually and show all their work, including the number sentences they wrote.

- When students have completed each problem, have them Pair/Share to discuss their solutions with a partner.

SOLUTIONS

Ex Tape diagrams and number sentences are used as examples for solving this problem. Students may also act it out using counters or playing cards.

16 *Solution:* 12 game pieces in the box; Students may act out the problem by drawing a picture or using a number line model. Students may also write a single number sentence: $6 - 2 + 8 = 12$. **(DOK 2)**

17 *Solution:* Rob got 9 baseball cards from Ella. See possible work above. Students may also try modeling with a number line or by drawing a picture. **(DOK 2)**

18 *Solution:* **B**; Add the money she got from her parents and subtract that from 18 to find out how much more money she needs.

Explain to students why the other two choices are not correct:

A is not correct because $10 + 2 \neq 18$.

D is not correct because 14 is equal to $18 - 4$, not $18 - 10$. **(DOK 3)**

©Curriculum Associates, LLC   Copying is not permitted.

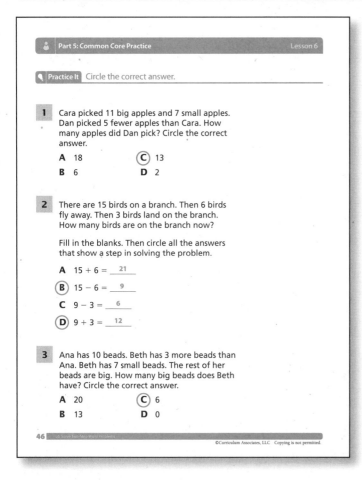

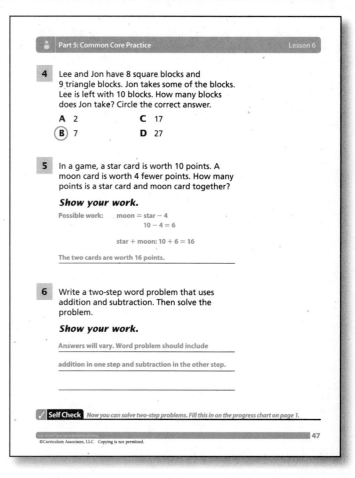

AT A GLANCE

Students will use addition and subtraction to solve two-step word problems that might appear on a mathematics test.

STEP BY STEP

• First, tell students they will use addition and subtraction to solve two-step word problems. Then have students read the directions and answer the questions independently.

• After students have completed the Common Core Practice problems, review and discuss correct answers.

SOLUTIONS

1 *Solution:* **C**; Cara picked 11 big and 7 small apples. Add $11 + 7 = 18$. Dan picked 5 fewer. $18 - 5 = 13$. (**DOK 2**)

2 *Solutions:* **B** and **D**; 15 birds and 6 fly away, $15 - 6 = 9$ (**B**); 3 more birds come, $9 + 3 = 12$. (**D**) (**DOK 2**)

3 *Solution:* **C**; Ana has 10 beads, Beth has 3 more, so $10 + 3 = 13$. 13 altogether $- 7$ small $= 6$ big beads. (**DOK 3**)

4 *Solution:* **B**; 8 squares $+ 9$ triangles $= 17$ shapes. $17 - ? = 10$ so $17 - 7$ shapes Jon takes $= 10$. Or, $17 - 10 = 7$ shapes Jon takes. (**DOK 2**)

5 *Solution:* 16 points together; star is 10, moon is $10 - 4 = 6$; $10 + 6 = 16$. (**DOK 2**)

6 *Solution:* Word problems should include addition in one step and subtraction in the other step. (**DOK 3**)

Assessment and Remediation

- There are 9 dogs playing in the park, and 2 dogs go home. Later 4 more dogs come to the park to play. Ask students to find the number of dogs that are in the park now. [11]

- For students who are still struggling, use the chart below to guide remediation.

- After providing remediation, check students' understanding using the following problem: Jenna puts 7 toys in a box. She finds 8 more toys to put in the box. Her little sister takes 3 toys out to play. How many toys are left in the box? [12]

If the error is . . .	Students may . . .	To remediate . . .
15	have added all the numbers.	Provide students with counters to act out the problem to see that when 2 dogs go home, subtraction is involved.
3	have written the number sentence $9 - 2 + 4 =$ and added $2 + 4$ before subtracting.	Read the problem again with the students, asking them to think about what is happening in the problem to make sense of the number sentence. Remind them to add and subtract in the order in which they are shown.
3	have subtracted all the numbers.	Reread the problem and help students build a number sentence that shows each step. Talk about why both addition and subtraction are involved

Hands-On Activity

Use an "act-it out strategy" to understand two-step word problems.

Materials: concrete objects, half sheets of paper with problems written on them

- Write two-step problems on a sheet of paper, one problem on each half. Write a total of four different problems. Make enough copies so that each pair has 2 or 3 problems to solve. Cut the paper in half so one problem is on each piece.

- Put students into pairs, and give each pair 2–3 problems and a set of counters.

- Instruct students to read a problem. Then one student acts out the first part of the problem, and the partner acts out the second part of the problem. Next, they draw a picture on the paper showing what they did. Finally, students write a number sentence and solve the problem.

Challenge Activity

Solve more difficult two-step problems.

This problem includes an unknown start.

- Stella took her rock collection to school. On the way home, 8 rocks fell out of her box of rocks. The next day, her Mom gave her 12 more rocks to add to her collection. She now has 35 rocks. How many rocks did she have to begin with? [31]

This problem requires organizing information to solve the multi-step problem.

- There are 10 hot dogs in each package and 8 hot dog buns in each package. Marcus has 3 packages of hot dogs and 3 packages of hot dog buns. He needs 40 hot dogs and 40 buns for his birthday picnic. How many packages of hot dogs and how many packages of buns does he need to buy? [1 package of hot dogs and 2 packages of buns]

©Curriculum Associates, LLC   Copying is not permitted.

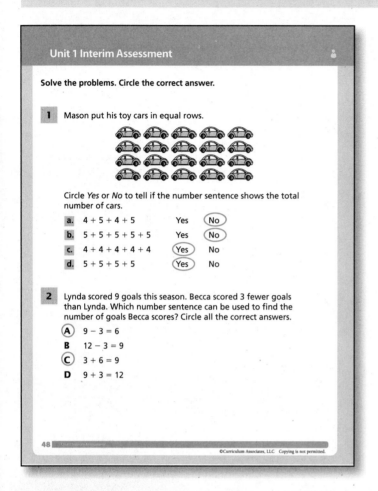

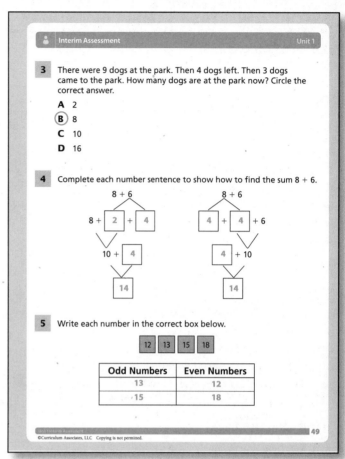

SCORING GUIDE AND ANSWER ANALYSIS

1 *Solution:* No, No, Yes, Yes; Correct number sentences will add the number of equal rows or number of equal columns to find a sum of 20.

$4 + 4 + 4 + 4 + 4 = 20$ (**c.**);
$5 + 5 + 5 + 5 = 20$ (**d.**)
(DOK 2)

2 *Solution:* **A**, **C**; Correct number sentences are members of the fact family that includes
$9 - 3 = 6$ (**A**); and $3 + 6 = 9$ (**C**). **(DOK 2)**

3 *Solution:* **B**; $9 - 4 = 5$; $5 + 3 = 8$ **(DOK 2)**

4 *Solution:* $8 + 2 + 4$; $10 + 4$; 14; and $4 + 4 + 6$; $4 + 10$; 14. In the expression on the left, the addend 6 is broken into $2 + 4$ so that a ten can be made with the addend 8. In the expression on the right, the addend 8 is broken into $4 + 4$ so that a ten can be made with the addend 6. **(DOK 2)**

5 *Solution:* Odd Numbers: 15, 17; Even Numbers: 12, 14. **(DOK 1)**

PERFORMANCE TASK SAMPLE RESPONSE

Common Core Standards: 2.OA.A.1, 2.OA.B.2, 2.OA.C.3, 2.OA.C.4, 2.NBT.B.5
Mathematical Practice Standards: SMP 2, 3, 4, 5, 6, 7
DOK: 3

About the Task

Students represent and solve problems using addition, subtraction, and equal groups. This task calls for students to add and subtract within 20 to solve one- and two-step word problems. Students also will need to work with an array and understand odd and even numbers.

Materials: (optional) tiles or counters

Getting Started

Read the problem out loud with your students. Review the information that is provided to them about Angie's DVD collection. Throughout the task, struggling students should be encouraged to model problems using tiles or counters, or create number bonds or other models using paper and pencil. **(SMP 4, 5)**

Completing the Task

Students first will need to solve a two-step problem using addition and subtraction. Guide them to understand that the number they first will be trying to find is the total or sum of cartoon and sports DVDs. Students might write a single equation using addition, such as $3 + 6 + ? = 20$, or they might write two equations, breaking the problem into steps, such as $3 + 6 = ?$ and $20 - 9 = ?$, to find the answer. **(SMP 4)**

Once students find the total number of cartoon and sports DVDs, they can select a pair of addends with a sum of 11. Any pair of addends is acceptable. **(SMP 2)**

Students next will need to consider patterns of sums of odd and even numbers. Have students classify the numbers of DVDs they selected in Part B as being either odd or even. Students who don't at first see the patterns in sums of odd and even numbers can be asked to give examples of different combinations of types of numbers and then look at the sums to see if any pattern emerges. **(SMP 2, 6, 7)**

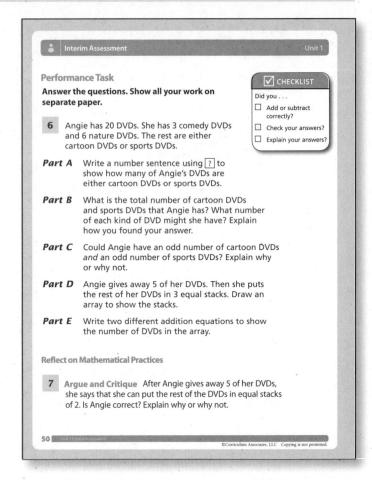

Before making an array for Part D, students will need to subtract to find the number of DVDs Angie has left. Make sure that students first are able to solve that subtraction problem before they attempt to make an array. Remind students that an array shows objects arranged in equal rows and equal columns. Encourage students to write addition equations using equal addends that represent those numbers of rows or columns.

Extension

Have students try this problem:

Angie kept all of her adventure and comedy DVDs. How many different ways can she arrange those DVDs in more than 1 equal stack so that there is more than 1 DVD in each stack? Explain how you know.

©Curriculum Associates, LLC   Copying is not permitted.

PERFORMANCE TASK SAMPLE RESPONSES AND RUBRIC

6 Sample 4-Point Solution

Part A Possible answer: $3 + 6 + ? = 20$

Part B Possible answer: Angie has 11 DVDs that are either cartoon or sports.

Angie's DVDs	
Type	**Number**
Comedy	3
Adventure	6
Cartoon	5
Sports	6

Possible explanation: Angie has 11 DVDs that are either cartoons or sports. $5 + 6 = 11$

Part C No; possible explanation: Angie has 11 DVDs that are either cartoon or sports, which is an odd number. Sums of two odd numbers always are even.

Part D Possible answer:

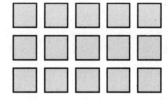

Student may also draw a 5×3 array.

Part E Possible answer: $3 + 3 + 3 + 3 + 3 = 15$ and $5 + 5 + 5 = 15$

REFLECT ON MATHEMATICAL PRACTICES

7 No; possible explanation: After Angie gives away 5 DVDs, she has 15 DVDs left. The number 15 is an odd number, and so it cannot be separated into equal groups of 2.

SCORING RUBRIC

4 points　The student's response is accurate and complete and all calculations are correct. All equations and models are correct. All explanations are complete and correct and exhibit an understanding of odd and even numbers.

3 points　Student has attempted all calculations but has made limited minor errors. Equations in Parts A and E are correct. Explanations are correct, though some might not be complete. Student correctly completed the table in Part B but might not have explained completely his or her reasoning. The equations in Part E might show the correct sum but not both use equal addends.

2 points　The student's response contains several mistakes in calculations and in equations and models. The student writes some equations that don't correctly model the situation. Responses show limited understanding of odd and even numbers.

1 point　The student's response contains an incorrect solution. The table is only partially correctly completed, and the student does not correctly write equations or make correct models. Explanations are missing or incorrect.

SOLUTION TO THE EXTENSION

One way; possible explanation: Angie has $3 + 6 = 9$ DVDs to arrange. The arrays she could use to represent 9 are 1 stack of 9 DVDs, 3 stacks of 3 DVDs, and 9 stacks of 1 DVD. With more than 1 stack and more than 1 DVD per stack, only an array of 3 stacks of 3 DVDs would work.

©Curriculum Associates, LLC　Copying is not permitted.

Unit 2: Number and Operations in Base Ten

Which lessons are students building upon?

Grade 1, Lesson 23
Add Tens to Any Number
1.NBT.C.4

Grade 1, Lesson 24
Add Tens and Add Ones
1.NBT.C.4

Grade 1, Lesson 25
Add and Regroup
1.NBT.C.4

Grade 1, Lesson 19
Understand 10 More and 10 Less
1.NBT.C.5

Grade 1, Lesson 20
Add and Subtract Tens
1.NBT.C.6

Grade 1, Lesson 25
Add and Regroup
1.NBT.C.4

Grade 1, Lesson 3
Add and Subtract in Word Problems
1.OA.A.1

Grade 1, Lesson 14
Make a Ten to Add
1.OA.C.6

Grade 1, Lesson 24
Add Tens and Add Ones
1.NBT.C.4

Grade 1, Lesson 17
Understand Tens
1.NBT.B.2a, 1.NBT.B.2c

Grade 1, Lesson 21
Understand Tens and Ones
1.NBT.B.2a, 1.NBT.B.2c

Grade 1, Lesson 22
Compare Numbers
1.NBT.B.3

Grade 1, Lesson 21
Understand Tens and Ones
1.NBT.B.2a, 1.NBT.B.2c

Grade 1, Lesson 22
Compare Numbers
1.NBT.B.3

Grade 2, Lesson 10
Understand Three-Digit Numbers
2.NBT.A.1a, 2.NBT.A.1b, 2.NBT.A.2

Grade 1, Lesson 22
Compare Numbers
1.NBT.B.3

Grade 2, Lesson 10
Understand Three-Digit Numbers
2.NBT.A.1a, 2.NBT.A.1b, 2.NBT.A.2

Grade 2, Lesson 11
Read and Write Three-Digit Numbers
2.NBT.A.3

Grade 1, Lesson 25
Add and Regroup
1.NBT.C.4

Grade 2, Lesson 10
Understand Three-Digit Numbers
2.NBT.A.1a, 2.NBT.A.1b, 2.NBT.A.2

Grade 2, Lesson 11
Read and Write Three-Digit Numbers
2.NBT.A.3

©Curriculum Associates, LLC   Copying is not permitted.

Which lessons are students preparing for?

Lesson 7
Add Two-Digit Numbers
2.NBT.B.5, 2.NBT.B.8

→ **Grade 3, Lesson 9**
Use Place Value to Add and Subtract
3.NBT.A.2

→ **Grade 4, Lesson 3**
Add and Subtract Whole Numbers
4.NBT.B.4

→

Lesson 8
Subtract Two-Digit Numbers
2.NBT.B.5, 2.NBT.B.8

→ **Grade 3, Lesson 9**
Use Place Value to Add and Subtract
3.NBT.A.2

→ **Grade 4, Lesson 3**
Add and Subtract Whole Numbers
4.NBT.B.4

→

Lesson 9
Solve One-Step Word Problems With Two-Digit Numbers
2.NBT.B.5, 2.OA.A.1

→ **Grade 3, Lesson 11**
Solve One-Step Word Problems Using Multiplication and Division
3.OA.A.3

→ **Grade 3, Lesson 12**
Model Two-Step Word Problems Using the Four Operations
3.OA.D.8

→

Lesson 10
Understand Three-Digit Numbers
2.NBT.A.1a, 2.NBT.A.1b, 2.NBT.A.2

→ **Grade 3, Lesson 8**
Use Place Value to Round Numbers
3.NBT.A.1

→ **Grade 3, Lesson 9**
Use Place Value to Add and Subtract
3.NBT.A.2

→

Lesson 11
Read and Write Three-Digit Numbers
2.NBT.A.3

→ **Grade 3, Lesson 8**
Use Place Value to Round Numbers
3.NBT.A.1

→ **Grade 3, Lesson 9**
Use Place Value to Add and Subtract
3.NBT.A.2

→

Lesson 12
Compare Three-Digit Numbers
2.NBT.A.4

→ **Grade 3, Lesson 8**
Use Place Value to Round Numbers
3.NBT.A.1

→ **Grade 3, Lesson 9**
Use Place Value to Add and Subtract
3.NBT.A.2

→

Lesson 13
Add Three-Digit Numbers
2.NBT.B.7, 2.NBT.B.9

→ **Grade 3, Lesson 9**
Use Place Value to Add and Subtract
3.NBT.A.2

→ **Grade 4, Lesson 3**
Add and Subtract Whole Numbers
4.NBT.B.4

→

©Curriculum Associates, LLC   Copying is not permitted.

Which lessons are students building upon?

Grade 1, Lesson 25 Add and Regroup **1.NBT.C.4**	**Grade 2, Lesson 13** Add Three-Digit Numbers **2.NBT.B.7, 2.NBT.B.9**
Grade 1, Lesson 25 Add and Regroup **1.NBT.C.4**	**Grade 2, Lesson 7** Add Two-Digit Numbers **2.NBT.B.5, 2.NBT.B.8**

©Curriculum Associates, LLC   Copying is not permitted.

Unit 2

Which lessons are students preparing for?

→ **Lesson 14**
Subtract Three-Digit Numbers
2.NBT.B.7, 2.NBT.B.9

→ **Grade 3, Lesson 9**
Use Place Value to Add and Subtract
3.NBT.A.2

→ **Grade 4, Lesson 3**
Add and Subtract Whole Numbers
4.NBT.B.4

→

→ **Lesson 15**
Add Several Two-Digit Numbers
2.NBT.B.6

→ **Grade 3, Lesson 9**
Use Place Value to Add and Subtract
3.NBT.A.2

→ **Grade 4, Lesson 3**
Add and Subtract Whole Numbers
4.NBT.B.4

→

©Curriculum Associates, LLC   Copying is not permitted.

Lesson 7 (Student Book pages 52–61)

Add Two-Digit Numbers

LESSON OBJECTIVES

- Break apart two-digit numbers as a strategy for adding place values.

- Recognize that in adding, tens are added to tens and ones to ones.

- Determine when regrouping a ten is necessary and carry out the regrouping to find a sum.

PREREQUISITE SKILLS

- Identify place values in two-digit numbers.

- Model two-digit numbers.

- Fluently add within 20.

VOCABULARY

There is no new vocabulary.

THE LEARNING PROGRESSION

In Grade 1, students explore the concept of place value by bundling groups of ten ones into one group of ten. They add two-digit numbers with and without composing a ten and mentally find 10 more or 10 less than a given number.

In Grade 2, students are expected to become fluent in two-digit addition and subtraction. They model two-digit numbers and write them in expanded form. Students fluently count by tens applying that skill to the count-up strategy for adding numbers. **In this lesson,** students add two-digit numbers with regrouping a ten. They break apart numbers to add place values and record the addition of partial addends before calculating the sum. Students interpret picture models, number models, and an open number line to understand addition of two-digit numbers.

In Grade 3, students gain fluency with addition and subtraction of numbers within 1000. They apply concepts of place value to multiplying two-digit numbers and add two-digit numbers when combining partial products.

▪ **Ready** *Teacher Toolbox*		*Teacher-Toolbox.com*
	Prerequisite Skills	*2.NBT.B.5 2.NBT.B.8*
Ready Lessons	✓ ✓ ✓	✓
Tools for Instruction	✓ ✓	✓ ✓
Interactive Tutorials	✓ ✓	✓ ✓

CCSS Focus

2.NBT.B.5 Fluently add and subtract within 100 using strategies based on place value, properties of operations, and/or the relationship between addition and subtraction.

2.NBT.B.8 Mentally add 10 or 100 to a given number 100–900, and mentally subtract 10 or 100 from a given number 100–900.

ADDITIONAL STANDARDS: 2.NBT.B.9 *(see page A42 for full text)*

STANDARDS FOR MATHEMATICAL PRACTICE: SMP 2, 3, 4, 5, 6, 7 *(see page A9 for full text)*

©Curriculum Associates, LLC Copying is not permitted.

Regrouping a Ten

Objective: Model and solve an addition involving regrouping.	**Materials for each student:** • Base-ten blocks

Overview

Students use base-ten blocks to add two numbers, exploring the purpose for regrouping ten ones into one ten.

Step by Step (10–15 minutes)

1 Build and add numbers without regrouping.

- Tell students to show 57 in tens and ones using base-ten blocks.
- Instruct students to add 32 blocks in tens and ones.
- Ask: *What is the sum?* [89] *What does that number tell you?* [how many unit cubes there are] *How many tens and how many ones are there?* [8 tens and 9 ones]
- Write *8 tens and 9 ones is 89* on the board.

2 Build and add numbers with regrouping.

- Have students replace all the blocks and then show 46 in tens and ones.
- Tell them to add 38 blocks.
- Ask: *What is the sum?* [84] *How many tens and how many ones are there?* [7 tens and 14 ones]
- Say: *When we added to get 89 blocks we put the 8 tens and 9 ones together to write 89.*
- Write *7 tens and 14 ones is 714* on the board and ask: *Can I write 7 tens and 14 ones like this? Why or why not?* Students should respond that there is a total of 84 blocks; 714 is not 84.
- Say and record on the board: *So you are telling me that 7 tens and 14 ones is 84? I don't see an 8 anywhere. Where did it come from?* Students should respond that there is another group of ten in 14 ones.

3 Pull it together.

- Ask students to compare the two additions and tell what is the same and what is different about them. Discuss that in both cases they combined tens and ones, but in the second case another ten needed to be made from the ones. You might press them to explain why they grouped the tens and ones separately instead of just counting how many blocks they had altogether. This may seem obvious, but it paves the way for the concept of adding "like terms" in algebra later in their schooling.

4 Generalize the concept.

- Ask: *When you look at two numbers to add, what tells you whether you will have to make another ten?* [If the sum of the numbers in the ones place is greater than ten, another ten will be regrouped.]

©Curriculum Associates, LLC   Copying is not permitted.

AT A GLANCE

Students examine a model of two-digit numbers. They add the numbers by combining each place value.

STEP BY STEP

- Read the problem at the top of the page. Ask students what operation will help them answer the question.

- Complete Explore It together. Make sure students are circling groups of ten. To ensure they count groups of ten accurately, have them mark each can as it is counted.

- Use the Hands-On activity to connect the concept of building tens to the problems on this page.

- Tell students they may use numbers or pictures or both to show how they thought about the question in part E.

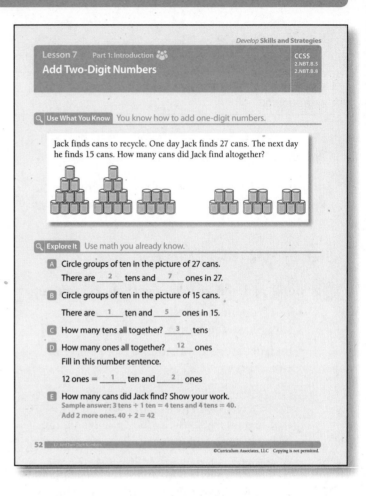

Hands-On Activity

Model two-digit numbers

Materials: locking cubes

- Tell the students to count 27 cubes and lock together groups of 10. Have them compare the tens and ones with what they found in the picture of the cans they circled.

- Have students count 15 cubes, lock together groups of 10, and compare to the picture of cans they circled.

- Ask: *If the blocks are the cans that Jack finds, how could you show how many he finds altogether?*

Mathematical Discourse

- *Why does it make sense to break numbers into tens and ones to add?*

  Students may respond that it makes it easier to see the place values in order to add tens to tens and ones to ones.

©Curriculum Associates, LLC   Copying is not permitted.

AT A GLANCE

Students connect a number model to a picture model for adding two-digit numbers.

STEP BY STEP

- Read Find Out More as a class. Refer to the problem on the previous page connecting the picture of base-ten blocks to the other models students explored.

- Compare the number models shown on this page. Students should recognize that these are all ways of representing the same addition. Ask why it might make sense to write 20 + 7 and 10 + 5 vertically. Reinforce the concept that while it might make sense, it isn't required. Thinking of the sum as 3 tens and 12 ones and finally 4 tens and 2 ones is as mathematically accurate as manipulating the numbers.

- Write the vertical form of the addition 27 + 15 on the board. Ask students to explain where the 30 and the 12 came from. Lead them to see that when written vertically the one ten from the 12 ones lines up with the 3 tens in 30. When the partial sums are added, the tens are automatically combined.

- Ask and discuss the Mathematical Discourse question. Listen to and accept all ideas. Although there are commonly used strategies, a mental strategy is individual. To be effective, it must make sense to the person using it. If a child perceives that the strategy was discovered by him/her, it is internalized and applied freely.

- After students discuss and write about the Reflect situation, have them share their responses with the class.

> **SMP Tip:** Exposing students to a variety of models reinforces the concept of the place value structure found in our base-ten number system. (*SMP 7*) Students use this structure to become fluent in mental calculation.

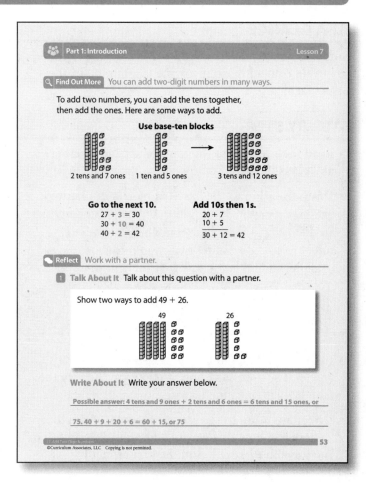

Mathematical Discourse

- *Which of the models helps you add in your head? Why?*

  Listen for responses that indicate that students are using mental calculation ("carrying" is not a mental strategy). Putting the tens together first and then adding on the ones is a commonly used mental strategy.

AT A GLANCE

Students use a quick drawing and break apart addends to evaluate an addition involving regrouping in the ones place.

STEP BY STEP

- Read the problem at the top of the page together as a class.

- Draw attention to the base-ten blocks in Picture It.

> **SMP Tip:** Ask why base-ten blocks are a good model to use for adding two-digit numbers. Students should recognize that the tens are already grouped. When using locking cubes, beans, or other counters, the tens have to be grouped first to be counted. *(SMP 5)*

- Instruct students to look at the sum in the first Model It section. Ask how it relates to the way the sum is written in the picture.

- Direct attention to the second Model It. Ask students to describe how this way of adding is different than the ways in Picture It and the first Model It.

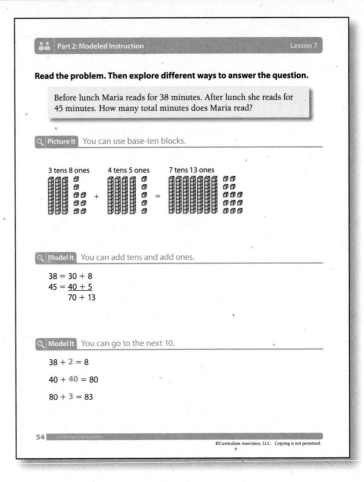

Visual Model

Use the following chart to help students focus on place values.

	Tens	Ones
	3	8
	4	5
Total	7	13

Write: 3 tens and 8 ones = 30 + 8
       4 tens and 5 ones = 40 + 5
       7 tens and 13 ones = 70 + 13

Mathematical Discourse

- *Would it make sense to write the sum of 7 tens + 13 ones as (write on the board) 713? Explain.*

  Students should respond that no, it would not make sense. The 7 is not in the tens place so the number cannot be written this way.

©Curriculum Associates, LLC   Copying is not permitted.

AT A GLANCE

Students revisit the problem on page 54 regrouping a ten to add.

STEP BY STEP

- Read Connect It as a class. Make sure students understand that the questions refer to the problem on page 54.

- To reinforce the regrouping process, you may want to use the Hands-On Activity as students answer the questions.

- Discuss the answers to Problems 6 and 7 together as a class. Allow students who employed different strategies to show their work on the board describing the strategy they used to find a sum.

- Ask students to describe the mental strategy they used (or could use) to find the sum of 8 and 5. Discuss how when they use the making a ten strategy, they think in terms of tens and ones. To make a ten, take 2 from the 5 to add to 8 and then add the extra 3 or add $10 + 3$. Helping students make this connection will build confidence in appling mental calculation strategies.

Hand-On Activity

Use base-ten blocks to understand regrouping.

Material: base-ten blocks

- Have students model the addends 38 and 45 with the blocks.

- Tell them that addition means they combine both groups of blocks. Remind them that when recording they must add tens to tens and ones to ones.

- Have students use the blocks to model making a ten as they answer Problem 3.

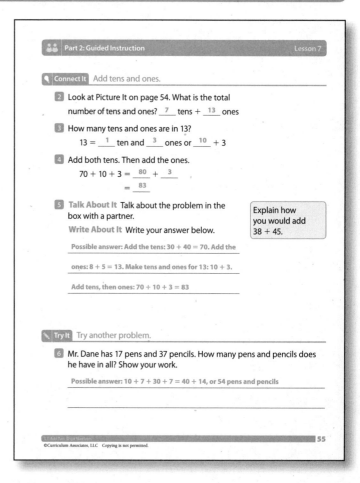

TRY IT SOLUTION

6 *Solution:* 54 pens; Break each number into tens and ones. Add the tens and then add the ones. Regroup the one ten from the sum of the ones to the tens place. **(DOK 1)**

ERROR ALERT: Watch for students who do not regroup the ten from the sum of the ones. Students who either wrote the sum as 414 or 44 did not regroup.

AT A GLANCE

Students examine a quick drawing and open number line model showing addition of two-digit numbers involving regrouping.

STEP BY STEP

• Read the problem at the top of the page together as a class. Ask students what operation will help them solve the problem.

• Draw attention to Picture It. Remind students that a quick drawing is an easy way for them to show tens and ones when adding numbers. You may want them to use white boards to replicate the addends as a quick drawing.

• Ask the first Mathematical Discourse question to help students connect what they already know to the strategy shown.

• Draw attention to the second Model It section. Have students evaluate the open number line by explaining what is happening. Tell them that this model shows one way to count up by making a ten first. Discuss other counting up strategies students may use such as first adding 40 to 48, counting 10s: 58, 68, 78, 88, and then adding the 3 ones by making a ten and then adding one more.

• Discuss the second discourse question as a class.

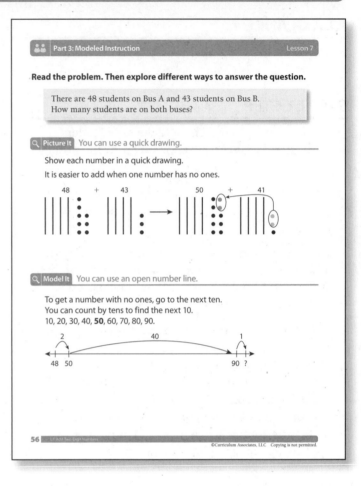

ELL Support

ELL students may find it difficult to express themselves in sharing strategies, so may not offer ideas. Yet it is important to get a window on their thinking. Encourage them to share ideas with a partner whom they trust, or talk to you later when there is no peer pressure.

Mathematical Discourse

• *How is the strategy used on this page like the making a ten strategy?*

Students should notice that when two is taken from 43 to add to 48, it is like taking 2 from the 3 to add to the 8. $8 + 2 = 10$ so $48 + 2 = 50$ (the next ten).

• *Do you think it is easier mentally to add the tens and then the ones, or count up? Why.*

Students will have a variety of responses showing personal preference. If students respond that one way is easier, ask them to tell you what makes it easier. Help struggling students articulate their reasoning.

©Curriculum Associates, LLC　　Copying is not permitted.

AT A GLANCE

Students revisit the problem on page 56, evaluating the models and applying strategies to a new problem.

STEP BY STEP

- Tell students that Connect It will help them think about the problem and models on page 56.

- You may want to complete the Concept Extension after students complete Problem 9. It shows that if they first jump 2 (add 2), they have to remember to subtract 2 from the total amount being added (43 − 2 = 41). That's why 40 + 1 is added next.

- Make sure students understand in Problem 12 that when making jumps to count up, a number is broken apart to make the addition easier.

- Have students discuss Talk About It in pairs and then write an answer using their own strategy. Suggest that they think about the strategies they have learned in this lesson.

Concept Extension

Materials: base-ten blocks

- Direct students' attention to Problem 9.

- Have students model the addends using base-ten blocks. Ask them to demonstrate what is happening when you add 2 to 48 and take 2 from 43. Discuss how reorganizing the blocks doesn't change the sum.

- Tell students they can think of reorganizing in another way. Write +2 and −2 on the board. Have students place 2 cubes in front of them to model the +2. Then take the 2 away to model −2. Ask: *How many are left?* [none] *When you add 2 and then subtract 2, how much have you added altogether?* [0] *When you add zero to a number, what happens to the number?* [It stays the same.]

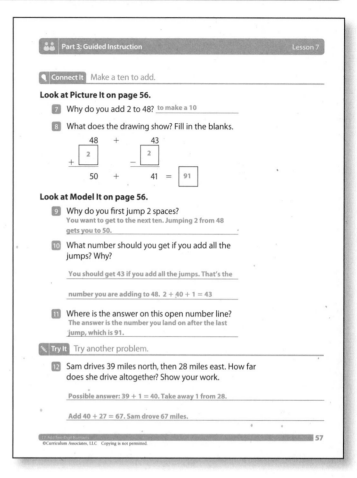

TRY IT SOLUTION

12 *Solution:* Sam drove 67 miles; Take one from 28 and add to 39: 39 + 1 = 40; Add the remaining 27 to 40: 40 + 27 = 67. **(DOK 1)**

ERROR ALERT: Students who answer 57 did not regroup a ten.

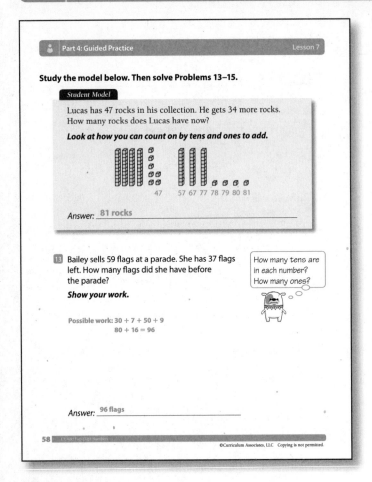

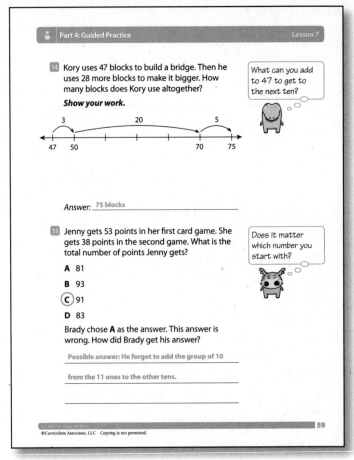

AT A GLANCE

Students use strategies to solve two-digit addition problems.

STEP BY STEP

- Ask students to solve the problems individually and show all their work, including the number sentences they wrote. Encourage students to describe their thinking.

- When students have completed each problem, have them Pair/Share to discuss their solutions with a partner.

SOLUTIONS

Ex A picture model is used as an example for employing the counting on strategy. Students may also think of an open number line to count on.

13 *Answer:* 96 flags; $59 + 1 = 60$; $60 + 36 = 96$. **(DOK 1)**

14 *Answer:* 75 blocks: $47 + 3 = 50$; $50 + 25 = 75$. **(DOK 1)**

15 Answer: **C**; $53 + 7 = 60$; $60 + 31 = 91$.

Explain to students why the other two choices are not correct:

B is not correct because $8 + 3 = 11$ not 13.

D is not correct because $53 + 30 = 83$. One addend is 38 not 30. **(DOK 3)**

©Curriculum Associates, LLC   Copying is not permitted.

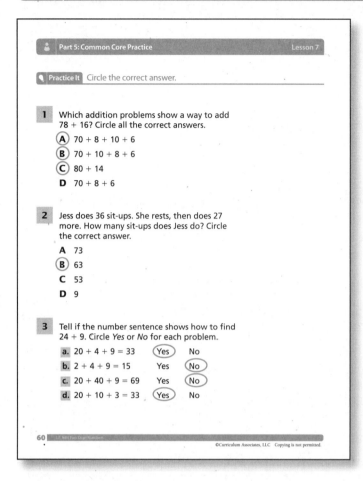

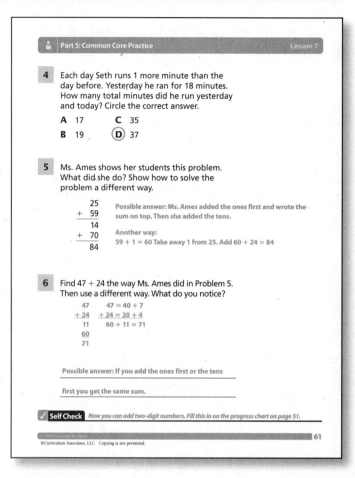

AT A GLANCE

Students use strategies to add two-digit numbers that might appear on a mathematics test.

STEP BY STEP

- First, tell students they will use strategies to solve addition problems. Then have students read the directions and answer the questions independently.

- After students have completed the Common Core Practice problems, review and discuss correct answers.

SOLUTIONS

1. *Solutions:* **A**, **B**, and **C**; Break each addend into tens and ones to add (**A**). Reorganize the tens and ones from each addend to add (**B**). Add the sum of the combined tens and combined ones (**C**). *(DOK 2)*

2. *Solution:* **B**; $36 + 4 = 40$; $40 + 23 = 63$. *(DOK 1)*

3. *Solution:* Yes, No, No, Yes. *(DOK 2)*

4. *Solution:* **D**; $18 + 19 = 18 + 2 + 17 = 20 + 17 = 37$. *(DOK 2)*

5. *Solution:* She added the ones first and recorded the sum. Then she added the tens and recorded the sum. Then she added the partial sums. Student strategies will vary. *(DOK 3)*

6. *Solution:* Ms. Ames way; $47 + 24 = 11 + 60 = 71$. Students' methods will vary. Check for accuracy. *(DOK 2)*

©Curriculum Associates, LLC   Copying is not permitted.

Assessment and Remediation

- Taylor picked 39 apples and Jordan picked 47 apples. How many apples did they pick together? [86]

- For students who are still struggling, use the chart below to guide remediation.

- After providing remediation, check students' understanding using the following problem: On Saturday morning 48 children and 35 adults visit the museum. How many people visit the museum on Saturday morning? [83]

If the error is . . .	Students may . . .	To remediate . . .
76	have failed to regroup ten ones.	Provide students with base blocks to model the problem recognizing that a ten needs to be regrouped. Have the student revisit the strategy employed adding the ten that was regrouped.
87	have counted on from 39 failing to subtract one from 47.	Help the student use a quick drawing to see that one is taken from 47 to make 39 equal 40. Remind the student that adding one without subtracting from the other addend changes the addend and makes the sum incorrect.
89	have counted on from 47 failing to subtract 3 from the 39.	Use the strategy discussed above to help students recognize the need for subtracting from one addend when adding to the other.

Hands-On Activity

Materials: a hundreds chart (Activity Sheet 2, page 309) and a counter for each student

- Distribute a hundreds chart and counter to each student.

- Write the addition problem 36 + 27 on the board.

- Tell students to find 36 on the chart and place the marker on it. Ask how they might use the chart to count on tens rather than ones first.

- Lead students to see that in the hundreds chart moving vertically adds or subtracts 10. They can add 20 by moving the counter vertically down the chart from 36 to 46 to 56 and then count on the additional 7.

- Write several problems on the board for the students to model with their hundreds chart and counter.

Challenge Activity

Devise a new addition strategy.

Challenge students to think of a strategy for adding two-digit numbers that no one in the class has discussed yet. Tell them to:

- Explain the strategy step-by-step so others can use it.

- Test the strategy on three or four addition problems to make sure it works all the time.

- Give the explanation and an addition problem to a classmate to see if they can use the strategy.

- Change any part of the strategy, if necessary, so that it is clear and will work all the time.

©Curriculum Associates, LLC   Copying is not permitted.

Lesson 8 (Student Book pages 62–71)

Subtract Two-Digit Numbers

LESSON OBJECTIVES

- Decompose a ten as a strategy for subtracting place values.

- Recognize that since addition is the inverse operation of subtraction, addition can be used to solve a subtraction.

- Evaluate mental strategies for subtracting a number from a two-digit number.

PREREQUISITE SKILLS

- Identify place values in two-digit numbers.

- Understand and apply the concept of fact families.

- Fluently add and subtract within 20.

- Apply the commutative property of addition.

VOCABULARY

There is no new vocabulary.

THE LEARNING PROGRESSION

In Grade 1, students subtract within 20 recognizing when decomposing a number leads to a ten and utilizing an addition to solve a subtraction. Students subtract multiples of ten within 100 and mentally find 10 more or ten less than a given number.

In Grade 2, students gain fluency addition and subtraction within 20. Students apply concepts of fact families as they explore how inverse operations can be a tool in solving addition and subtraction problems.

In this lesson, students subtract a two-digit number from another two digit number by mentally counting back to a ten and by decomposing a ten. Students interpret picture models, number models, and an open number line to understand subtraction of two-digit numbers.

In Grade 3, students fluently add and subtract numbers within 1000. They apply concepts of place value to division and recognize the role of subtraction in division with a remainder, and later in division of multi-digit numbers.

Ready *Teacher Toolbox*   Teacher-Toolbox.com

	Prerequisite Skills	*2.NBT.B.5 2.NBT.B.8*
Ready Lessons	✓ ✓ ✓	✓
Tools for Instruction	✓ ✓	✓ ✓
Interactive Tutorials	✓ ✓	✓ ✓

CCSS Focus

2.NBT.B.5 Fluently add and subtract within 100 using strategies based on place value, properties of operations, and/or the relationship between addition and subtraction.

2.NBT.B.8 Mentally add 10 or 100 to a given number 100–900, and mentally subtract 10 or 100 from a given number 100–900.

ADDITIONAL STANDARDS: **2.NBT.B.9** *(see page A42 for full text)*

STANDARDS FOR MATHEMATICAL PRACTICE: **SMP 2, 3, 4, 5, 6, 7** *(see page A9 for full text)*

©Curriculum Associates, LLC   Copying is not permitted.

Explore Subtraction Strategies

Objective: Model and solve a subtraction involving regrouping.

Materials for each student:
• Connecting cubes

Overview

Students use connecting cubes to subtract a two-digit number from another two-digit number, exploring and evaluating student directed strategies.

Step by Step (15–20 minutes)

1 Explore the concept of subtraction.

• Tell students to count out 42 connecting cubes.

• Ask: *Is it possible to take 17 cubes away? Why?* Make sure students understand that since there is a group of 17 within 42, it can be subtracted.

• Ask: *What will you do to take 17 cubes away?* Students will most likely respond that they count out 17 and remove them one by one. Discuss that trying to use the strategy of counting back 17 is not an efficient way to subtract larger numbers.

2 Use strategies to subtract.

• Have students construct groups of 10 cubes. Make sure they each have enough cubes to make 4 bars of 10 and 2 additional cubes.

• Instruct students to take 17 cubes away, while you observe their actions. You may want students to record each step on a white board to help them remember the process used.

3 Share and interpret strategies.

• Ask students to share the strategies used. Some students may have subtracted 2 first, then a 10, and finally the additional 5. Some may have subtracted 2, then 5, and finally 10. Others may have subtracted 10, then the two, and an additional 5. Allow students to express the strategy in their own way. If a student responds that 17 were taken away all at once, present him or her 4 groups of ten and 2 additional cubes. Have the student demonstrate taking 17 away while you record each movement.

• As students share their strategies, record their processes on the board. Have them compare and contrast each strategy, recognizing that in each case 17 was broken into a ten, a two, and a five.

4 Generalize strategies.

• Write the problem 53 − 25 on the board and tell students to apply the strategy they used with the previous problem to this one.

• Tell students that some strategies can only be used in certain situations such as doubles + 1, and some strategies can be used in many situations. This lesson will help them explore several different strategies that they might use for subtracting numbers. Make sure students understand that after learning about subtraction strategies, they can choose the ones they want to use in different situations.

©Curriculum Associates, LLC   Copying is not permitted.

AT A GLANCE

Students examine models of a two-digit number and evaluate subtraction based on the models.

STEP BY STEP

- Read the problem at the top of the page. Ask students what operation will help them answer the question.

- Complete Explore It together. For part C ask: *Are there enough art projects to subtract 9? Explain.* [Yes. Since there are 34 art projects, there is a group of 9 that can be removed]. Ask the Mathematical Discourse question to help students understand that within the set of whole numbers, a smaller number can be subtracted from a larger number, however, our place value system breaks numbers into tens and ones. **In that form** 9 ones cannot be subtracted without modifying the structure of the number.

- Use the Hands-On activity to connect the concept of decomposing a ten to the problem on this page.

Lesson 8   Part 1: Introduction
Subtract Two-Digit Numbers

Develop **Skills and Strategies**

CCSS
2.NBT.B.5
2.NBT.B.8

Use What You Know You know how to count tens and ones.

There are 34 art projects in a contest. There are 9 paintings. The rest are drawings. How many art projects are drawings?

Explore It Use math you already know to answer these questions.

A How many tens and ones are in 34?
   ___3___ tens and ___4___ ones

B Find 34 − 9 to find the number of drawings.
   How many ones do you need to subtract? ___9___

C Are there enough ones in 34 to subtract? ___no___
   Explain. No, there are only 4 ones in 34.

D Look at the second model.
   How many tens pieces are there? ___2___ tens
   How many ones pieces are there? ___14___ ones

E Now take away 9 ones. How many tens and ones
   are left? ___2___ tens and ___5___ ones

F How many art projects are drawings? ___25___

62   L8: Subtract Two-Digit Numbers   ©Curriculum Associates, LLC   Copying is not permitted.

Hands-On Activity

Model two-digit numbers

Materials: base-ten blocks

- Distribute base blocks to students.

- Tell the students to show 34 in tens and ones.

- Have students model decomposing a ten and subtracting 9 as they complete parts D–F.

Mathematical Discourse

- *We know that there is a group of 9 in 34, so why are there not enough ones to subtract 9?*

   Students should respond that since the blocks are grouped in tens and ones, there are not enough single units to subtract 9.

AT A GLANCE

Students examine and interpret strategies for subtracting from a two-digit number.

STEP BY STEP

- Read Find Out More as a class. Revisit the concept of fact families to justify using addition to solve a subtraction. You may want to write the problem on the board $34 - 9 = ?$. Ask students what an addition sentence would look like in this fact family. They should remember that $9 + ? = 34$ is the same as $34 - 9 = ?$

- Discuss with students that when they count up mentally it is important to keep track of the jumps so they know how much they added to 9 to get to 34. Have students talk about ways they mentally keep track of what they add.

- Tell students that for the Reflect section, they can talk about any strategy that makes sense. Choosing one from this page is acceptable but not required. Remind them that their strategy must make sense to their partner before writing it. Encourage students to ask for clarification.

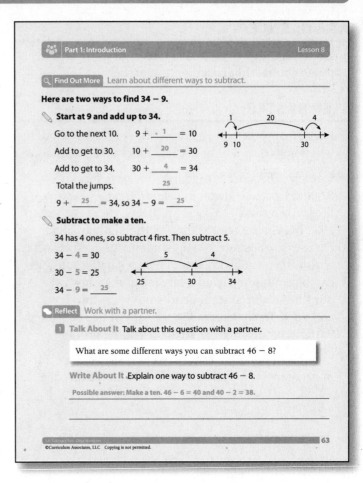

Concept Extension

- After students examine the second strategy shown for subtraction, say: *Dominick says that to subtract 9, he subtracts 10 and then adds one. What do you think of his strategy?*

- Lead students to recognize that when subtracting 10, one too many has been subtracted. That one needs to be replaced so that only 9 are subtracted. You may want to use locking cubes or a hundreds chart to model the strategy.

Mathematical Discourse

- *How does the number bond help you subtract 9?*

  The number bond shows how to break 9 apart with one addend being the 4 that is needed to subtract from 34 to get to 30.

SMP Tip: As students discuss their strategies in the Reflect section, roam the room encouraging students to ask questions of each other about a strategy and justify their own strategy using reasoning and/or models. *(SMP 3)*

©Curriculum Associates, LLC   Copying is not permitted.

AT A GLANCE

Students examine two counting-up strategies and apply them to subtracting a two-digit number.

STEP BY STEP

- Read the problem at the top of the page together as a class.

- Remind students that they are trying to find a part of a whole. Girls + boys = children at camp. To find the number of boys, subtract the number of girls from the total: $54 - 27 = ?$, or add the number of boys to the number of girls: $27 + \text{boys} = 54$.

- Discuss how 27 is broken into $20 + 3 + 4$ in both situations. Ask the Mathematical Discourse questions to reinforce use of these strategies. Discuss their value in performing mental calculations.

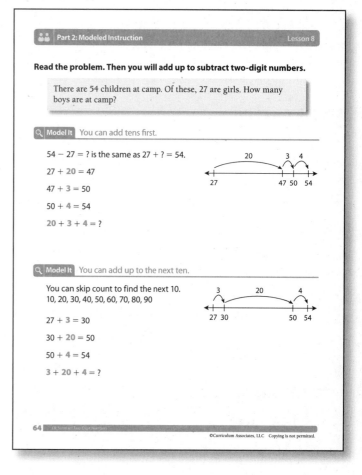

Concept Extension

- Say: *It doesn't matter the order you use when adding up. What about when you subtract down. Is $54 - 20 - 7$ the same as $54 - 7 - 20$? Why?*

  Allow students to discuss and justify their ideas in pairs before sharing with the class. You may want students to model the situation using locking cubes. Students should see that in both cases they are subtracting a **total** of 27 cubes. Make sure they understand that it is the $20 + 7$ that is being commuted, not $20 - 7$.

- Ask: *Does $20 - 7 = 7 - 20$? Explain.* Make sure students justify their responses. Help them clarify their thinking when necessary.

Teacher Note: This subtraction can be modeled as $54 - (20 + 7)$ or $54 - (7 + 20)$, not $54 - (7 - 20)$, in which case the subtraction in the parentheses would occur first.

Mathematical Discourse

- *Why doesn't it matter if you add up 20 first or 3 first?*

  A total of 27 is added. Numbers can be added in any order.

- *Which way of adding up do you think is easiest to do in your head? Why?*

  Listen for responses that show personal preference and justification. Make sure students understand that both ways are mathematically accurate and preference of one over the other is not an indication of superior intelligence.

©Curriculum Associates, LLC   Copying is not permitted.

AT A GLANCE

Students revisit the problem on page 64, analyzing counting up strategies to find a difference. They then select and apply a strategy to a new problem.

STEP BY STEP

- Read Connect It as a class. Make sure students understand that the questions refer to the problem on page 64.

- For Problem 3, discuss what Kim might be thinking when she wants to add 30. Students may reply that the difference between 50 and 20 is 30. Discuss what would happen if they added 30 first. Use the Visual Model to help students make sense of this strategy.

- Remind students that they may use any add up strategy that they prefer, but should show the process they used with an open number line or number sentences.

Visual Support

Explore a strategy.

- Draw an open number line on the board.

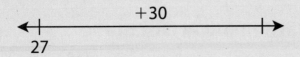

+30

27

- Ask a volunteer to show where the arrow would stop if 30 were added. Ask: *What might be confusing about adding 30?* [It stops at 57 which is greater than 54.] *Would it be possible to use Kim's idea to solve this problem? Explain.* Students should see that after adding 30, 3 must be subtracted making 27 the total number added.

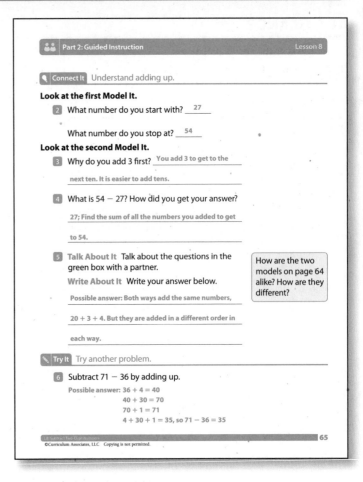

TRY IT SOLUTION

6 *Solution:* 35; Start at 36. Possible solutions include: $36 + 30 + 4 + 1$; $36 + 4 + 30 + 1$; $36 + 40 - 5$. **(DOK 2)**

ERROR ALERT: Watch for students who may lose track of the number of tens added on. They may try using taps or finger counts and in doing so add an additional ten.

©Curriculum Associates, LLC   Copying is not permitted.

AT A GLANCE

Students explore subtracting a two-digit number by breaking it into tens and ones, decomposing a ten and then subtracting tens from tens and ones from ones.

STEP BY STEP

- Read the problem at the top of the page together as a class. Ask students what operation will help them solve the problem.

- Draw attention to the first Model It. Have students explain what the model shows. You may want to have base-ten blocks available for students to physically model, if necessary.

- Ask: *Why is one ten decomposed into ten ones?* [It makes it easier to subtract 5 ones.]

- Have students evaluate the second Model It picture. Ask: *Why can we take away a ten first?* [There are enough tens to subtract one ten.]

- Notice that in the second step a ten is decomposed to subtract 5 ones. Some students may prefer to subtract 5 from 32 by counting back 2 to 30 and another 3 to 27. Make sure they understand that they are correct in their thinking, however there are many ways to think about subtraction and this model is showing one of those ways.

Note: The strategies on this page develop the thinking associated with the standard algorithm for subtraction. The algorithm itself is not introduced until grade 4.

ELL Support

ELL students may have learned a strategy differently, or represented it differently than presented. Encourage them to demonstrate for the class their ways of thinking. This validates their strategies and engenders confidence.

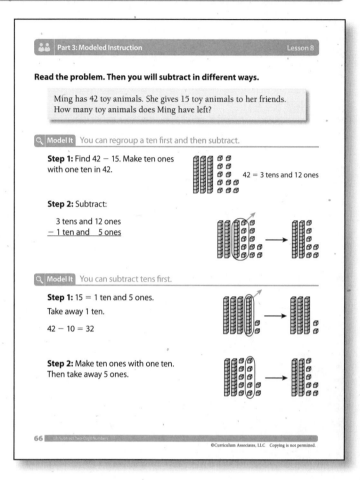

Mathematical Discourse

- *Do you think it is easier to subtract tens and ones, or count up in your head? Why?*

    Students will have a variety of responses showing personal preference. Make sure all preferences are justified using mathematical reasoning and equally valued.

SMP Tip: Encourage students to attempt to employ varied strategies in solving subtractions. Each strategy engages them in working within the structure of our number system somewhat differently, promoting flexibility in thinking as students search for the structure that allows them to solve problems mentally. (*SMP 7*)

AT A GLANCE

Students revisit the problem on page 66, evaluating models and applying strategies to a new problem.

STEP BY STEP

- Tell students that Connect It will help them think about the problem and models on page 66.

- Remind students that you want them to think about why the strategies on the previous page work rather than a strategy they may prefer to use.

- Have students discuss Talk About It in pairs and then write an answer using their own words.

- You may want to have base-ten blocks available for students to use as they complete Try It. Make sure they show either as a quick drawing or number sentence how they thought about the subtraction.

Concept Extension

- Display the problems posed in Modeled Instruction Parts 2 and 3, pages 64 and 66.

- Have students review the subtraction strategies modeled in each situation.

- Ask: *Why do you think the counting up strategy was used for the first problem and a take away strategy used for the second problem?* Students may respond that the first problem is a part of the whole problem so it was like a number bond. You can think of the missing part as an addition or subtraction. The second problem is a take away situation, so it makes sense to model subtraction as taking something away.

- Discuss with students that either strategy could be used in both situations. Have students talk in pairs about how they could use the "take away" strategy in the first problem and the "counting up" strategy in the second problem and then share their ideas with the class.

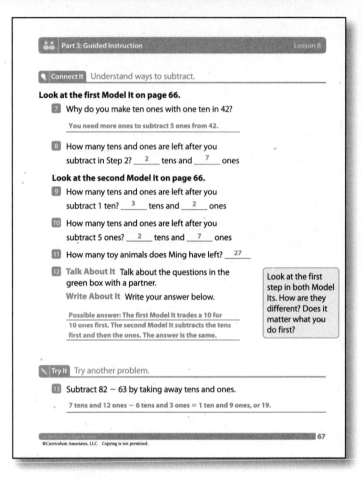

TRY IT SOLUTION

13 *Solution:* 19; 82 can be broken into 7 tens and 12 ones. $12 - 3 = 9$ and $70 - 60 = 10$, $10 + 9 = 19$; or $80 - 60 = 20$, 22 can be broken into 1 ten and 12 ones, $12 - 3 = 9$, $10 + 9 = 19$. **(DOK 1)**

ERROR ALERT: Students who answer 21 attempted to subtract mentally by subtracting 60 from 80 and 2 from 3.

©Curriculum Associates, LLC   Copying is not permitted.

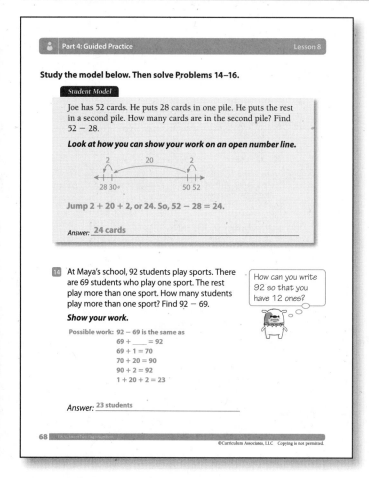

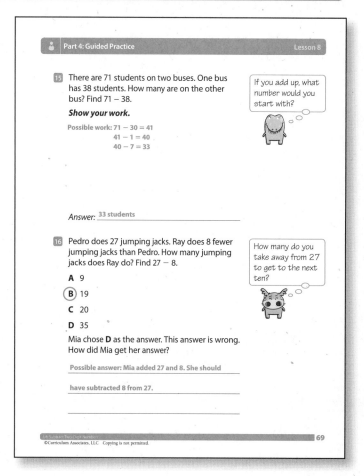

AT A GLANCE

Students use strategies to solve two-digit subtraction problems.

STEP BY STEP

- Ask students to solve the problems individually and show all their work, including the number sentences they wrote. Encourage students to describe their thinking.

- When students have completed each problem, have them Pair/Share to discuss their solutions with a partner.

SOLUTIONS

Ex An open number line is used to demonstrate the counting on strategy. Remind students that the jumps could be shown as $20 + 2 + 2$.

14 *Answer:* 23 students; $90 - 60 = 30$; $32 - 9 = 23$. **(DOK 1)**

15 *Answer:* 33 students; $38 + 30 = 68$; $68 + 3 = 71$; $30 + 3 = 33$. **(DOK 1)**

16 *Answer:* **B**; Break 8 into $7 + 1$; $27 - 7 = 20$; $20 - 1 = 19$.

Explain to students why the other two choices are not correct:

A is not correct because $8 + 9 \neq 27$. One more ten is needed.

C is not correct because $27 - 7 = 20$, one more needs to be subtracted. **(DOK 3)**

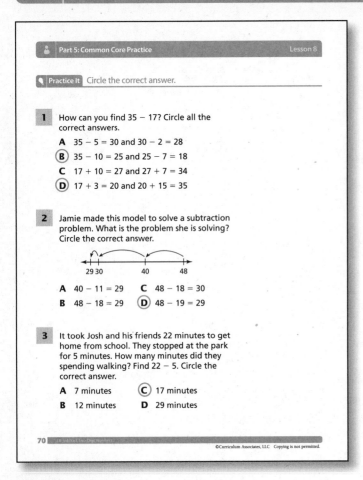

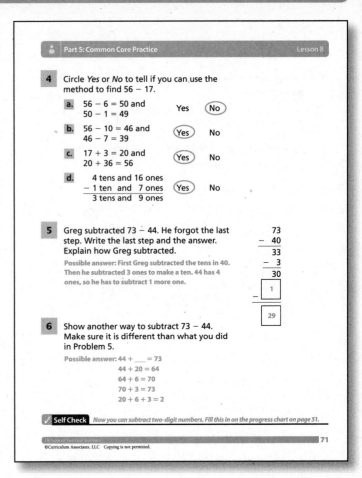

AT A GLANCE

Students use strategies to subtract two-digit numbers that might appear on a mathematics test.

STEP BY STEP

• First, tell students they will use strategies to solve addition problems. Then have students read the directions and answer the questions independently.

• After students have completed the Common Core Practice problems, review and discuss correct answers.

SOLUTIONS

1 *Solutions:* **B** and **D**; Count back a total of 17 (**B**). Add up a total of 18 (**D**). **(DOK 2)**

2 *Solution:* **D**; $48 - 8 - 10 - 1$. **(DOK 2)**

3 *Solution:* **C**; $22 - 2 = 20$; $20 - 3 = 17$. **(DOK 1)**

4 *Solution:* No, you must subtract $50 - 11$; Yes; Yes; Yes. **(DOK 2)**

5 *Solution:* The last step is $30 - 1$ to have subtracted a total of 44. **(DOK 3)**

6 *Solution:* Students may subtract in the following ways: $73 - 3 = 70$; $70 - 1 = 69$; $69 - 40 = 29$; or $44 + 20 + 9 = 73$; or $44 + 6 + 20 + 3 = 73$. **(DOK 2)**

©Curriculum Associates, LLC   Copying is not permitted.

Assessment and Remediation

- Stan saved 53 dollars and his brother saved 38 dollars. How many more dollars did Stan save than his brother? [15]

- For students who are still struggling, use the chart below to guide remediation.

- After providing remediation, check students' understanding using the following problem: 46 children are on the school playground. At the first bell 27 children go in. How many children are left on the playground? [19]

If the error is . . .	Students may . . .	To remediate . . .
91	have added instead of subtracted.	Model the two numbers on an open number line. Point out that when you are looking for "how many more" you are finding the difference between the two numbers. Help students write the subtraction and solve it.
13	have counted on from 38 to 48 and then added the extra 3.	Use a hundreds board to help students see the two that need to be counted to get from 48 to 50 before counting up 3.
25	have subtracted 30 from 50 and 3 from 8.	Model the subtraction using base-ten blocks. Students should see that after subtracting 30, 23 blocks are left. Guide students to see their error and encourage them to write down each step to make sense of the subtraction.

Hands-On Activity

Materials: a hundreds chart (Activity Sheet 2, page 309) and a counter for each student

- Distribute a hundreds charts and counter to each student and write the subtraction $63 - 27$ on the board.

- Tell students to find 63 on the chart and place the marker on it. Ask how they might use the chart to subtract 27.

- Students subtract 27 by moving the counter vertically up the chart from 63 to 56 to 46 and then count back the additional 7. Color in the 27 squares that were subtracted. You may want students to use one color for the tens, another for the 4 ones subtracted to get to 40 and another color for the additional 3.

- Repeat the process above using other problems involving subtraction.

Challenge Activity

Explore negative integers.

Remind students that in this lesson they discussed that $20 - 7 \neq 7 - 20$.

Tell students that although they are not equal, there is a solution for $7 - 20$.

Their challenge is to:

- Find the solution for $7 - 20$.

- Explain the strategy they used.

- Find a way to make sense of the solution using an everyday situation, a picture, or physical model to justify.

- Display their solution, strategy, and justification.

©Curriculum Associates, LLC   Copying is not permitted.

Lesson 9 (Student Book pages 72–81)

Solve One-Step Word Problems with Two-Digit Numbers

LESSON OBJECTIVES

- Analyze word problems to determine the operation needed to solve.

- Apply the use of fact families as a strategy to solve one-step problems and build number sense.

- Interpret models that represent a one-step problem with two-digit numbers.

PREREQUISITE SKILLS

- Add and subtract within 100.

- Use fact families fluently.

VOCABULARY

There is no new vocabulary. Review the following term.

one-step problem: A problem that requires a single step to solve.

THE LEARNING PROGRESSION

In Grade 1, students solve simple one step problems involving addition and subtraction within 20. They represent problems with objects, drawings, and number sentences that use a symbol to represent the unknown.

In Grade 2, students are expected to master solving one- and two-step problems with the unknown in all positions. They model problems using physical objects and diagrams and write number sentences using a symbol to represent the unknown. **In this lesson,** students interpret and solve problems involving two-digit numbers. They utilize concepts of fact families by representing a problem using more than one number sentence.

In Grade 3, students apply problem solving strategies to problems involving multiplication and division. At this level and beyond, students recognize mathematics as a tool for solving problems that arise within the context of a lesson and in daily life.

■Ready *Teacher Toolbox*		*Teacher-Toolbox.com*
	Prerequisite Skills	*2.NBT.B.5 2.OA.A.1*
Ready Lessons	✓ ✓ ✓	✓
Tools for Instruction		✓ ✓
Interactive Tutorials		

CCSS Focus

2.NBT.B.5 Fluently add and subtract within 100 using strategies based on place value, properties of operations, and/or the relationship between addition and subtraction.

2.OA.A.1 Use addition and subtraction within 100 to solve one- and two-step word problems involving situations of adding to, taking from, putting together, taking apart, and comparing, with unknowns in all positions e.g., by using drawings and equations with a symbol for the unknown number to represent the problem.

STANDARDS FOR MATHEMATICAL PRACTICE: *SMP 1, 2, 3, 4, 5, 6* (*see page A9 for full text*)

©Curriculum Associates, LLC   Copying is not permitted.

Explore One-Step Problems with Two-Digit Numbers

Objective: Solve a problem involving two-digit numbers using student selected strategies and models.	**Materials for each student:** • Plain paper, crayons, or colored pencils • Access to manipulative materials

Overview

Students are challenged to solve a one-step problem by interpreting the problem, representing it in a way that is meaningful to them, and finding a solution. Solutions and solution strategies are shared and analyzed by the class.

Step by Step (20–30 minutes)

1 Introduce the problem.

- Simon's mom has a piece of ribbon 85 inches long. Simon needs 67 inches for the tail of his kite. How much ribbon should he cut off?

- Tell students they can use any representation: a picture, drawing, or manipulative materials. They should show their thinking clearly on paper and find a solution. You may remind them of the problems they solved in Lesson 2, asking if any of those strategies would work here.

- Give students ample time to complete the task, allowing them to work in pairs, if they choose.

2 Support students as they solve the problem.

- Roam the room as students work, making sure they understand the problem and helping them find a meaningful representation and solution stragegy. Ask questions like: *What kind of drawing or model would make sense to use to show a piece of ribbon? What part of the ribbon does Simon need? How can you show that?*

3 Share solutions and solution strategies.

- Have students or student pairs take turns sharing their strategy and showing the representation they used.

- Ask: *Why do you think this is a good way to show the problem? What strategy did you use to solve the problem? Did you think of any other strategy that might work? Why did you choose the one you did?*

- As students share solutions, guide them in using mathematical vocabulary and clearly articulating the strategy they employed.

4 Critique the work of others.

- Invite the class to ask questions of each other, seek clarification, and acknowledge the work of their peers. Highlight innovative strategies or representations as an encouragement for all students to attempt diverse ways of thinking.

©Curriculum Associates, LLC   Copying is not permitted.

AT A GLANCE

Students explore one-step problems involving two-digit numbers by examining a bar model and an open number sentence.

STEP BY STEP

- Read the problem together as a class. Review with students the possible positions for an unknown.

- Ask: *In this problem, are you trying to find the start, the change, or the result?* [the change] *How do you know?* [They need 75 so that's the total. They have 49, so that's the start. We need to find how many more are needed to get to 75.]

- Work through Explore It as a class. Discuss with students how the top bar in the model shows the whole and the bottom boxes are the parts that make up the whole.

- Ask: *What operation will you use to find the missing part?* [Addition] Some students may respond that they could subtract 49 from 75. Discuss that subtraction is an acceptable operation since the three numbers are part of a fact family.

- As students complete Problem D, use the second discourse question to encourage flexible thinking.

> **SMP Tip:** Asking students to evaluate that the use of a model makes them aware of the types of models that are appropriate to use in this kind of problem situation as well as its usefulness in organizing the information found in the problem. This promotes good decision making when students are asked to select a model for solving a problem independently. *(SMP 5)*

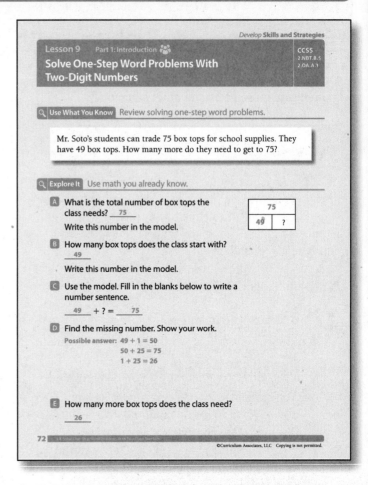

Mathematical Discourse

- *Why might this be a good model to use for this problem?*

    Since we are looking for a part of the whole, this model shows the parts and the whole.

- *What are some ways you could mentally solve this problem?*

    Students may suggest strategies such as counting up from 49 to 75, or subtracting 50 from 75 and adding one back.

©Curriculum Associates, LLC   Copying is not permitted.

AT A GLANCE

Students use varied models to represent a word problem and analyze the three positions for an unknown.

STEP BY STEP

- Ask students to look at the models in Find Out More. Ask: *What shows the parts in each model?* [the two boxes at the bottom] *What shows the whole?* [the box or number at the top] Encourage students to describe how each model shows addition and how it shows subtraction.

- Discuss the positions for the question mark. You may want to use the Hands-On Activity to physically model each of these situations. Reinforce the fact that these models and number sentences resemble the ones they explored in Lesson 2. Students should recognize that the models used here can be applied to any fact family and used with numbers of any size.

- Have student pairs read and solve the Reflect problem.

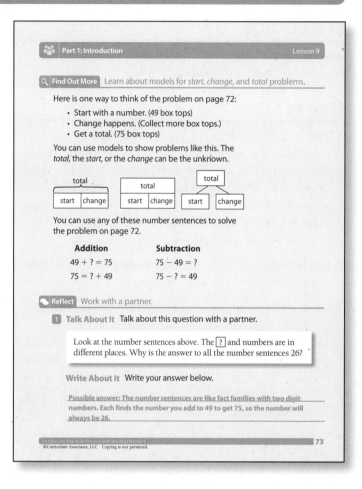

Hands-On Activity

Use physical models to understand visual models.

Materials: 1 set of 3 rectangles (9×3, $4\frac{1}{2} \times 3$, $4\frac{1}{2} \times 3$) and a set of cards with $+$, $-$, and $=$ printed on them for each student pair

- Tell students to place the two small rectangles below the large one to resemble the models on this page.

- Instruct students to print a 75 on the long piece of paper at the top and a 49 on the paper representing the start and a ? on the third paper. You may want students to reposition the papers to resemble each model shown.

- Tell students to use the operation and equal signs to show each number sentence on this page.

Mathematical Discourse

- *How are the models on this page alike? How are they different?*

  Listen for responses such as: They are the same because the whole is at the top and the two parts are under it.

  They are different because some are put together next to each other and one is spread apart.

- *How is finding the unknown part like using fact families?*

  You can either add the parts to the get the whole or subtract the known part from the whole to get the unknown part.

AT A GLANCE

Students use a part-whole model and number sentences to show a one-step problem.

STEP BY STEP

- Read the problem at the top of the page as a class. Ask students to tell if this is a "find the total," "find the change," or "find the start" question and how they know. Then ask: *What would the chart look like if we needed to find the change? The total?* [The question mark would be on Level 2 for the change and in place of 55 for the total.]

- Draw students' attention to Picture It and relate it to the models from the previous page.

- Have students look at the two number sentences in Model It. Ask why the problem can be modeled in either way? Students should respond that by adding the points from Level 2 to the points from Level 1, a total of 55 points will be reached. By subtracting the points made in Level 1 from the total, you will have 16 points from Level 2.

- Say, *I really like to use the counting up strategy. I'm wondering if I could use counting up to find the start?* Encourage students to "assist" you in using the counting up strategy. Reinforce the application of the commutative property of addition that allows them to begin at 16 and count up to 55.

- Provide students time to share their methods of counting up from 16 to 55, listening for accurate calculations. If no student employs the following strategy say: *Janell said she could count up by adding 40 to 16 to get 56 and then subtract one from 40. Does this strategy make sense? Why?*

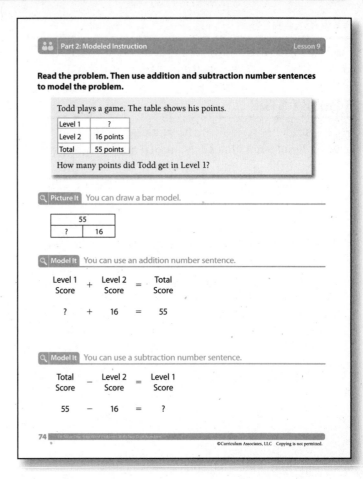

Visual Model

- Project a hundreds chart and use a colored pencil or marker to trace the right side of the square containing the number 55. Ask students what 55 represents.

- Trace around the entire block of 55 squares to indicate the total. Lead students to recognize that since the start is unknown, you can count back 16 squares and shade them in to represent the change.

- Students should notice that the first 39 squares are not shaded. This represents the start.

- You may want to use the chart to model some of the mental strategies students employed to calculate.

©Curriculum Associates, LLC   Copying is not permitted.

AT A GLANCE

Students revisit the problem on page 74 by writing number sentences to represent what is shown in the models. They then solve the problem using both addition and subtraction.

STEP BY STEP

- Read Connect It as a class. Make sure students understand that the questions refer to the problem on page 74.

- For problem 3, some students may write 55 in the first blank. Assure them that 55 is the correct number, but ask if they could write what part of the problem 55 represents. If a student doesn't understand, refer to the problem and picture on the previous page.

- As students complete Problem 4, remind them to think of what they know about fact families to help them find a different number sentence.

Concept Extension

Extend mental calculation strategies.

- After students discuss mental strategies in Problem 6, say: *I'm wondering if it would make sense to subtract 20 from 55 to get 35 and then add 4 to get 39?*

- Lead students to recognize that since 20 is greater than 16, subtracting 20 is subtracting 4 too many. Those need to be added back to the 35 so that only 16 have been subtracted.

- You may want to use an open number line or hundreds chart to help students visualize this calculation strategy.

- Encourage students to be creative in mental calculations.

SMP Tip: Encourage students to share responses to problem 6 articulating the strategy used to solve and the steps involved in mentally calculating the answer through an open number line. *(SMP 6)*

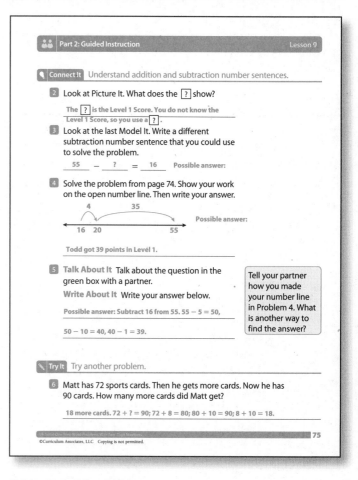

TRY IT SOLUTION

6 *Solution:* 18; $72 + ? = 90$; $72 + 8 = 80$; $80 + 10 = 90$; $8 + 10 = 18$. **(DOK 1)**

ERROR ALERT: Students who wrote $90 + 18 = 108$ added the numbers shown in the problem to find a whole rather than finding an unknown part.

AT A GLANCE

Students solve a word problem using a number bond model.

STEP BY STEP

- Read the problem at the top of the page as a class. Discuss what is known and what is unknown. Since the information given refers to the parts, the total is unknown.

- Direct attention to the models shown. Ask: *Is this an "add to" or "take from" problem? How do you know?* [It is a "take from" problem. Some of the books were taken off of the shelf.]

- Have students tell you a number sentence that would make sense for this problem. Write them on the board and discuss why each sentence would or would not make sense. ? − 24 = 38 makes sense because 24 books were taken from the total number on the shelf leaving 38 books. This number sentence models what occurs in the problem. For some students, this is the easiest way to interpret the problem. The other possible number sentences can also make sense. If a student suggests using addition, ask the second discourse question.

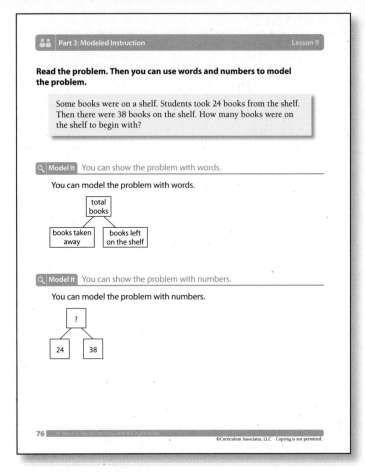

ELL Support

Some students may struggle comprehending the language used in a word problem. You may want to pair an English language learner with a proficient reader to complete this task and the ones that follow. You may want to write the information given in the problem on the board:

24 books taken away.
38 books left.
How many books to start with?

Mathematical Discourse

- *Why does it make sense to always put the total at the top of a number bond model?*

  Students should respond that if the total was placed in one of the other positions, it would mean something is added to it. If you did that, it would no longer be the total.

- *You told me this is a "take from" problem, so why can you add to find the answer?*

  Students may respond that the number bond shows the addends. Accept it, but help students see how addition applies to the problem situation. Some books were taken and some books were left. Their sum represents all the books that were on the shelf.

©Curriculum Associates, LLC   Copying is not permitted.

AT A GLANCE

Students revisit the problem on page 76 writing a number sentence to model the situation. Then students solve a one-step word problem involving two-digit numbers.

STEP BY STEP

- Read Connect It as a class. Remind students that the questions on this page refer to the problem on page 76.

- Allow students to complete Problems 8–10 independently. For Problem 10, make sure students describe the step-by-step procedure they used to mentally calculate the answer.

- Listen to students as they discuss Talk About It. They should have both arrived at the same answer but possibly in different ways. Make sure each student describes the strategy used clearly enough so the partner can write it out.

- If the partners did not arrive at the same answer for Problem 10, have them check each other's work to see if a calculation error or an error in thinking was made. Make sure students know that if they are not able to find an error, they should alert you for assistance.

SMP Tip: Remind students that for problem 12, they can use a picture or physical model to help them make sense of the problem, but they should also try to write a number sentence and show how they calculated an answer. *(SMP 1)*

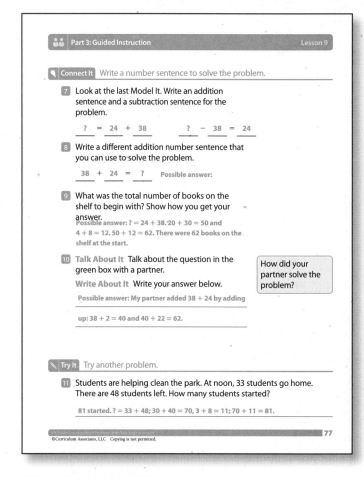

TRY IT SOLUTION

11 *Solution:* 81 students started.
$? - 33 = 48$; $48 + 33 = ?$; $48 + 30 = 78$; $78 + 3 = 81$. *(DOK 1)*

ERROR ALERT: Students who answer 6 subtracted 2 from 8.

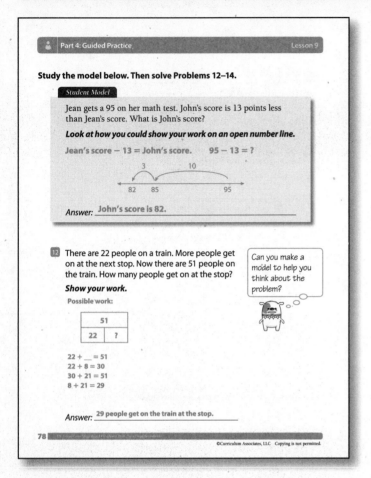

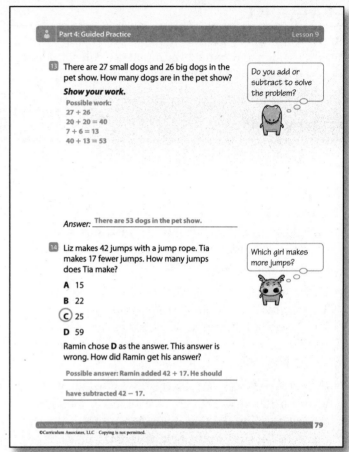

AT A GLANCE

Students model and solve one-step problems involving addition and subtraction of two-digit numbers.

STEP BY STEP

- Ask students to solve the problems individually and show all their work including the number sentence(s) they wrote. Encourage students to describe their thinking.

- When students have completed each problem, have them Pair/Share to discuss their solutions with a partner.

SOLUTIONS

Ex An open number line and a number sentence are used as examples for solving this problem. Students may also use a number bond or hundreds chart to make sense of the problem.

12 *Solution:* 29 people got on the train; Students may use a number line or number bond model. Students may also write as a subtraction number sentence: $51 - 22 = 29$. **(DOK 1)**

13 *Solution:* There are 53 dogs in the pet show. See possible work above. Students may also try modeling by using a number bond. **(DOK 1)**

14 *Solution:* **C**; 42 jumps $-$ 17 jumps $=$ 25 jumps.

Explain to students why the other two choices are not correct:

A is not correct because $25 + 15 \neq 42$.

B is not correct because $42 - 20 = 22$ not 25. **(DOK 3)**

©Curriculum Associates, LLC   Copying is not permitted.

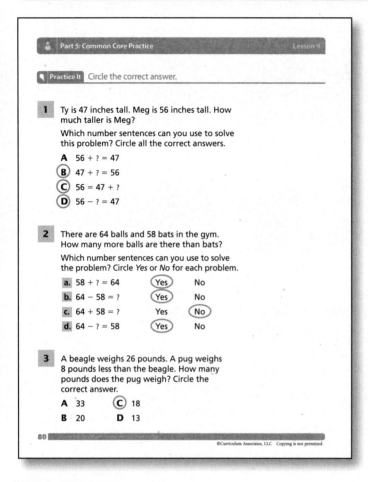

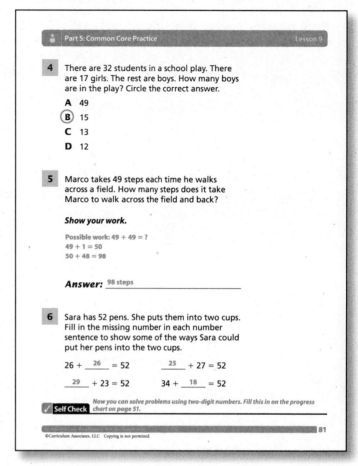

AT A GLANCE

Students will use addition and subtraction to solve one-step word problems involving two-digit numbers that might appear on a mathematics test.

STEP BY STEP

- First, tell students they will use addition and subtraction to solve one-step word problems. Then have students read the directions and answer the questions independently. Remind students to fill in the correct answer choices on the Answer Form.

- After students have completed the Common Core Practice problems, review and discuss correct answers. Have students record the number of correct answers in the box provided.

SOLUTIONS

1 *Solution:* **B, C,** and **D**; Ty's height + the additional inches needed = his sisters height (**B**). Sister's height = Ty's height + additional inches needed (**C**). Sister's height − additional inches = Ty's height (**D**). **(DOK 2)**

2 *Solutions:* Yes; Yes; No, 64 + 58 represents the total, not the difference; Yes. **(DOK 2)**

3 *Solution:* **C**; 26 − 8 = 18. **(DOK 1)**

4 *Solution:* **B**; 32 − 17 = 15. **(DOK 1)**

5 *Solution:* 49 + 49 = 98. **(DOK 1)**

6 *Solution:* 26 + 26; 25 + 27; 29 + 23; 34 + 18. **(DOK 1)**

©Curriculum Associates, LLC   Copying is not permitted.

Assessment and Remediation

- Sue collects 27 cans of food for the food drive. Her goal is to collect 65 cans. How many does she have left to collect? [38]

- For students who are still struggling, use the chart below to guide remediation.

- After providing remediation, check students' understanding using the following problem: There are 79 passengers on the plane. The plane holds 93 people. How many seats are empty? [14]

If the error is . . .	Students may . . .	To remediate . . .
42	have subtracted 20 from 60 and 5 from 7.	Have students check their work by adding 42 to 27. Once they realize the answer is incorrect, lead them to use a strategy such as counting up to insure accuracy.
92	have added the numbers instead of subtracting.	Ask students to describe the total number of cans Sue has to collect. Ask if it makes sense that 92 are left. Then help students organize the information using a number bond or hundreds board.
any other number	have subtracted inaccurately or misrepresented the problem.	As students read each sentence, have them describe what the sentence says and model with base blocks or a picture model. Have students write the number sentence, solve, and check for computational accuracy.

Hands-On Activity

Solve one-step word problems.

Materials: number bond mats, (Activity Sheet 5, page 312) blank paper rectangles to fit number bond mats

- Write 2–3 word problems involving two-digit numbers with the unknown in different positions on a piece of paper. Photocopy so that there are enough for each student. Cut the problems apart and distribute them to students.

- Tell students to write the known numbers from one of the problems on the paper rectangles and arrange them on the number bond mat.

- Have students glue the problem on a plain sheet of paper, draw the number bond under it, and then write a number sentence that models the problem.

- Have students solve the problem and show their strategy. Repeat for each problem.

Challenge Activity

Writing one-step problems.

Write two-digit numbers such as 53, 67, 46, etc. on separate cards.

Have each student select a card. Provide the following directions:

- Make up 3 word problems in which the number they selected is the answer in each problem.

- The unknown must be in a different position in each problem.

- Each problem must be about a different topic and the numbers used must be different from those used in the other problems.

- When finished, give each problem to a different classmate to solve. If they do not each have the same solution, the student who wrote the problems must check his/her problem for possible errors.

©Curriculum Associates, LLC   Copying is not permitted.

Lesson 10 (Student Book pages 82–87)

Understand Three-Digit Numbers

LESSON OBJECTIVES

- Identify ones, tens and hundreds in a three-digit number.

- Interpret models to determine the combinations of hundreds, tens and ones in a number.

- Write a three-digit number in terms of varied combinations of hundreds, tens and ones.

PREREQUISITE SKILLS

- Count to 100.

- Count by 10s and by 100s.

- Understand the concept of place value in two-digit numbers.

VOCABULARY

There is no new vocabulary.

THE LEARNING PROGRESSION

In first grade, students were introduced to the concept of place value as it applies to two-digit numbers. This concept has been reinforced in grade 2 as students add and subtract two-digit numbers.

In this lesson, students use base block to understand that one hundred can be seen as 100 ones or 10 groups of ten. As students count groups of blocks, they record the number in a chart to aid in connecting the concept that a digit is used to indicate the number of groups of objects within a number. This leads to the realization that a digit's value is dependent upon its placement in a number. The 4 in 420 represents 4 groups of one hundred, while the 4 in 42 represents 4 groups of ten. This concept will be further developed in the next lesson as students learn to accurately read and write three-digit numbers.

As early as kindergarten, students are led to recognize the inclusive nature of numbers. Within 7 there is a group of 3 and a group of 4 or 2 groups of three and 1 more, etc. This concept is extended into grade 1 with two-digit numbers and in grade 2 with three-digit numbers. This understanding is foundational for upcoming work with subtraction and other operations in the future.

Ready *Teacher Toolbox*   *Teacher-Toolbox.com*

	Prerequisite Skills	*2.NBT.A.1a* *2.NBT.A.1b* *2.NBT.A.2*
Ready Lessons	✓ ✓ ✓	✓
Tools for Instruction	✓	✓
Interactive Tutorials	✓	✓ ✓

CCSS Focus

2.NBT.A.1 Understand that the three digits of a three-digit number represent amounts of hundreds, tens, and ones; e.g., 706 equals 7 hundreds, 0 tens, and 6 ones. Understand the following as special cases:

    a. 100 can be thought of as a bundle of ten tens – called a "hundred."

    b. The numbers 100, 200, 300, 400, 500, 600, 700, 800, 900 refer to one, two, three, four, five, six, seven, eight, or nine hundreds (and 0 tens and 0 ones).

2.NBT.A.2 Count within 1000; skip count by 5s, 10s, and 100s.

STANDARDS FOR MATHEMATICAL PRACTICE: *SMP 2, 3, 7 (see page A9 for full text)*

101

©Curriculum Associates, LLC   Copying is not permitted.

Tens and Hundreds

Objective: Explore three-digit numbers	**Materials for each student:** • connecting cubes

Overview

Students explore hundreds as ten groups of ten by connecting cubes into groups of ten and bundling into groups of hundreds.

Step by Step (15–20 minutes)

1 Build stacks of cubes.

- Organize students into pairs and provide them with connecting cubes.

- Ask students to build 4 stacks of 10 cubes each.

- Ask: *How many cubes did you stack?* [40] *How do you know?* [I counted them all; I counted by tens.]

- Tell students to combine their stacks with a partner. Ask: *How many cubes do you have now?* [8 stacks or 80 cubes.]

2 Building hundreds.

- Ask partners to discuss how many more stacks they will need to have 100 cubes and then make the extra stacks.

- Ask: *How many extra stacks did you make?* [2] *How many total stacks do you have?* [10] *How can you be sure you have 100 cubes stacked?* [count by tens]

- Ask: *How many stacks would you need to show 200 cubes?* Have partners discuss this question and explain how they know.

- Share student ideas as a class. You may want them to think about and suggest how many stacks would be needed to show 300, 400, 500, . . . cubes.

3 Apply the concept to multiples of ten.

- Have student pairs build three more stacks of ten and combine them with the ten stacks they made earlier. Ask partners to identify the total number of cubes they have in terms of both ones, tens, and hundreds and tens.

4 Extend the concept.

- Engage students in thinking about how they would show other multiples of 10 cubes. You may want to challenge them to think beyond the 100s using numbers such as 240, 350, etc.

©Curriculum Associates, LLC   Copying is not permitted.

AT A GLANCE

Students explore the meaning of one hundred through two different models. They see that 100 can be expressed as 100 ones or 10 tens.

STEP BY STEP

- Introduce the question at the top of the page. Emphasize that there are many ways to count to 100. Have students generate ideas of how they could count to 100 [by 1s, 2s, 5s, 10s, etc].

- Draw students' attention to the number 100 shown on the chart. Discuss the differences among the one-digit, two-digit and three-digit numbers shown on the chart helping students recognize that the number of place values is what gives the number its designation. This may be difficult for students to articulate, so emphasize that each of the individual "numbers" in 100 are called digits.

- Read the Think section together. After students circle groups of 10 ones, compare what they did to the model of the 10 tens. Students should notice that they circled ten groups of 10 and the model shows ten groups of 10.

- Refer students back to the hundreds chart on the page. Ask if they can find groups of 10 in the chart. Students may identify groups either horizontally or vertically. Although both are accurate, you may want to point out that the horizontal groups include the counting numbers within each ten.

SMP Tip: Analyzing a hundreds chart for skip counting and identifying groups of ten helps students recognize the patterns and structure inherent in our number system (*SMP 7*), enabling them to become proficient with the base ten number system.

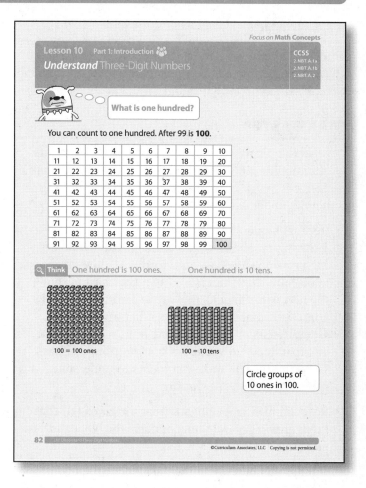

Mathematical Discourse

- *Why do you think 100 is called a three-digit number?*

  Students should recognize that there are 3 digits or 3 place values designated in the number 100.

- *Look at the hundreds chart. How is the number 100 the same and how is it different from the other numbers in its column?*

  Possible responses: It has all zeros after the first "number" (digit) like the other numbers, but it has two zeros instead of only one.

- *How does counting by tens help you think about 100?*

  Instead of counting all the ones, I can count groups of ten gets to 100 much more quickly. I have to count by tens 10 times, but it is the same as counting 100 ones.

©Curriculum Associates, LLC   Copying is not permitted.

AT A GLANCE

Students explore ways in which 100 can be represented, analyze picture models and a chart and then use symbols to represent a three-digit number.

STEP BY STEP

- Read the Think statement together. Draw students' attention to the three picture models and ask what each one represents. Instruct students to fill in the blanks under each model.

- Instruct students to look at the chart and talk to a partner to decide which of the pictures matches each row on the chart and justify. As they share ideas make sure they understand that the chart is showing the number of blocks that are locked together. The 1 hundred block is locked together, there are no separate tens or ones. The one hundred block can be separated into groups of tens or groups of ones. This concept will enable students to understand subtraction with regrouping.

- Read Think and emphasize that the zeros tell that there are no separate tens or ones; the blocks form one large 100 flat.

- Have students reply to the Talk About It question. Allow students to draw pictures, if necessary, but encourage them to use number representations also.

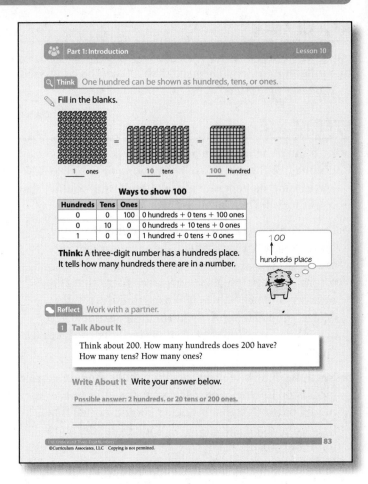

Hands-On Activity

Materials: base blocks

- Distribute the blocks so that each student has at least 30 units, 12 rods and 2 flats.

- Instruct students to use their blocks to show 3 groups of 10. Ask students to show how many ones are in 3 groups of 10. Ask them to show 6 groups of 10. Ask: *How many ones do you think there are in 6 groups of 10?* [60] *Justify.* Make sure students recognize that the ten rods can be broken into individual ones.

- Ask students how many ones they would have if they broke the rods or the flat apart [100].

Mathematical Discourse

- *How are the three pictures on this page alike?*

  They all show 100 using squares or rectangles.

- *How are the pictures on this page different from each other?*

  In the first one the pieces are all locked together. In the second one, the tens are locked together, but there are spaces between them. In the third one, all the pieces are separate.

- *Why do you think there are two zeros after the 1 in 100?*

  Students should recognize that the zeros indicate that there are no additional tens or ones.

©Curriculum Associates, LLC   Copying is not permitted.

AT A GLANCE

Students use counting strategies to understand large numbers.

STEP BY STEP

- Tell students that they will have time to work individually on the Explore It problems on this page and then share their responses in groups. Ask students to look at the first set of drawings and count the groups of 100. Ask: *How many groups of 100 are shown?* [3]. Instruct students to write that number on the blank. Encourage students to continue counting by hundreds to 900. Use the first discourse question to connect counting strategies.

- For Problem 3, reinforce the concept that the zeros following the 3 indicate that there are no separate tens or ones. You may want to write the addition on the board: 100 + 100 + 100 = 300. Explain that they are putting groups together just as they do when adding.

- Ask students to look at the second group of models and ask how these compare to the first group. They should note that in this case there are extra groups of ten that are not connected.

- As students complete this page individually, circulate among them. This is an opportunity to assess student understanding and address student misconceptions. Use the second Mathematical Discourse question to engage student thinking.

- Take note of students who are still having difficulty and wait to see if their understanding progresses as they work in their groups during the next part of the lesson.

> **SMP Tip:** Using counting strategies to interpret large numbers builds a sense of quantities in students and enables them to use symbolic representations in a meaningful way. *(SMP 2)*

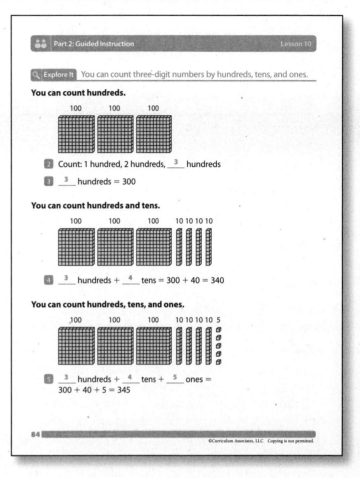

Mathematical Discourse

- *How is counting by hundreds like counting by tens?*

  You count 1 group of a hundred, 2 groups of a hundred, 3 groups of a hundred and so on just like you count 1 group of 10, 2 groups of ten, 3 groups of ten and so on.

- *Why doesn't it make sense to write 300 instead of 3 on the first blank or 40 instead of 4 on the second blank?*

  There aren't 300 groups of a hundred, but 3; and there aren't 40 groups of ten, but 4 groups of ten.

©Curriculum Associates, LLC   Copying is not permitted.

AT A GLANCE

Students interpret models and organize three-digit numbers in varied ways.

STEP BY STEP

- Organize students in pairs to answer Problems 6–8 on this page. You may choose to work through the first Talk About It problem together.

- Walk around to each group, listen to, and join in on discussions at different points. Use the Mathematical Discourse questions to help support or extend students' thinking.

- Direct the group's attention to Try it Another Way. Instruct them to work in pairs to fill in the charts.

- Invite volunteers to come to the board to show how they completed the charts for problems 9 and 10.

- Make sure students include a zero as a placeholder in each of the problems. Discuss that in the chart, it may not seem important to include the zero, but when the number is written out of the chart, it is very important. Write 530 on the board and ask children to read the number. Then write the number 53 on the board and ask them to read it. Ask: *Why is it important to add the zero on the end?* (It makes the 53 mean 53 tens, not 53 ones.)

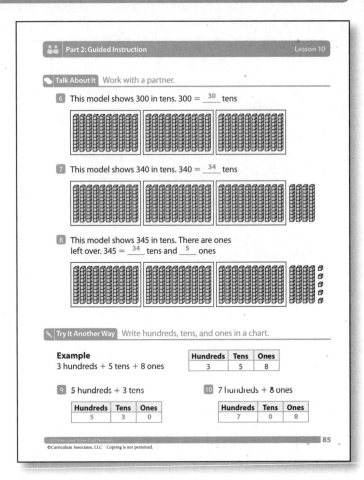

Visual Model

- Tell students that they can draw simple models to help them understand placeholders. Draw the following on the board:

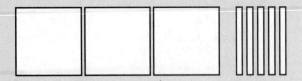

- Write 100 inside each square and 10 inside each rectangle and write 3 hundreds + 5 tens = 350.

- Draw the following:

- Ask children to write the number shown [35]. Compare the models to see that they are not equal.

Mathematical Discourse

- *Why do you think there is a box around some of the tens? What does it represent?*

  Students should recognize that there are 10 tens in each box that represents 100. The box around them makes it easier to count the groups.

- *How do the pictures help you think about the number 345?*

  It is easy to see the 10 tens in each hundred and the extra tens and ones. In 345 there are 3 hundreds 4 tens and 5 ones or 34 tens and 5 ones or it could be broken into 345 ones.

©Curriculum Associates, LLC   Copying is not permitted.

AT A GLANCE

Students demonstrate their understanding of three-digit numbers by analyzing and comparing different ways to represent large numbers.

STEP BY STEP

- Discuss each Connect It problem as a class using the discussion points outlined below:

Evaluate:

- Ask students to explain the error Lana made. [She didn't write a zero in the tens place to show there are no extra tens.] *Why do you think she may have made this error?* [She doesn't understand what hundreds tens and ones mean.]

- Invite a volunteer to come to the board and write the number Lana should have written. Then ask: *How would you help Lana understand what she did wrong?* Allow students to talk in pairs about how they could help Lana. Encourage volunteers to share their ideas with the class. **(DOK 3)**

> **SMP Tip:** Providing opportunities for students to analyze the reasoning of others and then communicate accurately builds the awareness that math must make sense and enables students to clarify and refine their own thinking. *(SMP 3)*

Analyze:

- Write the way each student represented the number 572 on separate sections of the board. Ask students to talk to a partner about what each student did and whether or not it is mathematically accurate. Encourage volunteers to come to the board to justify how both Sam and Sue can be correct. If students do not use a visual model to justify, you may want to ask students to come to the board to draw a model using ☐ for 100 | for 10 and • for one. Make sure that for the 57 tens, groups of 10 tens are boxed to represent a group of 100. This will make the models more visually similar. **(DOK 3)**

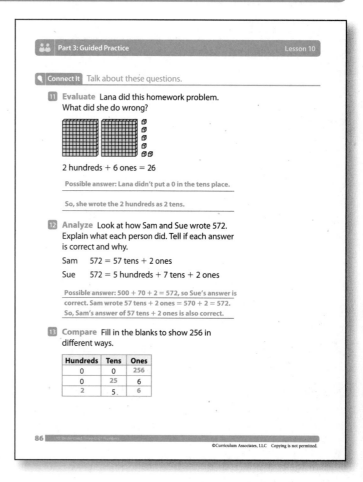

Compare:

- Draw the chart shown on the board, or on paper to project, leaving the bottom open. Ask students to tell you what belongs in each blank space and explain their thinking. **(DOK 2)**

- Ask: *Can you think of another way to show 256?* Listen to student responses expecting justification for each one. You may want to have base blocks available as a tool for justifying. If there are no viable responses, make suggestions such as: *How would you fill the rest of the chart if there are 20 tens?* Or: *What if I put 126 in the ones column?* Write those numbers and allow students to determine what they might put in the other columns. They should notice that there are many other ways to complete the chart. **(DOK 3)**

AT A GLANCE

Students demonstrate their understanding of three-digit numbers by drawing a picture, representing the solution in two ways and writing an original word problem.

STEP BY STEP

- Direct students to complete the Put It Together task on their own. **(DOK 3)**

- Have counter such as tiles available for students to stack, if necessary, to make sense of the problem.

- Suggest that students draw rectangles or simple cylinders to represent the stacks of coins. It is not necessary to show the ten coins in each stack, however, some students may need to do this. Encourage students to focus on the task rather than on an artistic drawing.

- Make sure students are aware that the word problem they write should have an answer in the hundreds.

- As students work on their own, walk around to assess their progress and understanding, to answer their questions, and to give additional support, if needed.

- If time permits, have students share the strategies they used in completing the task.

Put It Together Use what you have learned to complete this task.

14 Nate puts his coins in stacks of ten. He has 12 stacks of coins with 4 coins left over.

A Draw a picture to show Nate's coins.

B How many coins does Nate have? Write the answer in two different ways.

Possible answer: 12 tens + 4 ones; 120 + 4 or

124 coins

C Suppose Nate gets 30 more coins from a friend. Write this new number of coins in two different ways.

Possible answer: 12 tens + 3 tens + 4 ones =

15 tens + 4 ones; 150 + 4 = 154.

L10: Understand Three-Digit Numbers
©Curriculum Associates, LLC   Copying is not permitted.
87

SCORING RUBRICS

A

Points	Expectations
2	The student draws an accurate picture to represent the situation.
1	The student is partially correct. Some elements of the picture may be accurate but not all of them.
0	The student is not able to accurately complete the picture.

B

Points	Expectations
2	The student answers correctly and writes it in two different ways.
1	The answer is correct, but only one written representation is accurate.
0	The student is not able to accurately answer or write in two ways.

C

Points	Expectations
2	The student writes a word problem involving a number in the hundreds.
1	The student writes a word problem, but not one that involves a three-digit number.
0	The student is not able to write a word problem.

©Curriculum Associates, LLC   Copying is not permitted.

Intervention Activity

Break apart numbers

Materials: base blocks; place value mats (Activity Sheet 6, page 313); cards with single digit numbers written on them (Activity Sheet 1, page 308); cards with multiples of ten written on them; cards with 3-digit numbers written on them (Activity Sheet 7, page 314); and blank cards

- Provide each student with base blocks, blank cards, multiples of ten cards, single digit cards and a place value mat. Place the 3-digit number cards face down. Allow each student to draw a card. Remind students that if they used all unit blocks to make the number they would need to count that many units. Have the student use the blank card to cover the tens and ones place and count the number of hundreds flats equal to the number shown and place them on the mat. Slide the blank card to show the number of ten rods to place on the mat and finally add the number of units shown. (You may want to repeat this activity several times before moving on.)

- Have students move the hundreds flats off the mat and substitute 10 rods for them. Ask them to find the card (multiple of 10) that tells how many rods there are. Add them to the rods that are on the mat and cover the ones place on the corresponding 3-digit card. Students should see that the number revealed equals the total number of rods on the mat with one units left. You may wish to record each step on a chart.

On-Level Activity

Play three-digit number "around the table"

Materials: base blocks; a place value mat (Activity Sheet 6, page 313) for each student; and cards each with a different three-digit number written on it

- Divide students into groups of 3. Provide each student with a place value mat and base blocks. Place the cards face down in a pile. Allow one student to pick a card and use blocks to represent it on the mat. The student to the right must represent it in a different way and then the last student must represent it in another way also. The only rule is that no one can use ALL ones to represent the number. Once they have agreed that all the representations are accurate they record each representation. The second student in the group picks a card and play resumes as in the first round. Continue until time is up or the cards have all been used.

Challenge Activity

Organizing data

Refer back to the Compare activity students did as a class during Guided Practice. Help students draw a chart, or have one drawn for each of them, and ask them to label it Hundreds, Tens, Ones (you will need to have extra paper or extra charts available).

Tell students you want them to try to find **all** the ways to show 127 on the chart. Encourage them to think of possible strategies they may use before beginning. Allow students to discuss those strategies with each other or with you.

After students have completed the task, have them present their charts to the class discussing the patterns they used and then display them on the wall or bulletin board.

©Curriculum Associates, LLC   Copying is not permitted.

Lesson 11 (Student Book pages 88–95)

Read and Write Three-Digit Numbers

LESSON OBJECTIVES

- Identify place values: ones, tens, hundreds.
- Model three-digit numbers.
- Interpret a model and write the number value.

PREREQUISITE SKILLS

In order to be proficient with the concepts/skills in this lesson, students should:

- Understand two-digit numbers.
- Count by tens and hundreds.
- Add two-digit numbers.

VOCABULARY

digit: any one of the ten symbols used to write numbers: 0, 1, 2, 3, 4, 5, 6, 7, 8, 9

value: the amount a digit is worth

THE LEARNING PROGRESSION

In Grade 1, students explored the concept of place value by bundling 10 ones to make groups of ten. They learned to read numbers between 9 and 99 and write them using proper digit placement. In grade 2, this concept is extended to include the hundreds place as a group of 10 tens. Through active involvement, students make sense of the place value system recognizing a digit as a symbol that tells the number of groups of hundreds, tens and ones in a number. They are then led to read the numbers accurately.

In Grade 2, a firm grasp of this concept is essential for students to fully understand addition and subtraction of numbers with more than three digits that will follow after grade 2 as well as to understand multiplication and division of multi-digit numbers in grades 3 and 4. Place value concepts are then extended to decimal places in grade 5.

	Prerequisite Skills	2.NBT.A.3
Ready *Teacher Toolbox*		*Teacher-Toolbox.com*
Ready Lessons	✓ ✓	✓
Tools for Instruction	✓	✓
Interactive Tutorials	✓	✓ ✓

CCSS Focus

2.NBT.A.3 Read and write numbers to 1000 using base-ten numerals, number names, and expanded form.

STANDARDS FOR MATHEMATICAL PRACTICE: SMP 2, 4, 7 (*see page A9 for full text*)

©Curriculum Associates, LLC   Copying is not permitted.

Put Together Hundreds, Tens, and Ones

Objective: Express three-digit numbers in terms of hundreds, tens and ones.	**Materials for each student:** • Base-ten blocks • Place value mats (Activity Sheet 6, page 313) • Digit cards

Overview

Students build numbers involving hundreds, tens and ones and express the value of each one.

Step by Step (10–15 minutes)

1 Build a number.

- Provide students with base-ten blocks and a large place value mat.

- Ask students to place 3 hundreds, 2 tens and 7 ones in their proper location on the mat.

2 Read a number.

- Hold up a hundred block. Ask: *What does this show?* [a hundred units] *How many hundreds are on your mat?* [3] Have students place the digit card "3" under the hundreds place.

- Display a tens block. Ask: *What does this show?* [ten units] *How many tens are on your mat?* [2] Have students place the digit card "2" under the tens place.

- Ask: *What does a unit cube show?* [one] *How many ones are on your mat?* [7] Have students place the digit card "7" under the ones place.

3 Put it all together.

- Ask: *What number is used to show 3 hundreds?* [300] *What number is used to show 2 tens?* [20] *What number is used to show 7 ones?* [7]

- Now put together the numbers you just used for hundreds, tens, and ones. How do you say this new number? [three hundred twenty-seven]

4 Apply to other numbers.

- Repeat the activities above using other numbers such as 452, 691, 758.

- Tell students that in this lesson, they will learn more about reading and writing numbers in the hundreds.

©Curriculum Associates, LLC   Copying is not permitted.

AT A GLANCE

Students use what they know about hundreds, tens and ones to interpret a model.

STEP BY STEP

- Tell students that this page shows them how to think about and write a three-digit number.

- Have students read the problem at the top of the page. Ask: *Is the number of packs Jan buys the same as the number of balloons she buys? Explain.* Students should recognize that since each pack contains more than one balloon, she buys many more balloons than packs. This discussion prepares students for the idea of place "value" that is explored in this lesson.

- Work through Explore It as a class. Make sure students connect the models to the initial problem. They should see the hundred flats and ten rods as the packs of balloons from the problem and the units as single balloons.

- Encourage students to underline or highlight the word value in each sentence in which it appears. Discuss that each flat contains 100 ones just as a pack of 100 contains 100 balloons. The *value* of the flat or the pack is in terms of ones. Repeat with the value of a ten rod and ten pack. You may want to use the Real-World Connection to reinforce this concept and prepare students for upcoming activities.

- Once students complete part D, ask them to tell what numbers they wrote in the blanks and explain why.

- Instruct students to circle the 2, the 7 and the 5 that they wrote in the blanks for the first parts of A, B and C. Ask where they see those numbers located in the sum. Discuss that the 2 is in the hundreds *place*, the 7 is in the tens place and the 5 is in the ones *place* of the sum.

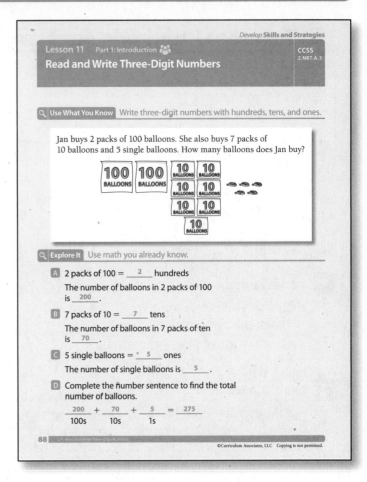

Real-World Connection

Show students a ten dollar bill (you may use realistic play money). Ask: *How many bills do you see?* [1]. *If I traded this in for $1 bills, how many should I get?* [10]. Hold the ten dollar bill in one hand and the 10 ones in the other and ask which is more—the one ten or the ten ones. Students should recognize that they represent the same amount of money. Then show a $100 dollar bill and ask how many ten dollar bills you should get if you traded it in for ones. How many ones? Reinforce the concept that one bill can have a value of more than one dollar.

SMP Tip: Providing students opportunities to experience large numbers in a variety of contexts enables them to make sense of the values represented by digit placement and the quantity as a whole. *(SMP 2)*

AT A GLANCE

Students determine the value of a digit based on its placement in a number.

STEP BY STEP

- Read Find Out More as a class.

- Use the Concept Extension and the first Mathematical Discourse question to reinforce the concept of digit.

- Help students interpret the information in the place-value chart. Explain that a 4 in the tens place means 4 tens or 40. A 4 in the ones place means 4 ones, or 4. You may want to use base-ten blocks to support these ideas.

- Ask students to work with a partner to answer the Talk About It questions. After students complete Write About It, have them share their numbers, evaluating them for accuracy.

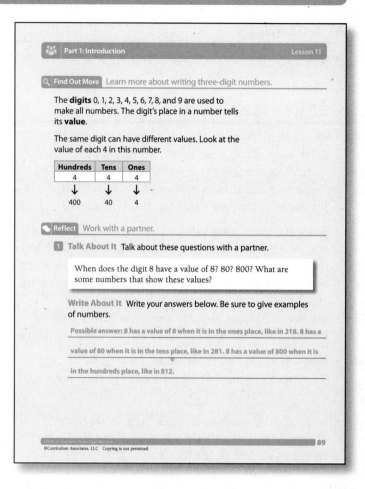

Concept Extension

- Explain to students that we use many symbols in our world. They might see a ⤷ on a bike trail to tell them to turn right. In math we use symbols like + and = to tell us what to do. A digit is a symbol that tells how many groups of ones, tens, hundreds, and so on there are in a number. Since a digit is one symbol, the only symbols or digits we use are 0–9. Emphasize that the number 37 tells how many of something, such as crayons, there are, and the digits 3 and 7 tell how many groups there are within the number—3 groups of 10 and 7 groups of one. You may want to note that when a digit is used alone it is a number since it is describing the number of what you have.

- Write several two and three-digit numbers on the board. Ask students to tell you what the number is and identify the digits.

Mathematical Discourse

- *Why isn't the number 23 called a digit?*

  Students should respond that 23 uses two symbols or digits. A digit is only one symbol.

- *Why might a student write two hundred seventy-five as 200705? Why is it incorrect?*

  The student just wrote all the values next to each other. It is not correct because the number is too big. The 7 is in the hundreds place instead of the 2 and the zero is in the tens place instead of the 7.

©Curriculum Associates, LLC   Copying is not permitted.

AT A GLANCE

Students represent a three digit number in pictures and in a chart.

STEP BY STEP

- Read the problem at the top of the page as a class. Refer back to the Real-World Activity in Part One reminding students that a ten dollar bill is equal to ten one dollar bills so its value is ten dollars. The same is true for a one hundred dollar bill.

- Draw students' attention to Picture It. Ask them to describe what the picture shows. Ask how many bills they see [6]. Ask: *Do the number of bills tell how much money Mike has? Explain.* Students should be able to articulate that since each one hundred dollar bill is equal to 100 ones and the ten dollar bill is equal to 10 ones, Mike must have more money than 6 dollars.

- Connect the quick drawing to the bills by asking students to write 100, 10, or 1 next to each part of the quick drawing.

- Instruct students to place the digit in each space of the chart that tells the number of hundreds, tens and ones shown in the pictures.

SMP Tip: To reinforce modeling, use the problem on this page, but change Mike's winnings to 6 hundreds bills, 3 tens bills and 5 ones bills. Ask a volunteer to show the number of bills he wins using play money. Instruct students to make a quick drawing to represent the winnings and then show it in a chart. *(SMP 4)*

ELL Support

For students who are not familiar with American dollars, use money from their native country whose denominations are in powers of ten such as the Mexican1 peso coin, 10 peso coin and 100 peso bill.

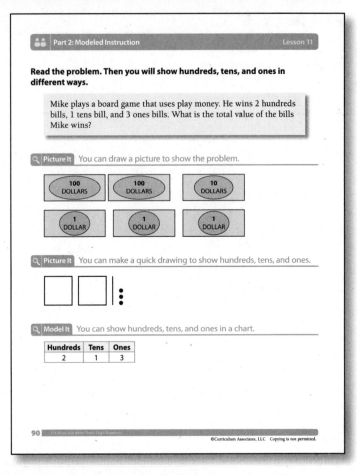

Hands-On Activity

Materials: base blocks

- Distribute blocks to students and ask them to show the amount of money Mike wins using the blocks.

- Have students tell the blocks they used and justify their choices.

- Ask them to compare the blocks to the quick drawing on this page. Ask how they knew each of the flats drawn on the page was equal to 100 and how they know that the base block flat is equal to or worth 100. Students should see that the physical blocks are divided into 100 units. Tell them that the quick drawings are just like the blocks but without all the ones shown to make them "quick" to draw.

©Curriculum Associates, LLC   Copying is not permitted.

AT A GLANCE

Students revisit the problem on page 90 by connecting the digits to the values they represent.

STEP BY STEP

- Read Connect It as a class. Make sure students understand that the questions refer to the problem on page 90.

- For Problem 3, ensure students understand that the value they are finding is the combined value of each kind of bill, not the value of only one bill.

- As students complete Problem 4, ask them why it makes sense to add all the values together.

- For Problem 5 make sure students understand that the 2 tens Mike wins are in addition to the money he has already won.

- Tell students that they may use a picture or other model help solve the Try It problem. Have students explain the thinking they used in solving the problem.

Hands-On Activity

Materials: base blocks; place value charts (Activity Sheet 6, page 313); number cards 0–9

- Distribute the materials and ask the students to show the number 324 with base blocks. (Do not write the number)

- Have them place the digit cards in the proper places on their chart to show the number. Connect the digit and placement with the 3 hundreds flats, 2 ten rods and 4 ones. Have students write the expanded form and sum $300 + 20 + 4 = 324$.

- Repeat as necessary to solidify the concept. Include numbers such as 420 and 205 to reinforce the concept of 0 as a placeholder.

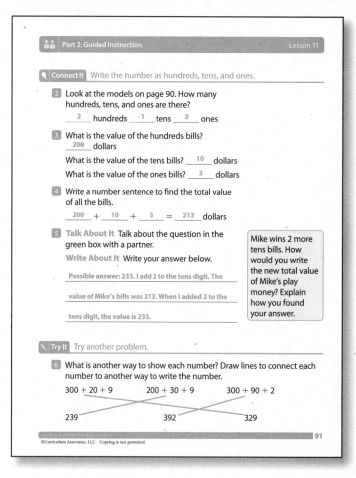

TRY IT SOLUTION

6 *Solution:* $300 + 20 + 9 = 329$; $200 + 30 + 9 = 239$; $300 + 90 + 2 = 392$. *(DOK 1)*

ERROR ALERT: Watch for students who may invert the 9 and 2 in 329 and 392.

SMP Tip: Ask students to describe the structure that is inherent in our place value system. In a three-digit number, the first digit represents the number of hundreds, the second digit the number of tens and the third digit the number of ones that collectively equal the number. *(SMP 7)*

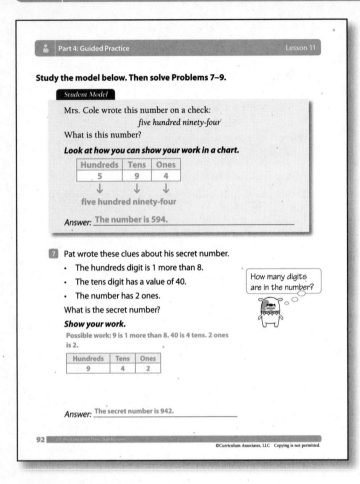

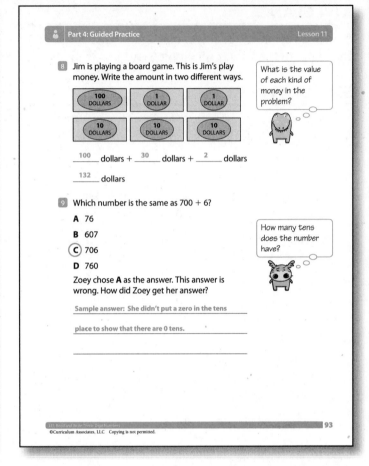

AT A GLANCE

Students connect representations to base ten numbers.

STEP BY STEP

- Ask students to solve the problems individually and show all their work. Tell students to describe their thinking. For problem 7, encourage students to describe how they found each digit. For students who are struggling with problem 9, suggest that they draw a hundreds chart.

- When students have completed each problem, have them Pair/Share to discuss their solutions with a partner.

SOLUTIONS

Ex A hundreds chart is used to help students organize the place values described in the number word. Students could also write the number in expanded form $500 + 90 + 4 = 594$. **(DOK 1)**

7 *Solution:* The secret number is 942; 9 is one more than 8, 40 equals 4 tens, and 2 ones is 2. **(DOK 2)**

8 *Solution:* 100 dollars + 30 dollars + 2 dollars is 132 dollars. **(DOK 2)**

9 *Solution:* **C**; $700 + 6 = 706$.

Explain to students why the other choices are not correct:

B is not correct because $607 = 600 + 7 \neq 700 + 6$.

D is not correct because $760 = 700 + 60 \neq 700 + 6$. **(DOK 3)**

©Curriculum Associates, LLC   Copying is not permitted.

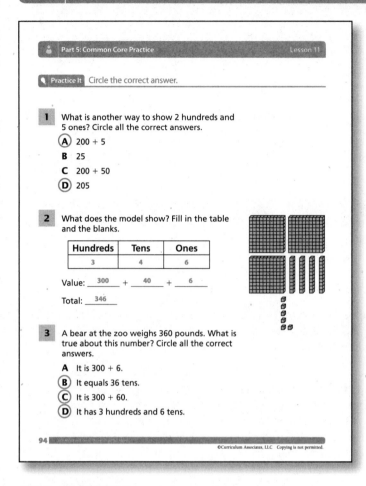

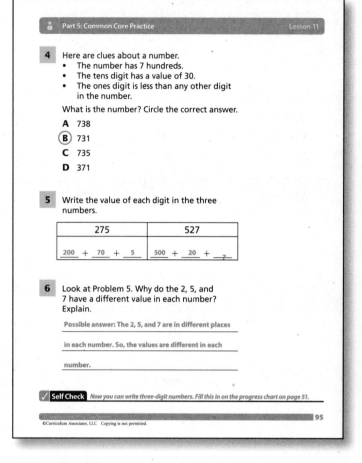

AT A GLANCE

Students find appropriate ways to represent three-digit numbers that might appear on a mathematics test.

STEP BY STEP

• First, tell students they will find ways to show three-digit numbers. Then have students read the directions and answer the questions independently. Remind students to fill in the correct answer choices on the Answer Form.

• After students have completed the Common Core Practice problems, review and discuss correct answers. Have student record the number of correct answers in the box provided.

SOLUTIONS

1 *Solution:* **A** and **D**; 2 hundreds = 200 and 5 ones = 5 (**A**). The 2 is in the hundreds place and 5 is in the ones place (**D**). (*DOK 2*)

2 *Solution:* 3, 4, 6; 300, 40, 6; 346. (*DOK 2*)

3 *Solution:* **B**, **C** and **D**; 36 tens = 360 ones (**B**). 300 + 60 = 360 (**C**). 360 = 300 + 60 or 3 hundreds and 6 tens (**D**). (*DOK 2*)

4 *Solution:* **B**; 7 hundreds = 700, 30 is 3 tens, 1 is less than both 3 and 7. (*DOK 3*)

5 *Solution:* 200 + 70 + 5; 500 + 20 + 7. (*DOK 1*)

6 *Solution:* Possible answer: The 2, 5, and 7 are in different places in each number. The place it is in gives the digit its value. (*DOK 3*)

Assessment and Remediation

- Jamie is collecting coins. She has 4 jars of one hundred coins in each jar and 7 more coins. How many coins does Jamie have? [407]

- For students who are still struggling, use the chart below to guide remediation.

- After providing remediation, check students' understanding using the following problem: Sam is the banker for a board game. Each player gets $240 to start the game. How many hundred, ten and one bills should he give each player? [2 hundred bills and 4 ten bills]

If the error is...	Students may...	To remediate...
47	have placed the digits 4 and 7 together.	Provide students a place value chart. Help them model the situation by placing the digit in the chart that represents the number of jars and the number of extra coins Jamie has. Assist students in writing the number correctly.
470	have placed the 4 in the hundreds place and placed the 7 next to it followed by a zero.	Help the student write the value of the total number of coins in the jars and the extra coins in expanded form: 400 + 7. Help them to see that there are no groups of ten so they should write 400 with a 7 in the ones place.
11	have added the two numbers shown.	Use base blocks to model the situation ensuring the student recognizes the 100 units in the hundreds flats. Remind students that the total tells the number of units that are shown. Have the student count by 100s to find the total in the 4 flats (or 4 jars) and then add the additional ones. Write the total in a place value chart and as a sum.

Hands-On Activity

Race to 500

Materials: base blocks (one set per pair), place value charts (Activity Sheet 6, page 313; one per student), 0-9 digit cards (at least 2 of each), and two dice one white and one colored (one set per team)

- Organize students into pairs and distribute the materials to each student. Instruct students to take turns rolling the dice and use base blocks to model what they roll. The number on the white die tells how many ones they take and the number on the colored die tells the number of ten rods. Place digit cards on the place value mat to show the total. On the next and subsequent rolls students add the number of blocks rolled to what they already have, organize their blocks into groups of ones, tens and hundreds and display with digit cards on the place value chart. Continue until one player reaches 500.

Challenge Activity

On Beyond Hundreds

Challenge students to explore numbers greater than 999 by giving them a place value chart showing at least 6 place value positions. Ask them to fill in the place values they already know. They should be able to fill in ones, tens, and hundreds.

Tell them that their task is:

1) to find out what label belongs in the remainder of the place value positions on the chart (allow them to use whatever resources they need).

2) figure out the value of each of the labels.

3) write numbers with six or more place values in expanded form and read them using the proper place value names.

©Curriculum Associates, LLC   Copying is not permitted.

Lesson 12 (Student Book pages 96–105)

Compare Three-Digit Numbers

LESSON OBJECTIVES

- Evaluate models of three-digit numbers to determine whether numbers are greater than, less than or equal to each other.

- Express equalities and inequalities in number sentences using proper notation.

- Solve problems and justify solutions involving inequalities.

PREREQUISITE SKILLS

In order to be proficient with the concepts/skills in this lesson, students should:

- Identify place values in three-digit numbers.

- Model three-digit numbers.

- Understand the concept of greater than, less than and equal to.

VOCABULARY

There is no new vocabulary.

THE LEARNING PROGRESSION

In Grade 1, students explored the concept of greater than and less than comparing place values of two-digit numbers. They recorded comparisons using the symbols for inequalities. Students learned the meaning of the equal sign and applied it to number sentences.

In Grade 2, students expand their understanding of numbers and place values as they explore three-digit numbers. They model three digit numbers attending to the additional place value position of the hundreds place. The concept of inequality is explored further as students measure and compare lengths. **In this lesson,** students compare three-digit numbers through picture models, charts and sentences involving numbers. Numbers are applied to a variety of settings extending the concept of number beyond physical quantity yet modeling and comparing them in the same way. Students model situations involving inequalities using number sentences with the appropriate symbol.

In Grade 3 and beyond, students apply their understanding of inequalities to fractions and decimals. They model inequalities on a number line and explore the meaning of the greater than or equal to symbol used in algebraic sentences.

Ready *Teacher Toolbox*   *Teacher-Toolbox.com*

	Prerequisite Skills	*2.NBT.A.4*
Ready Lessons	✓	✓
Tools for Instruction		✓
Interactive Tutorials	✓	✓ ✓

CCSS Focus

2.NBT.A.4 Compare two three-digit numbers based on meanings of the hundreds, tens, and ones digits, using >, =, and < symbols to record the results of comparisons.

STANDARDS FOR MATHEMATICAL PRACTICE: **SMP 2, 3, 4, 6, 7** *(see page A9 for full text)*

©Curriculum Associates, LLC   Copying is not permitted.

Compare Two-Digit Numbers

Objective: Compare two-digit numbers using *greater than* and *less than*.	**Materials for each student:** • a set of cards per student pair (Activity Sheet 8, pages 315–316)

Overview

Students practice the concept of *greater than* and *less than* by playing a card game comparing 2-digit numbers.

Step by Step (15–20 minutes)

1 Prepare the game.

• Make a set of 30–40 cards with varied 2-digit numbers for each student pair.

• Put students in pairs and give them a set of cards.

2 Play the game.

• Instruct students to divide their cards into two equal piles, placing them face down. Tell them how many cards to put in each pile. Each partner takes a pile. Tell them they are going to play a game of "greater than".

• Have students turn the card from the top of their pile face up. They compare the cards and decide whose number is greater. The player with the greater number keeps both cards.

• Students continue to play until all cards have been played. To avoid excessive competition have students mix the cards back together without counting the number each student "won".

• Replay the game as a "less than" game.

• As students play, make sure they understand the concept of *greater than* and *less than*. Have a hundreds chart available for reference, if necessary.

• You may want students to replay the game when finished. Allow them to trade cards with another group for variety.

3 Discuss the game.

• Use this question to assess students' understanding of comparing two-digit numbers: *How did you know if your number was greater than or less than your partner's number?* Make sure students can analyze by comparing the tens place. If the tens digits are the same, then compare the ones digits. You can use a hundreds chart to reinforce this concept.

©Curriculum Associates, LLC   Copying is not permitted.

AT A GLANCE

Students use what they know about place value to interpret and compare two numbers.

STEP BY STEP

- Tell students that this page will help them decide what number is greater than the other.

- Have students read the problem at the top of the page. Tell them that the number in each box represents a digit. When the digits are written one next to the other, they form a larger number. Use the first Mathematical Discourse questions to reinforce this concept. Write the numbers the students generate on the board.

- Work through Explore It as a class. You may want to suggest that students use quick drawings of hundreds, tens and ones if they find this helpful. Use the second Mathematical Discourse questions and the Hands-On Activity to help students review using place values to read and write numbers.

Develop Skills and Strategies

Lesson 12   Part 1: Introduction

Compare Three-Digit Numbers   CCSS 2.NBT.A.4

Use What You Know   Compare hundreds and tens.

Kim and Jon toss beanbags at a target. What is the greatest number each person can make using the digits they land on? Whose number has the most hundreds?

Kim				Jon		
1	2	3		1	2	3
4	5	6		4	5	6
7	8	9		7	8	9

Explore It   Use math you already know.

A. What is the greatest number Kim can make? Why?

421; Kim has 3 numbers so put the greatest number in the hundreds place. Then the next greatest number in the tens place.

B. One of Jon's beanbags did not land on the board, so he can only use two numbers. What is the greatest number Jon can make? Why?

97; Jon has 2 numbers, so put the greatest number in the tens place.

C. How many hundreds, tens, and ones are in each number?

Kim's number: __4__ hundreds + __2__ tens + __1__ ones

Jon's number: __0__ hundred + __9__ tens + __7__ ones

D. Compare the numbers. Which has more hundreds?

421 has 4 hundreds. 97 has 0 hundreds. So Kim's number has more hundreds.

96   L12: Compare Three-Digit Numbers   ©Curriculum Associates, LLC   Copying is not permitted.

Hands-On Activity

Materials: base blocks, 0–9 cards (optional; Activity Sheet 1, page 308), place value charts (optional; Activity Sheet 6, page 313)

- Record the numbers generated from the first Mathematical Discourse question on the board. Ask students to show the number of ones, tens and hundreds contained in each number. This activity can be used to support student responses to the second discourse question.

- If students require additional support, have them place a corresponding 0–9 card under each group of blocks. Students should notice that the numbers formed are the same as the numbers written on the board.

- Compare each number Kim might have made to the number Jon might have made and ask: *Which number has more hundreds? Why?* [In each case, Kim's has more hundreds since there are no hundreds in any of Jon's numbers.]

Mathematical Discourse

- *What other numbers could Kim have made with her tosses? What other number could Jon have made? Why is there only one other number Jon could make?*

  Kim could have made 142, 214, 241, 412, 421; Jon could have made 79. Jon could only make one other number because there are only 2 digits so only 2 ways to arrange them.

- *How would you show the hundreds, tens and ones for the other numbers Kim could have made? For the other number Jon could have made?*

  Student responses should indicate that they understand place value by expressing the correct number of ones, tens and hundreds for each number.

AT A GLANCE

Students compare numbers by evaluating place values. They use the equality and inequality notation to write number sentences.

STEP BY STEP

- Read Find Out More as a class. Use the first Mathematical Discourse question to help students develop flexibility with number comparisons and, in turn, build number sense.

- To help students remember which symbol to use when comparing numbers, use the Visual Model.

- Have students write a number sentence using two numbers that would be connected with the equal sign. Make sure they understand that = is used only when the value on each side of it is exactly the same.

- As students discuss the Reflect question, encourage them to use reasoning. Allow the use of base-ten blocks to support their thinking, if necessary. Use the last Mathematical Discourse question to help students reason logically.

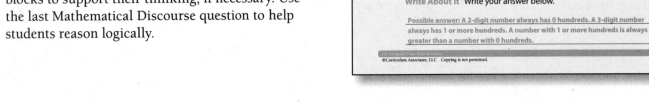

Visual Model

- Draw the inequality symbols on the board. Connect the two ends with an arc to resemble a pie with a slice missing. Tell students to think of it as a hungry creature that likes to eat whatever number is the greatest.

- Write the numbers 421 and 97 on the board in that order. Have a volunteer write the correct inequality symbol between them. Tell students that we read number sentences in the same direction as word sentences. Since 421 is *greater* and is listed first we read the sentence 421 > 97. Have students write a number sentence on white boards listing the 97 first. Help them see that when the smaller number is written first, the symbol is inverted and is read as *less than*.

Mathematical Discourse

- *How can thinking of 421 as tens and ones help you compare the numbers?*

  Since there are 42 tens in 421, you can compare those with the 9 tens in 97. 42 tens are more than 9 tens so 421 is greater than 97.

- *Why can't you use the equal sign to compare the numbers 421 and 97?*

  The equal sign means they are exactly the same amount. 421 and 97 are not the same amount.

- *Why is the **smallest** three-digit number always greater than the **greatest** two-digit number?*

  No matter how many are in the tens place of a two-digit number, the number can never equal 100 or be greater than 100. A three-digit number is always greater than or equal to 100.

©Curriculum Associates, LLC　Copying is not permitted.

AT A GLANCE

Students compare three-digit numbers by observing a situation modeled in a picture and in expanded form.

STEP BY STEP

- Tell students that they will find out how to decide what number is greater than or less than when both numbers are in the hundreds.

- Read the problem at the top of the page together as a class. Ask students what number they are supposed to find, the greater or the smaller.

- Draw attention to the base-ten models. Use the first Mathematical Discourse question to help students recognize that, in this model, there are an equal number of hundreds flats. Ask the second Mathematical Discourse question to help students analyze the models and find a strategy for determining greatest and least.

- Use a series of "What if?" questions to extend students' thinking. Ask questions like: *What if there were 4 tens in Diego's guess? Would it be smaller or greater than Bart's? Explain. What if there were 6 ones in Bart's guess?*

- Compare the visual models to the expanded form in the Model It section. Make sure students connect the written models to the visual models.

- Remind students of the previous page where they thought of 124 as 12 tens and 4 ones. Ask students to write both numbers from this page on white boards or paper in terms of tens and ones.

> **SMP Tip:** Write several three-digit numbers on the board. Ask students to describe each number in terms of tens and ones. They should recognize that the number represented by the hundreds and tens digits is equal to the total number of tens in each number. *(SMP 7)*

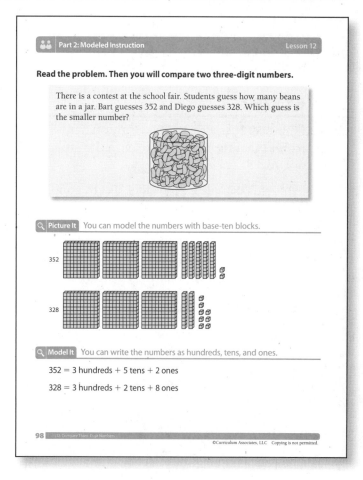

Mathematical Discourse

- *How are these models different from the ones you drew on the first page of the lesson?*

  Listen for or encourage responses that identify the models on this page as both having an equal number of hundreds.

- *What might you do to decide which number is the smaller number when the hundreds are the same? Explain.*

  You could look at the tens. Since the hundreds match up, you can see there are more tens in 352 and fewer tens in 328.

- *What is a number other than 328 that has 3 hundreds and is less than 352? Tell how you know.*

  Listen for accurate numbers and justification that compares the numbers in terms of tens and ones.

©Curriculum Associates, LLC   Copying is not permitted.

AT A GLANCE

Students revisit the problem on page 98 comparing numbers with an equal number of hundreds.

STEP BY STEP

- Read Connect It as a class. Make sure students understand that the questions refer to the problem on page 98.

- After students complete Problem 4, ask them to write a different numbers sentence using > to compare the two numbers.

> **SMP Tip:** Ask students to describe Bart's faulty reasoning using what they have learned about comparing numbers. (*SMP 3*)

Visual Model

Compare numbers on an open number line.

- Write the names of two towns/cities on the board whose distances are greater than 100 miles, but have the same number of hundreds of miles, from your school.

- Draw an open number line similar to the one shown using the names of the towns selected.

Our town   Town A
    o────────────o
        (distance)

Our town   Town B
    o──────────────o
        (distance)

- Ask: *Which town is the greater distance from our town?* [Town B] *How do you know?* [The line is longer.]

- Have students write the inequality that represents this situation on whiteboards or paper. Ask a volunteer to share the number sentence that was written. Discuss how two sentences one using > and another using < can both represent the same situation.

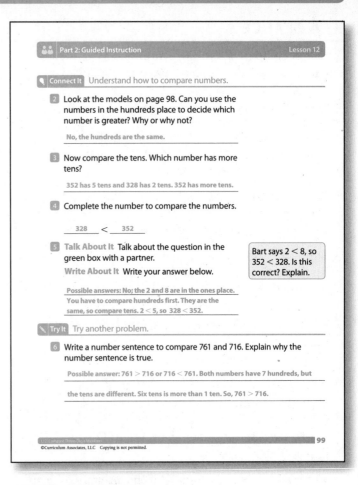

TRY IT SOLUTION

6 *Solution:* 761 > 716 or 716 < 761; both numbers have 7 hundreds, but the tens are different. Six tens is more than 1 ten so 761 is greater than 716. (*DOK 2*)

ERROR ALERT: Watch for students who may invert the 1 and 6 in one of the numbers, seeing the numbers as equal.

©Curriculum Associates, LLC   Copying is not permitted.

AT A GLANCE

Students model three-digit numbers when the hundreds and tens are equal in picture form and in a chart.

STEP BY STEP

- Tell students that they will find out how to decide what number is greater than or less than when both the hundreds and the tens are the same.

- Read the problem at the top of the page together as a class. Ask students what number they are supposed to find, the greater or the smaller.

- Draw attention to the quick drawing models. Use the first Mathematical Discourse question to help students recognize that, in this model, there are an equal number of hundreds and tens.

- Have students compare the numbers in the chart to the quick drawings. Guide them to see that the chart is a "shortcut" for writing 4 hundreds, 6 tens, 7 ones.

- Use the second Mathematical Discourse question to help students recognize that the only difference between these two numbers is found in the ones place.

- Replicate the chart on the board. Use a piece of paper to cover the digits in the hundreds place since the number of hundreds are the same. Cover the digits in the tens place since the number of tens are the same. Students can now compare the ones place to determine which number is greater.

> **SMP Tip:** Have students compare the models they have seen in this lesson. Ask them to tell which model(s) make it easier to write a number sentence comparing two numbers and why. (*SMP 4*)

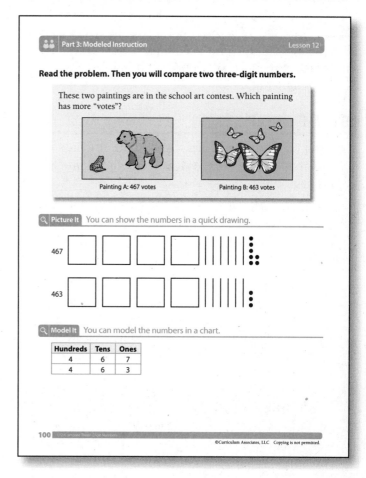

Mathematical Discourse

- *How do these models compare to the ones from the last section?*

  Listen for or encourage responses that identify the models on this page as both having an equal number of hundreds and tens.

- *How can thinking about the number of tens and ones help you decide which of these numbers is the greatest?*

  Since they both have 46 tens, the ones place will tell you which number has more likes.

AT A GLANCE

Students revisit the problem on page 100 comparing numbers with an equal number of hundreds and an equal number of tens.

STEP BY STEP

- Read Connect It as a class. Make sure students understand that the questions refer to the problem on page 100.

* For Problem 9, write the two number sentences on the board. Ask a volunteer to read the number sentence from left to right and attending to the direction of the inequality sign.

* After students complete the Try It section, ask them to tell how they knew which direction to write the inequality. Use this opportunity to correct student misunderstandings. Help individuals who struggle to find a method that is personally meaningful for remembering how to properly position the symbol.

SMP Tip: Have students describe the strategy they used in Problem 12 to determine which number was greater and which one was smaller, and explain how they know they are correct. *(SMP 6)*

ELL Support

Students may struggle with the terms "greater than" and "less than." Try using terms more familiar to them like bigger and smaller. When a term is found that makes sense, provide each student with a card that has the words "greater than" printed on it. Write the synonym that is most familiar to the student under it. Do the same for "less than."

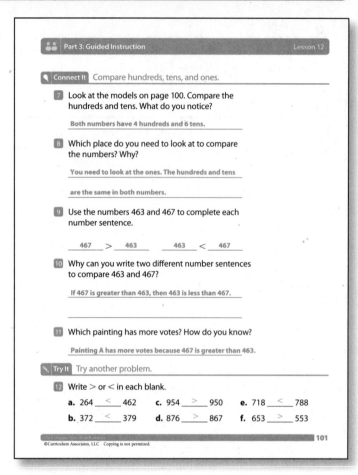

TRY IT SOLUTIONS

12 *Solutions:*

    a. 264 < 462   **c.** 954 > 950   **e.** 718 < 788

    b. 372 < 379   **d.** 876 > 867   **f.** 653 > 553

    (DOK 1)

©Curriculum Associates, LLC   Copying is not permitted.

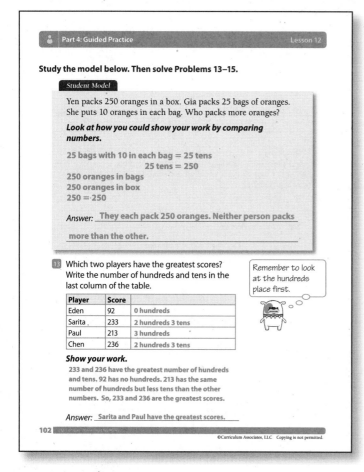

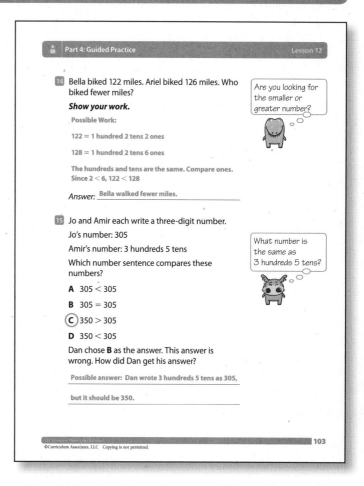

AT A GLANCE

Students evaluate the digits in four different numbers to determine how they relate to each other.

STEP BY STEP

- Ask students to solve the problems individually and show all their work. Review the sample problem together telling students that using a visual or number model can help them compare numbers. They should choose a model that makes the most sense to them.

- When students have completed each problem, have them Pair/Share to discuss their solutions with a partner.

SOLUTIONS

Ex A number model is used to describe each situation demonstrating that 25 tens is equal to 250. Therefore, the answer to the question is that neither person packs more. They pack the same number of oranges.

13 *Solution:* Sarita and Chen; 92 has no hundreds, so it's the smallest. The other numbers all have 2 hundreds, so compare tens. 233 and 236 have 3 tens, and 213 has only 1 ten. **(DOK 3)**

14 *Solution:* Bella walked fewer miles; The hundreds and tens are the same. Compare the ones. Since $2 < 8$, $122 < 128$. **(DOK 1)**

15 *Solution:* **C;** 3 hundreds 5 tens = 350, 350 > 305. Explain to students why the other two choices are not correct.

A is not correct because 305 = 305.

D is not correct because the inequality symbol should be pointing at the smaller number. This sentence is read 350 is less than 305. **(DOK 3)**

©Curriculum Associates, LLC Copying is not permitted.

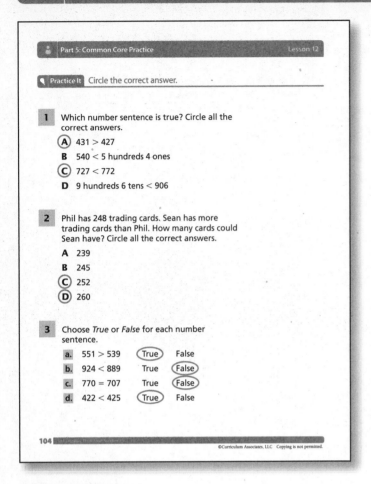

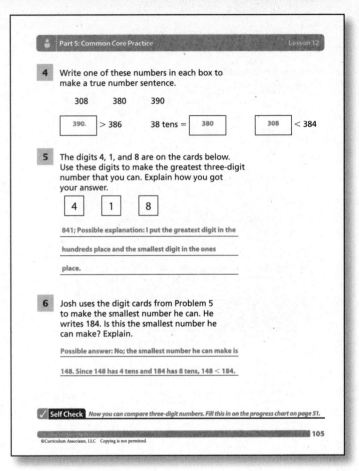

AT A GLANCE

Students compare numbers to answer questions that might appear on a mathematics test.

STEP BY STEP

- First, tell students they will answer questions by comparing three-digit numbers. Then have students read the directions and answer the questions independently. Remind students to fill in the correct answer choices on the Answer Form.

- After students have completed the Common Core Practice problems, review and discuss correct answers. Have student record the number of correct answers in the box provided.

SOLUTIONS

1 *Solution:* **A** and **C**; There are the same number of hundreds in each numbers, but 431 has one more tens (**A**). There are the same number of hundreds in each number but 772 has more tens (**C**). **(DOK 2)**

2 *Solution:* **C** and **D**; 252 has 5 tens, 248 has 4 tens (**C**). 260 has 6 tens which is more than 4 tens (**D**). **(DOK 2)**

3 *Solution:* True, 551 has more tens than 539; False, 924 has more hundreds than 889; False, There are more tens in 770 than in 707; True, There are fewer ones in 422. **(DOK 1)**

4 *Solution:* 390, 380, 308. **(DOK 2)**

5 *Solution:* 841; When the digits are ordered from greatest to least the higher place value always has the greater number in it. **(DOK 3)**

6 *Solution:* 148; Order the digits from least to greatest to write the smallest number possible.

©Curriculum Associates, LLC   Copying is not permitted.

Assessment and Remediation

- Tory and Sam are playing a video game. They get points for moves they make. At the end of the game, Tory has 228 points and Sam has 241 points. Write a number sentence to show who has more points. [Sam: 241 > 228.]

- For students who are still struggling, use the chart below to guide remediation.

- After providing remediation, check students' understanding using the following problem: Juan and his family travel 498 miles on a trip. Jay and his family travel 568 miles on a trip. Write a number sentence to show who travels the shorter distance. [Juan: 498 < 568.]

If the error is . . .	Students may . . .	To remediate . . .
241 < 228	have missed the inequality symbol.	Review how the inequality symbol is always "gobbling up" the larger number or "points to" the smaller number.
241 < 228	have compared the ones place rather than the tens place.	Provide the student with base ten blocks or ask the student to make a quick drawing of each number. Compare each place value reinforcing the concept that digits in a higher place value represent 10x that of the digit in the lower place value next to it.
other answers	not understand the concept of greater than and less than.	Use physical models or models such as a hundreds chart or a number line with one and two-digit numbers to review and reinforce what it means to be greater than or less than. Put the number comparisons into situations familiar to the child providing a meaningful context.

Hands-On Activity

Make it Greater or Less

Materials: one set of 10, 3-digit number cards per student pair (Activity Sheet 7, page 314), four sets of 0–9 digit cards per pair, one card with > drawn on it (Activity Sheet 1, page 308)

- Organize students into pairs. Place each set of cards face down between the student pairs. Either label the piles or color code them.

- One student turns a number card face up and places it on the table. The other student selects 3 digit cards and places them together to form a 3-digit number and places it next to the card with the number printed on it, leaving a space. The first student then places the inequality between the numbers and explains the reasoning for the placement. Mix the digit cards back into the digit pile and repeat the activity, changing roles until all number cards have been used.

Challenge Activity

How far is it?

Materials: a list of 5–10 cities throughout the United States

- Challenge students to explore greater than and less than as they relate to distances. Give each student a list of cities in the United States and tell them to find the distance to that city from the town or city in which they live. Once they find the distances, they compare to determine which city is the greatest and least distance. Ask students to record their findings and share them with each other justifying the decision.

- Challenge them further by asking them to find a destination whose distance is greater than the greatest distance among the cities they researched.

©Curriculum Associates, LLC   Copying is not permitted.

Lesson 13 (Student Book pages 106–115)

Add Three-Digit Numbers

LESSON OBJECTIVES

- Break apart three-digit numbers as a strategy for adding place values.

- Recognize that in adding, hundreds are added to hundreds, tens to tens, and ones to ones.

- Determine when regrouping a hundred or a ten is necessary and carry out the regrouping to find a sum.

PREREQUISITE SKILLS

In order to be proficient with the concepts/skills in this lesson, students should:

- Identify place values in three-digit numbers.

- Model three-digit numbers.

- Perform two-digit addition with and without regrouping.

VOCABULARY

There is no new vocabulary.

THE LEARNING PROGRESSION

In Grade 1, students explore the concept of place value by bundling groups of ten ones into one group of ten. They add two-digit numbers with and without composing a ten and mentally find 10 more or 10 less than a given number.

In Grade 2, students extend their understanding of numbers and place values as they explore three-digit addition and subtraction. They model three-digit numbers and write them in the expanded form. Students fluently count by hundreds and tens using that skill to count on. **In this lesson,** students add three-digit numbers with and without regrouping a hundred and/or a ten. They break apart numbers to add place values and record the addition of partial addends before calculating the sum. Students interpret picture models, number models, and an open number line to understand addition of multi-digit numbers. They apply models to addition and select models most meaningful to the individual student.

In Grade 3, students gain fluency with addition and subtraction of numbers within 1000. In later years, students will draw on the understanding of place values as they multiply and divide multi-digit numbers and apply place-value concepts to decimal numbers.

▮ Ready *Teacher Toolbox*

Teacher-Toolbox.com

	Prerequisite Skills	2.NBT.B.7 2.NBT.B.9
Ready Lessons	✓	✓
Tools for Instruction	✓ ✓	✓
Interactive Tutorials	✓ ✓	✓

CCSS Focus

2.NBT.B.7 Add and subtract within 1000, using concrete models or drawings and strategies based on place value, properties of operations, and/or the relationship between addition and subtraction; relate the strategy to a written method. Understand that in adding or subtracting three-digit numbers, one adds or subtracts hundreds and hundreds, tens and tens, ones and ones; and sometimes it is necessary to compose or decompose tens or hundreds.

2.NBT.B.9 Explain why addition and subtraction strategies work, using place value and the properties of operations.

ADDITIONAL STANDARDS: 2.NBT.B.8 *(see page A42 for full text)*

STANDARDS FOR MATHEMATICAL PRACTICE: SMP 2, 3, 4, 6, 7 *(see page A9 for full text)*

©Curriculum Associates, LLC   Copying is not permitted.

Explore Addition with Three-Digit Numbers

Objective: Students explore adding three-digit numbers through an open-ended problem.	**Materials for each student:** • manipulative materials • hundreds charts

Overview

Students practice adding three-digit number by solving a problem with two unknown addends. They find different combinations of addends that result in a given sum.

Step by Step (15–20 minutes)

1 Introduce the problem.

- Students set up chairs for the winter program. They need to set up 465 chairs. They set up some chairs on one day and the rest the next day. How many chairs do they set up each day?
- Write the given information on the board: 465 chairs. Ask students to tell you what they are supposed to find out.
- Organize students into pairs and give them paper and writing/coloring tools. Set out the manipulative materials so all students have access.

2 Support students as they solve the problem.

- Tell students they can work in pairs and use any models they want to solve the problem. They then record their solution on paper and tell how they know it is correct.
- You may need to discuss that this is a problem with many correct answers. Make sure students understand that they are finding two numbers whose sum is 465.
- Watch out for students who struggle to find an entry point into the problem. To break 465 in two groups, suggest a number that they might begin with, such as 200.
- As students work, circulate and make sure they understand the task and are recording their solutions.
- Once students find and record one answer, encourage them to try to find others.

3 Share solutions and solution strategies.

- When students are finished ask them to share their solutions. Ask how they know their solution is correct. Encourage students to share the strategy they used. Listen for accurate mathematical language and sound reasoning. Write each solution on the board as an addition sentence.

4 Extend the problem.

- Ask students if it is possible to set the chairs up in equal rows and columns, like an array. Let them explore the idea using models. They should notice that they can make rows of 10 using the base-ten blocks, but there will be 5 left over. Lead them to see that they could break each of the rows of ten into rows of 5 to form arrays.

©Curriculum Associates, LLC   Copying is not permitted.

AT A GLANCE

Students examine a model of two three-digit numbers. They add the numbers by combining each place value.

STEP BY STEP

- Tell students that this page will help them add three-digit numbers.

- Have students read the problem at the top of the page. Ask students what operation will help them answer the question.

- Remind students of what they learned about digits and their values in Lesson 11. The digit tells how many groups of 100, 10, or 1 are in a number. The value of the digit depends on its place in the number.

- Guide students to understand that placing the digits of the numbers in the chart helps them to focus on the value of each digit. As they answer the questions in Explore It, make sure they refer to the column headings of the chart.

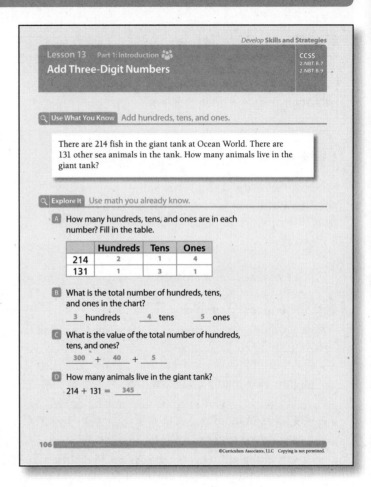

Concept Extension

- Tell the students: *Stuart remembers that there are 21 tens in 214 and 13 tens in 131. He wonders if he can write, 21 tens + 13 tens + 5 ones = 34 tens and 5 ones. What should I tell him?*

- Ask students to discuss this situation in pairs and decide if Stuart's strategy will work, and explain why or why not.

- Invite students to share their ideas with the class. They should notice that within 21 tens there are 2 groups of 100 and within 13 tens there is one group of 100, so adding the tens is like adding the hundreds and tens. In the sum of 34 tens, there are 3 groups of 100 and 4 groups of ten.

Mathematical Discourse

- *Why does it make sense to break numbers into hundreds, tens, and ones to add?*

  Students may respond that it makes it easier to see the place values in order to add hundreds to hundreds, tens to tens, and ones to ones.

- *What makes these numbers easy to add in your head?*

  The numbers of hundreds, tens, and ones are easy to add and there is no regrouping.

©Curriculum Associates, LLC   Copying is not permitted.

AT A GLANCE

Students break apart addends and use an open number line to find the sum of two three-digit numbers.

STEP BY STEP

- Read Find Out More as a class. Refer to the chart on the previous page, making the connection to the expanded form shown on this page.

- Write the vertical form of the addition on the board leaving a small amount of space between each digit. Draw vertical lines separating the place values. Ask students why adding the columns makes sense. They should notice that adding the digits in each column preserves place value.

- Ask students to examine the open number line. Help them to interpret it by using the Hands-On Activity.

- After students discuss and answer the Reflect question, ask the second Mathematical Discourse question.

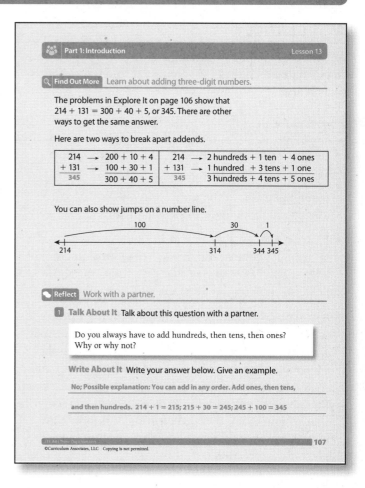

Hands-On Activity

Use base-ten blocks to understand counting on.

Materials: base-ten blocks

- Replicate the open number line from this page on the board.

- Distribute base-ten blocks to each student.

- Tell students to place 214 blocks in front of them showing 2 hundreds flats, one tens rod, and 4 ones units.

- Have students use blocks to model the thinking involved in the open number line. Adding one hundreds flat changes the hundreds, but not the tens or ones. Repeat adding the tens rods either as a group or individually. Adding tens rods changes the number of tens, but not the number of hundreds or ones. Then add on the unit block.

Mathematical Discourse

- *How is the open number line like counting by hundreds, tens, and ones?*

  Students should notice that when starting at 214, two hundreds have already been counted so count on another hundred to get 3**14**. There is already one ten in 314 so when adding the thirty it is like counting on by tens to 324, 334, 3**44**. Then count on the extra one to get 34**5**.

- *Do you think it is easier to add in your head starting with the hundreds or starting with the ones? Why?*

  Listen for students to demonstrate the flexible use of mental strategies, honoring each idea presented. As students hear the strategies of others, they will refine their own mental approach to calculations.

AT A GLANCE

Students use a quick drawing and break apart addends to evaluate an addition involving regrouping in the ones place.

STEP BY STEP

- Read the problem at the top of the page together as a class.

- Draw attention to the quick draw in Picture It, asking students to describe what they see.

- Instruct students to look at the sum in the Model It section. Ask the Mathematical Discourse question to help students recognize that this addition requires more steps than the previous addition.

- Ask students what they might do with the 12 ones to make the sum make sense. Listen for responses that show they understand that 12 is one ten and 2 ones. The one ten needs to be grouped with the other tens. Ask: *How would you know, just by looking at the sum of the ones, that you need to regroup?* Help them recognize that when there is a two-digit sum, regrouping is necessary since there can only be one digit in each place-value position.

- Encourage students to show the addition on their white boards or paper using an open number line. Have volunteers show their models on the board. Discuss how when adding on the ones, another ten was composed leaving 2 extra ones.

> **SMP Tip:** Exposing students to a wide variety of models reinforces the concept of the place-value structure found in our base-ten number system. (*SMP 7*)

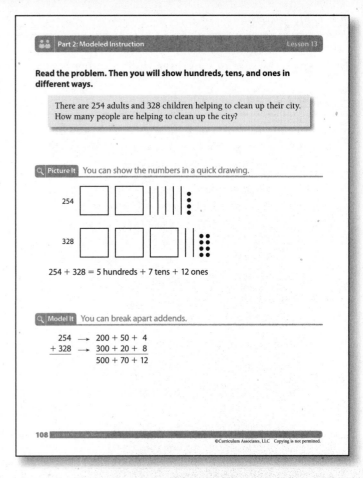

Mathematical Discourse

- *Would it make sense to write the sum of 5 hundreds + 7 tens + 12 ones as (write on the board) 5712? Explain.*

  Students should respond that the 5 is not in the hundreds place and the 7 is not in the tens place, so the number cannot be written this way.

©Curriculum Associates, LLC   Copying is not permitted.

AT A GLANCE

Students revisit the problem on page 108 regrouping a ten to add.

STEP BY STEP

- Read Connect It as a class. Make sure students understand that the questions refer to the problem on page 108.

- To reinforce the regrouping process, use the Hands-On Activity before moving on to the Try It problems.

- Discuss the answers to Problems 5 and 6 together as a class. Allow students who employed different strategies to show their work on the board, describing the strategy they used to find a sum.

Hand-On Activity

Use base-ten blocks to understand regrouping.

Material: base-ten blocks

- Have students model the two addends with their blocks. Since addition is the process of grouping together, ask them to organize all the blocks together into groups of hundreds, tens, and ones and count each group. When they count the ones place, help them recognize that they can regroup ten of the units into another rod making a total of 8 rods.

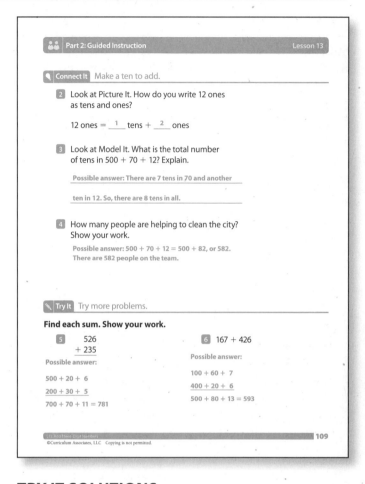

TRY IT SOLUTIONS

5 *Solution:* 781; Add the hundreds, tens, and ones, then regroup the one ten from the sum of the ones to the tens place. **(DOK 1)**

ERROR ALERT: Watch for students who do not regroup the ten from the sum of the ones. Students who either wrote the sum as 7711 or 771 did not regroup.

6 *Solution:* 593; Add the hundreds, tens, and ones, then regroup the ten from the sum of the ones to the tens place. **(DOK 1)**

AT A GLANCE

Students evaluate models of three-digit addition involving regrouping in the ones and tens places.

STEP BY STEP

- Read the problem at the top of the page together as a class. Ask students what operation will help them solve the problem.

- Have students evaluate the first Model it section by asking what they notice about the sums of the tens and ones. They should see that there are two-digit sums in both places, therefore the tens and ones need to be regrouped.

- Ask students to write 5 hundreds + 11 tens + 14 ones as numbers. Check to make sure they include the correct number of zeros.

- Draw attention to the second and third Model It sections. Have students evaluate by explaining each row. Help them see that the sums are the same sums they wrote on their boards. Ask the Mathematical Discourse question to ensure students notice the regrouping that occurs when writing partial sums vertically.

- Ask students if the sum is the same or different if they add and record the hundreds place first. Guide students to see that the partial sums are the same, and the order in which they are added doesn't matter.

> **SMP Tip:** Asking students to check work using alternate methods of adding facilitates the attention to precision and accuracy in calculation that plays a vital role in computational fluency. *(SMP 6)*

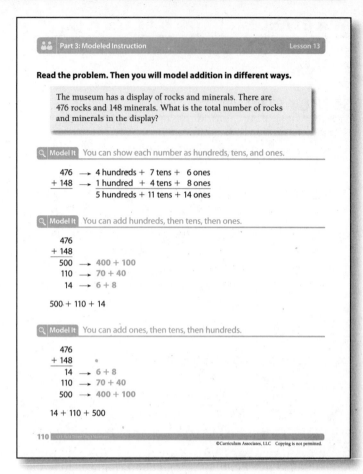

Mathematical Discourse

- *Why is it helpful to write the sums in rows the way they are written in the second model?*

    The extra ten from the addition of the ones and the extra hundred from the addition of the tens are added to the other tens and hundreds so you don't have to regroup again.

©Curriculum Associates, LLC   Copying is not permitted.

AT A GLANCE

Students revisit the problem on page 110 regrouping a ten and a hundred when adding.

STEP BY STEP

- Read Connect It as a class. Make sure students understand that the questions refer to the problem on page 110.

- For Problem 9, make sure students recognize that there are multiple ways to think about or write numbers. The purpose is to help us understand numbers in order to use them to solve problems. Have students think of other ways to write the sums and record them on the board. If no ideas are generated, write: $500 + 100 + 10 + 10 + 4$ and ask how this could represent the sums. Help students see that you broke apart the 110 and the 14 to clearly see the one hundred and one ten that need to be regrouped.

- After students complete the Try It section, ask them to share their calculations on the board. Try to have as many different strategies displayed as possible. This validates students' strategies and allows all students to see that there are many ways to calculate, all resulting in the same sum.

SMP Tip: Have students compare the strategies used to calculate. Discuss the similar elements and differences of each one and ask students to justify their computational approaches. (SMP 3)

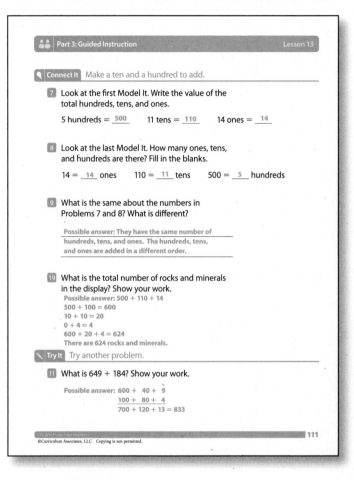

TRY IT SOLUTION

11 *Solution:* 833; Add the hundreds, tens, and ones, then regroup a hundred and a ten. **(DOK 2)**

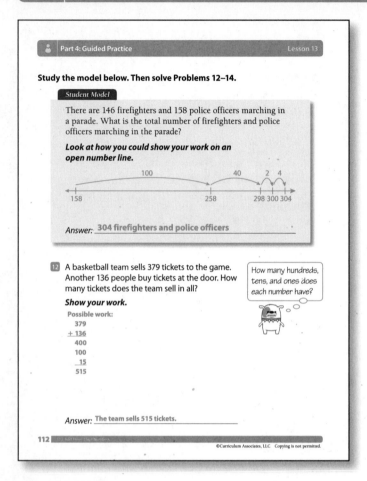

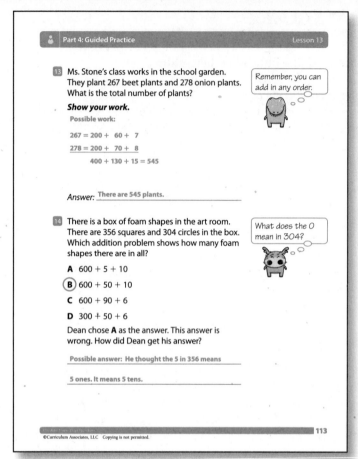

AT A GLANCE

Students interpret word problems to find a solution involving the addition of two three-digit numbers.

STEP BY STEP

- Ask students to solve the problems individually and show all their work. Review the sample problem together telling students that using a visual or number model can help them think about breaking numbers apart to add. Make sure they know they can use whatever strategy is most meaningful to each student.

- When students have completed each problem, have them Pair/Share to discuss their solutions with a partner.

SOLUTIONS

Ex An open number line is used to interpret the problem by adding on 146 to 158 to arrive at 404.

12 *Solution:* 515 tickets; 400 + 100 + 15 = 515. **(DOK 2)**

13 *Solution:* 545 plants; 400 + 130 + 15 = 545. **(DOK 2)**

14 *Solution:* **B**; 300 + 300 = 600, 50 + 0 = 50, 6 + 4 = 10. **(DOK 3)**

Explain to students why the other two choices are not correct.

C is not correct because the numbers in the tens and ones places were miscalculated.

D is not correct because the hundreds and ones places were miscalculated.

©Curriculum Associates, LLC   Copying is not permitted.

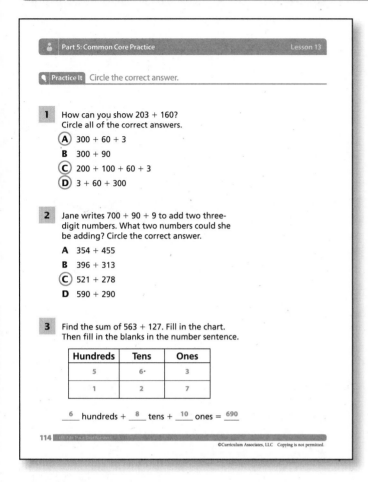

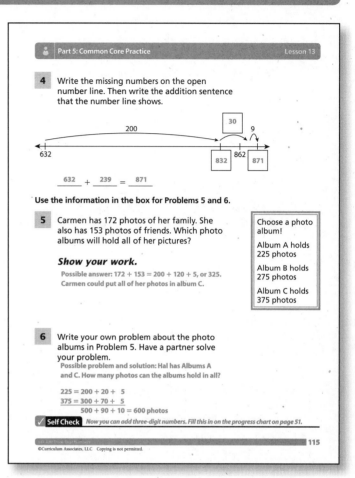

AT A GLANCE

Students solve three-digit addition problems that might appear on a mathematics test.

STEP BY STEP

- First, tell students they will answer questions about adding three-digit numbers. Then have students read the directions and answer the questions independently. Remind students to fill in the correct answer choices on the Answer Form.

- As students write their own addition in Problem 6, make sure they are adding at least two three-digit numbers. If students wish to write a more challenging problem, ensure that the partner is able to solve it.

- After students have completed the Common Core Practice problems, review and discuss correct answers. Have student record the number of correct answers in the box provided.

SOLUTIONS

1 *Solutions:* **A**, **C**, and **D**; $300 + 60 + 3 = 363$ (**A**); $200 + 100 + 60 + 3 = 363$ (**C**); $3 + 60 + 300 = 363$ (**D**). *(DOK 2)*

2 *Solution:* **C**; $500 + 200 = 700$, $70 + 20 = 90$, $1 + 8 = 9$. *(DOK 2)*

3 *Solution:* 690; Break apart 563 and 127 into hundreds, tens, and ones, then add each place value and find the sum. *(DOK 2)*

4 *Solution:* 871; Jump +200 to 832, then +30 to 862, and finally +9 to 871. *(DOK 2)*

5 *Solution:* Album C; $172 + 153 = 200 + 120 + 5 = 325$. Carmen needs an album that holds at least 325 pictures. *(DOK 2)*

6 *Solution:* Answers will vary. *(DOK 3)*

Assessment and Remediation

- There were 278 people at the art fair on the first day and 364 people the second day. How many people went to the two-day art fair? [278 + 364 = 500 + 130 + 12 = 642 people]

- For students who are still struggling, use the chart below to guide remediation.

- After providing remediation, check students' understanding using the following problem: The Park City school children planted 157 trees for Arbor Day. The flower club planted 65 trees. How many trees were planted on Arbor Day in Park City? [158 + 65 = 100 + 110 + 13 = 223 trees]

If the error is . . .	Students may . . .	To remediate . . .
532	not have regrouped the hundred or the ten.	Provide the student with base-ten blocks to model the problem. The student records the number of hundreds, tens, and ones in the sum. Lead the student to notice that 10 rods can be grouped into a hundreds flat and ten units can be grouped into a tens rod.
632	have regrouped the hundred but not the ten.	Check the student's partial sums to make sure the addition was completed accurately. If so, ask the student what was done with the extra ten found in the ones place. Lead the student to recognize the error by writing the partial sums vertically.
Other answers	have miscalculated.	Have the student work the problem using an addition strategy other than the one originally employed to check for accuracy.

Hands-On Activity

Target number game

Materials: 3 number cubes for each student pair, 5–10 cards with three-digit numbers written on them for each pair of students (Activity Sheet 7, page 314), white boards and marking pens

- Organize students into pairs and distribute the number cubes, number cards, and a white board to each pair.

- Students turn up one of the number cards. This is the target number. The first player rolls the number cubes, arranges the digits to form a three-digit number and records it on the white board. The second player rolls the number cubes and tries to make a three-digit number that, when added to the first number, has a sum close to without going over the target number. If the student is successful, a point is awarded. If the first player can make a number that is even closer without going over, two points are awarded. Students switch turns and the game continues until the number cards have all been used.

Challenge Activity

Switch-a-roo

Materials: a list of 5–10 cities throughout the United States

- Show students the sum: 360 + 230 = 330 + 260. Make sure they notice that the groups of tens have been switched around being paired with a different hundred.

- Challenge students to determine if this will always work, even when there are digits in the ones places.

- Require students to justify whether it does or does not always work using at least 10 examples.

- If they find that it does always work, explain why they think it does work using visual models and/ or blocks to justify.

- If students find that it does not always work, they should provide examples and tell when it will and when it will not work.

©Curriculum Associates, LLC   Copying is not permitted.

Lesson 14 (Student Book pages 116–125)

Subtract Three-Digit Numbers

LESSON OBJECTIVES

- Determine when regrouping a ten and/or a hundred is necessary to subtract and carry out the regrouping to find a difference.

- Recognize that in subtracting, hundreds are subtracted from hundreds, tens from tens, and ones from ones.

- Explore subtraction as a process of "taking away" or "counting on."

PREREQUISITE SKILLS

In order to be proficient with the concepts/skills in this lesson, students should:

- Identify place values in three-digit numbers.

- Model three-digit numbers.

- Perform two-digit subtraction with and without regrouping.

VOCABULARY

There is no new vocabulary.

THE LEARNING PROGRESSION

In Grade 1, students explore the concept of two-digit subtraction using physical models and drawings. They subtract multiples of 10, applying strategies based on place values and the relationship between addition and subtraction.

In Grade 2, students subtract two- and three-digit numbers with and without regrouping. They use varied models to represent subtraction and connect models and strategies to a written expression. **In this lesson,** students subtract three-digit numbers with and without regrouping a hundred and/or a ten. They analyze a subtraction to determine when a ten or hundred needs to be decomposed before subtracting. Students interpret picture models, number models, and an open number line to understand subtraction of multi-digit numbers.

In Grade 3, students gain fluency with subtraction of numbers within 1000. They rely less on concrete models and pictures focusing on the numerical representation in preparation for learning standard algorithms in the following year.

▣ Ready *Teacher Toolbox*

Teacher-Toolbox.com

	Prerequisite Skills	2.NBT.B.7 2.NBT.B.9
Ready Lessons	✓	✓
Tools for Instruction	✓ ✓	✓
Interactive Tutorials	✓ ✓	✓

CCSS Focus

2.NBT.B.7 Add and subtract within 1000, using concrete models or drawings and strategies based on place value, properties of operations, and/or the relationship between addition and subtraction; relate the strategy to a written method. Understand that in adding or subtracting three-digit numbers, one adds or subtracts hundreds and hundreds, tens and tens, ones and ones; and sometimes it is necessary to compose or decompose tens or hundreds.

2.NBT.B.9 Explain why addition and subtraction strategies work, using place value and the properties of operations.

ADDITIONAL STANDARDS: 2.NBT A.1 *(see page A42 for full text)*

STANDARDS FOR MATHEMATICAL PRACTICE: SMP 1, 2, 3, 4, 6, 7 *(see page A9 for full text)*

141

©Curriculum Associates, LLC   Copying is not permitted.

Explore Three-Digit Subtraction

Objective: Solve a subtraction problem using any form of representation.

Materials for each student:
- Plain paper, crayons or colored pencils
- Access to manipulative materials

Overview

Students are challenged to solve a subtraction by interpreting a problem, representing it in a way that is meaningful to each student, and finding a solution. Solutions and solution strategies are shared and analyzed by the class.

Step by Step (20–30 minutes)

1 Introduce the problem.

- Pablo's family takes a trip to grandma's house. Pablo's grandmother lives 213 miles away. They drive 127 miles and stop for lunch. How much farther do they have to drive to get to grandma's house?

- Tell students they can use any representation: a picture, drawing (like a map or diagram), or manipulative materials. They should show their thinking clearly on paper and find a solution.

- Give students ample time to complete the task and allow them to work in pairs, if they choose.

2 Support students as they solve the problem.

- Circulate the room as students work, making sure they understand the problem. Help them find a meaningful representation and reasonable solution strategy, if necessary. Ask questions like: *What kind of drawing or model would make sense to use to show how far they drove? What part of the drive do you need to find out about? What might you do to find out?*

3 Share solutions and solution strategies.

- Have students or student pairs take turns sharing their strategy and showing the representation they used.

- Ask: *Why did you choose this way to show the problem? What strategy did you use to solve the problem?*

- As students share solutions, guide them in using mathematical vocabulary and clearly articulating the strategy they employed.

4 Critique the work of others.

- Invite the class to ask questions of each other, seek clarification, and acknowledge the work of their peers. Highlight innovative strategies or representations as an encouragement for all students to attempt diverse ways of thinking.

©Curriculum Associates, LLC   Copying is not permitted.

AT A GLANCE

Students model subtraction as a "take away" process in finding the difference of two three-digit numbers.

STEP BY STEP

- Tell students that this page will help them understand subtracting large numbers.

- Have students read the problem at the top of the page.

- Work through Explore It as a class.

- Make sure students understand that they are crossing out the number of cards Dora has. Discuss how hundreds are subtracted from hundreds, tens from tens, and ones from ones.

- Complete the remainder of the problems and ask the first Mathematical Discourse question. Use the Visual Model to reinforce the concept.

Visual Model

A bar graph can be used to model the concept of a difference among two numbers.

- On the board, draw a graph similar to the one below, but without the horizontal line at 243.

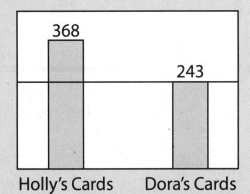

- Ask students how they can use the graph to show how many more cards Holly has. Listen to student ideas and then draw a line as shown. Point out that the portion above the line shows how many more cards Holly has than Dora. Cover the portion that is equal and tell students that when you subtract the amount that is equal, what's left is the "difference" between them. Remind them that the answer to a subtraction is called a difference.

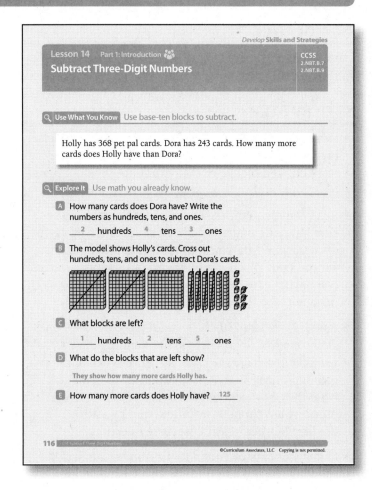

Mathematical Discourse

- *Why do you subtract to find how many more?*

    Students may respond that when you take away the number of cards Dora has, what is left is the number of cards that Holly has that Dora does not.

- *How could you subtract 368 − 243 in your head?*

    Students may respond that they can subtract the numbers in each place value position.

AT A GLANCE

Students explore regrouping tens as a strategy for finding a difference.

STEP BY STEP

- Read Find Out More as a class. Refer to the models on the previous page, reminding them that there were enough blocks in each group to cross out ones, tens, and hundreds making the subtraction simple.

- Read the inequalities shown with the class. Make sure students understand they are comparing digits of corresponding place values in the minuend and subtrahend. Discuss with them that the purpose of comparing is to determine whether there are enough in each place value position to be subtracted.

- Ask: *If Dora had 249 cards, could you cross out 9 ones on the models?* [No. There are not enough.] *How could you get enough ones to cross out?* [Break apart a ten rod into ones.] Check to ensure they remember what they have learned about the commutative property as it applies to subtraction by asking the first Mathematical Discourse question.

- Direct students' attention to the number model showing the regrouping. Ask why a 4 and 18 are shown in the tens and ones place respectively. Discuss how when adding 10 ones can be regrouped or composed into a ten rod. When subtracting we can break down or decompose a ten into ones. Remind them of the importance of recording what they did.

- After students discuss and answer the Reflect question, have them share their answers with the class.

ELL Support

The term "regroup" may not be familiar to ELL students. In some cultures the term "compose" and "decompose" are used. Explain that regrouping can mean putting blocks together to make a larger block or breaking a block into smaller parts.

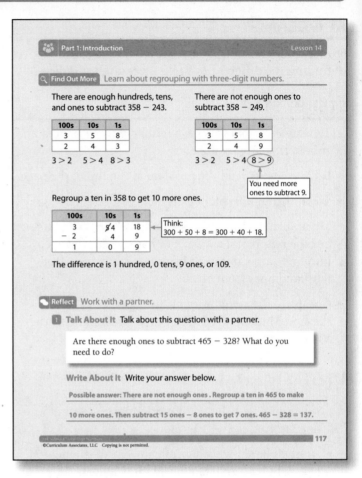

Mathematical Discourse

- *Would it make sense to subtract the 8 from the 9? Why?*

  Students should respond no. The problem instructs them to take 9 from 8. Subtraction is not commutative.

- *What would happen if you forgot to record the ten that was decomposed?*

  You would have too many tens in the answer. It would be like adding a ten to Holly's cards.

SMP Tip: Ask students to mentally calculate $358 - 243$ as shown in the first model. Write the calculation on the board. Ask them what the calculation would be in the second model if you forgot to record the regrouped ten. Ask if the answer makes sense and explain why. (*SMP 1*)

©Curriculum Associates, LLC   Copying is not permitted.

AT A GLANCE

Students examine a base-ten model for subtraction with regrouping. They apply the process to subtracting groups of 100, groups of 10, and groups of ones.

STEP BY STEP

- Read the problem at the top of the page together as a class.

- Draw attention to the base-ten model shown in Picture It. Have students describe what they see and help them interpret the model. Make sure they interpret the gray pieces as the decomposed ten. You may want to use the Hands-On Activity to support student understanding. Ask: *Does this show taking a ten away from 5 tens? Why?* [No. It shows taking a ten away from 4 tens. One ten was broken into ones to take away 8 ones.]

- Instruct students to look at and interpret the subtraction in the Model It section. Ask the Mathematical Discourse questions to reinforce mental strategies.

Read the problem. Then you will show subtraction in different ways.

There are 450 kids at Camp Cody. One day 218 kids do art projects. The rest do sports. How many kids do sports that day?

Picture It You can subtract using base-ten blocks.

Show 450.

Regroup 1 ten as ten ones.

Then take away 218.

Model It You can subtract hundreds, tens, and ones.

Think: 218 = 200 + 10 + 8

$$
\begin{array}{r}
450 \\
-\ 200 \\
\hline
250 \\
-\ 10 \\
\hline
240 \\
-\ 8 \\
\hline
? \\
\end{array}
$$

118   L14: Subtract Three-Digit Numbers

©Curriculum Associates, LLC   Copying is not permitted.

Hands-On Activity

Use base-ten blocks to model subtraction.

Materials: base-ten blocks, place value mats

- Distribute base-ten blocks to students and have them show 450 on the place value mat.

- Ask: *What do you need to think about when subtracting 218?* [You need to think if there needs to be regrouping.] *Why does the picture in the book show a ten being regrouped?* [There aren't enough ones to take 8 from.] *Where can you find some ones?* [From the tens place.]

- Have students demonstrate the regrouping. Ask: *Can you subtract now? Why?* [Yes, there are enough ones now to subtract.]

- Return to the picture in the book asking the questions above. Allow students to model the subtraction.

Mathematical Discourse

- *How might the Model It strategy help you subtract in your head?*

  It is easy to count back hundreds and count back tens. Then just subtract the extra ones.

- *How can you subtract 8 from 240 in your head?*

  Some students may say they need to regroup a ten because there aren't enough ones. Others may recognize that 8 fewer than 40 is 32 so 8 fewer than 240 is 232.

AT A GLANCE

Students revisit the problem on page 118, regrouping a ten to subtract.

STEP BY STEP

- Read Connect It as a class. Make sure students understand that the questions refer to the problem on page 118.

- As students complete Talk About it, discuss how the partial sums shown in Problem 3 is a recording of what they did when they regrouped using base-ten blocks.

- Remind students as they complete Try It, they are free to use either of the strategies they learned on the previous pages or one of their own. Tell them to be sure and include a number sentence or recording of their work to show how they subtracted.

- Discuss the answers to Problem 6. Encourage students to share their strategies. Some may choose to regroup while others may use subtraction of hundreds, tens, and then ones. If one of these is not employed, ask a volunteer to come to the board and show how it could be used to solve the subtraction.

SMP Tip: As students explain their thinking, guide them to use accurate vocabulary and clear explanations. Help them evaluate their solutions to ensure that they make sense in the context of the problem. (*SMP 6*)

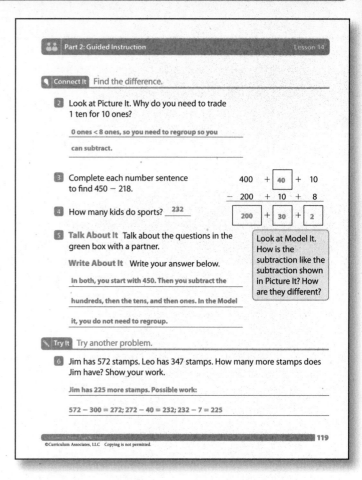

TRY IT SOLUTION

6 *Solution:* 225; Either regroup a ten or subtract hundreds, tens, and then ones. (**DOK 1**)

ERROR ALERT: Students who wrote 235 subtracted the 2 from the 7 rather than regrouping.

©Curriculum Associates, LLC   Copying is not permitted.

AT A GLANCE

Students evaluate models of three-digit subtraction involving regrouping in the tens and hundreds places.

STEP BY STEP

- Read the problem at the top of the page together as a class.

- Have students evaluate the base-ten model in Picture It. Ask how this model is different from the one on the previous pages. They should notice that both a ten and a hundred have been regrouped.

- Reinforce the concept of regrouping by having students add the value of each digit in the regrouped number to see that it still represents 305.

- Write the problem vertically on the board and say: *Mitchell asks, "Can't I just cross out the 3, make it a 2 and then put a 1 next to the 5?" What should I tell him?* You may want students to model this problem with base-ten blocks to help them see that by putting the one next to the 5 without first regrouping a hundred into the tens place makes the value 105, not 15.

- Draw attention to the Model It section. Put the addition back into the context of the problem to help students make sense of the correlation. Ask: *When you put together the 276 students that are at school and the ones that are on a field trip, how many students should there be? Why?*

- Have students describe what is happening in the open number line. Make sure they see the counting on strategy that is used. You may want to refer back to the Visual Model in the Introduction.

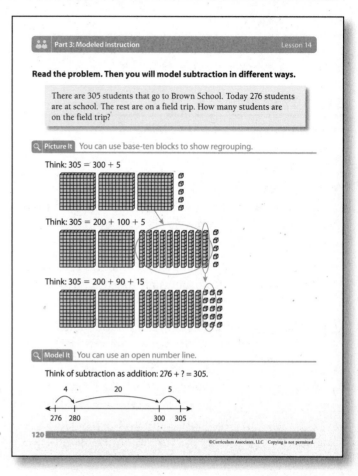

Mathematical Discourse

- *How is subtracting three-digit numbers like subtracting two-digit numbers? How is it different?*

  Students should recognize that in both cases they subtract tens from tens and ones from ones and they need to decide if a ten needs to be regrouped.

  When subtracting three-digit numbers, they need to subtract hundreds from hundreds and may need to regroup a hundred.

SMP Tip: Have students restate each problem posed, making sure they understand the context of the problem, what they need to find, and what number to subtract. (*SMP 2*)

©Curriculum Associates, LLC   Copying is not permitted.

AT A GLANCE

Students revisit the problem on page 120 regrouping a ten and a hundred when subtracting.

STEP BY STEP

- Read Connect It as a class. Make sure students understand that the questions refer to the problem on page 120.

- Connect Problem 9 to the model or the way in which students physically modeled the problem from the previous page. The number they record in each place value position represents the regrouped number.

- Have students share their number line strategies in Problem 10. As they do, continue to ask if anyone has solved the problem in a different way.

- Encourage students to attempt a solution strategy in the Try It problem that they have not yet tried.

- After students complete the Try It section, ask them to share their calculations on the board.

SMP Tip: Have students compare the strategies used to calculate. Discuss the similar elements and differences of each one and ask students to justify their computational approaches. *(SMP 3)*

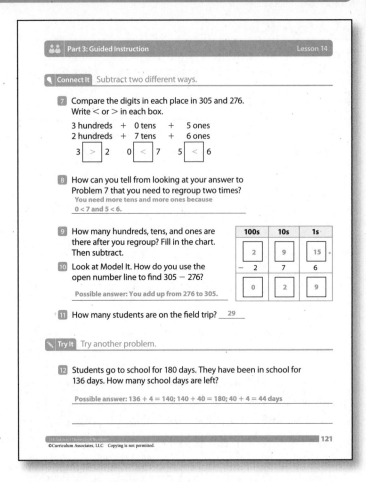

TRY IT SOLUTION

12 *Solution:* 44 days; Students may subtract by regrouping a ten or use the counting on model demonstrated in the number line model. **(DOK 1)**

©Curriculum Associates, LLC   Copying is not permitted.

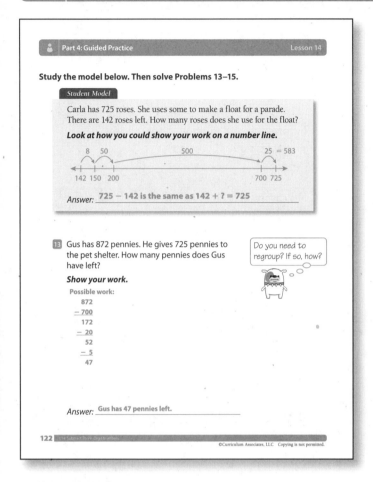

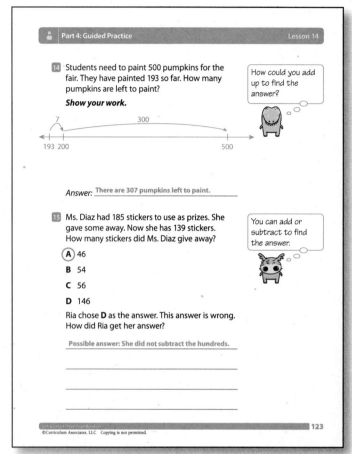

AT A GLANCE

Students interpret word problems to find a solution involving the subtraction of two 3-digit numbers.

STEP BY STEP

- Ask students to solve the problems individually and show all their work. Review the sample problem together, discussing how the number line shows the subtraction as an addition.

- Draw attention to the Study Buddies on each page. Tell students that the buddies help them think of a strategy to use. Encourage students to attempt a variety of strategies in solving the problems.

- When students have completed each problem, have them Pair/Share to discuss their solutions with a partner.

SOLUTIONS

Ex An open number line is used to interpret the problem by adding $142 + ? = 725$.

13 *Solution:* 47 pennies; $872 - 700 = 172$; $172 - 20 = 52$; $52 - 5 = 47$. **(DOK 1)**

14 *Solution:* 307 pumpkins; $193 + 300 = 493$; $493 + 7 = 500$; $300 + 7 = 307$. **(DOK 1)**

15 *Solution:* **A**; $185 - 139 = 46$. **(DOK 3)**

Explain to students why the other three choices are not correct.

B is not correct because $139 + 54 = 193$; $193 \neq 185$. $5 - 9 \neq 9 - 5$.

C is not correct because the number of tens should be 4, not 5.

©Curriculum Associates, LLC   Copying is not permitted.

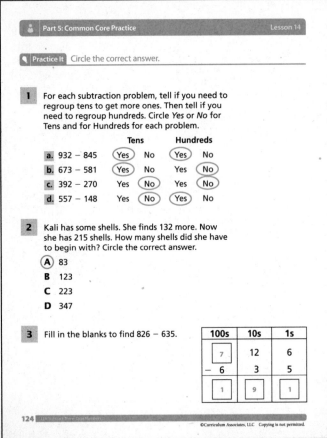

Part 5: Common Core Practice — Lesson 14

Practice It Circle the correct answer.

1 For each subtraction problem, tell if you need to regroup tens to get more ones. Then tell if you need to regroup hundreds. Circle *Yes* or *No* for Tens and for Hundreds for each problem.

		Tens	Hundreds
a.	932 − 845	(Yes) No	(Yes) No
b.	673 − 581	(Yes) No	Yes (No)
c.	392 − 270	Yes (No)	Yes (No)
d.	557 − 148	Yes (No)	(Yes) No

2 Kali has some shells. She finds 132 more. Now she has 215 shells. How many shells did she have to begin with? Circle the correct answer.

(A) 83
B 123
C 223
D 347

3 Fill in the blanks to find 826 − 635.

	100s	10s	1s
	[7] 7	12	6
−	6	3	5
	[1]	[9]	[1]

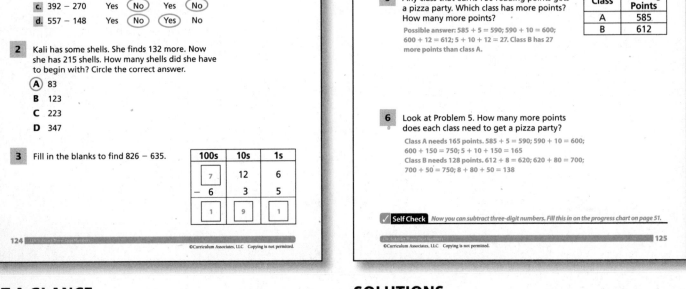

4 Add up to find 524 − 395. Fill in the blanks.

[5]   100   [24]

[395] 400   [500] 524

524 − 395 = ___129___

5 Any class that earns 750 reading points gets a pizza party. Which class has more points? How many more points?

Possible answer: 585 + 5 = 590; 590 + 10 = 600; 600 + 12 = 612; 5 + 10 + 12 = 27. Class B has 27 more points than class A.

Class	Reading Points
A	585
B	612

6 Look at Problem 5. How many more points does each class need to get a pizza party?

Class A needs 165 points. 585 + 5 = 590; 590 + 10 = 600; 600 + 150 = 750; 5 + 10 + 150 = 165
Class B needs 128 points. 612 + 8 = 620; 620 + 80 = 700; 700 + 50 = 750; 8 + 80 + 50 = 138

✓ Self Check *Now you can subtract three-digit numbers. Fill this in on the progress chart on page 51.*

AT A GLANCE

Students solve 3-digit subtraction problems that might appear on a mathematics test.

STEP BY STEP

- First, tell students they will answer questions about adding three-digit numbers. Then have students read the directions and answer the questions independently. Remind students to fill in the correct answer choices on the Answer Form.

- Tell students to be sure to show work to explain their solution strategy for Problems 4–6.

- After students have completed the Common Core Practice problems, review and discuss correct answers. Have students record the number of correct answers in the box provided.

SOLUTIONS

1 *Solutions:* **a.** Yes, Yes; **b.** Yes, No; **c.** No, No; **d.** No, Yes. **(DOK 2)**

2 *Solution:* **A**; 215 − 132 = 83. **(DOK 1)**

3 *Solution:* 191; hundreds place should read 7 − 6. **(DOK 1)**

4 *Solution:* 129; 395 + 5 = 400; 400 + 100 = 500; 500 + 24 = 524. **(DOK 1)**

5 *Solution:* Class B has 27 more points than class A. 612 − 585 = 27. **(DOK 1)**

6 *Solution:* Class A needs 165 more points, class B needs 128 more points. 750 − 585 = 165; 750 − 612 = 128. **(DOK 2)**

©Curriculum Associates, LLC   Copying is not permitted.

Assessment and Remediation

- Cody wants to buy a bike that costs 250 dollars. He has saved 169 dollars. How much money does he need to have enough to buy the bike? [81 dollars]

- For students who are still struggling, use the chart below to guide remediation.

- After providing remediation, check students' understanding using the following problem: The Park City school children planted 157 trees for Arbor Day. The flower club planted 65 trees. How many trees were planted on Arbor Day in Park City? [158 + 65 = 100 + 110 + 13 = 223 trees]

If the error is . . .	Students may . . .	To remediate . . .
119	have subtracted 0 from 9 and 50 from 60 rather than regrouping.	Provide students with base-ten blocks to model the problem. When trying to remove 9 blocks, the students should notice there are no ones to take away. Demonstrate how regrouping in a number sentence is a recording of what was done with the blocks.
91	have regrouped a ten but failed to record one less ten in the tens place.	Ask students to review their subtraction to see if it makes sense. Point out the tens place and ask what the problem is with that calculation. Guide students to self correct.
other answers	have miscalculated.	Have students check their answers using addition. After recognizing an error was made, have them check their work to find the error. You may need to point out where the error was made, but allow each student to identify it.

Hands-On Activity

Model subtraction using base-ten blocks.

Materials: base-ten blocks, place value mats (Activity Sheet 6, page 313)

- Distribute base-ten blocks to each student.

- Write several subtraction problems on the board involving regrouping a ten, a hundred, or both.

- Have students copy one problem at a time, use models to solve. Students may use the models to think about regrouping or to subtract hundreds, then tens, then ones.

- Make sure students record on their paper what they did in number form.

Challenge Activity

- Give each student a card containing a three-digit number such as 247 (Activity Sheet 7, page 314). Make sure each student has a different number.

- Challenge students to write as many subtraction problems as they can think of in which their number is the difference.

- Have them record the number sentences and see if they notice any patterns or consistencies. If so, describe what they notice.

©Curriculum Associates, LLC   Copying is not permitted.

Lesson 15 (Student Book pages 126–133)

Add Several Two-Digit Numbers

LESSON OBJECTIVES

- Break apart three or more 2-digit numbers as a strategy for adding place values.
- Develop strategies for adding more than two numbers.
- Apply the commutative and associative properties of addition.

PREREQUISITE SKILLS

In order to be proficient with the concepts/skills in this lesson, students should:

- Identify place values in two-digit numbers.
- Model two-digit numbers in expanded form.
- Perform two-digit addition with and without regrouping.
- Use addition facts fluently.

VOCABULARY

There is no new vocabulary.

THE LEARNING PROGRESSION

In Grade 1, students add one- and two-digit numbers within 100 using concrete models and pictures. They apply strategies based on place values and properties of operations. Students at this level develop strategies for computing mentally and learn tens facts.

In Grade 2, students build on their knowledge of number and place value through a wide variety of models. Number models are used more extensively, transitioning students into abstract thinking and mental computation. They notice consistencies in addition and subtraction that enable them to become proficient in computation. **In this lesson,** students add three or more two-digit numbers with and without regrouping a hundred and/or a ten. Students interpret number models and explore strategies including breaking apart numbers to add place values and making tens and hundreds.

In Grade 3, students gain fluency with addition of numbers within 1000. They apply the strategy of breaking apart numbers to multiplication of whole numbers and use place values to round numbers.

Ready *Teacher Toolbox*　　*Teacher-Toolbox.com*

	Prerequisite Skills	2.NBT.B.6
Ready Lessons	✓	✓
Tools for Instruction	✓ ✓	
Interactive Tutorials	✓ ✓	

CCSS Focus

2.NBT.B.6 Add up to four two-digit numbers using strategies based on place value and properties of operations.

ADDITIONAL STANDARDS: 2.NBT.B.5, 2.NBT.B.9 *(see page A42 for full text)*

STANDARDS FOR MATHEMATICAL PRACTICE: SMP 2, 3, 4, 5, 6, 7, 8 *(see page A9 for full text)*

©Curriculum Associates, LLC　Copying is not permitted.

Making Hundreds

Objective: Recognize patterns involved in combinations of two numbers with a sum of 100.	**Materials for each student:** • Sheet with 2–4 10 × 10 grids printed on it • Colored pencils or crayons

Overview

Students apply their knowledge of tens facts to hundreds facts. They then create facts on a 10 × 10 grid and search for the patterns and structure that enables them to easily recognize any two numbers with a sum is 100.

Step by Step (20–30 minutes)

1   Relate tens facts to hundreds facts.

- Ask students to recite tens facts together. Help them start by saying: *0 + 10, 10 + 0 , 1 + 9, 9 + 1 …*

- Ask students how many tens facts there are. [11] Ask: *How many hundred facts do you think there are?* Allow students to respond and justify their responses. Tell them that in this activity, they will find out what the hundreds facts are.

- Ask students if they can think of a way to use their tens facts to find some hundreds facts. Listen for them to tell you that 50 + 50 = 100, 60 + 40 = 100, etc. Make sure the student tells how each hundred fact relates to a ten fact.

2   Explore hundreds facts on a 10 × 10 grid.

- Distribute the 10 × 10 grids and colored pencils or crayons.

- Have students use a hand or another piece of paper to cover 5 rows of ten on the grid and tell how many rows are showing; cover 3 rows of ten and tell how many are showing. Have them find all combinations. This will reinforce the connection between these hundreds facts and tens facts.

- Ask students if they can think of other ways to combine two numbers to make 100. Listen to ideas and then show students how to model on the grid combinations such as 53 + 47 and 28 + 72.

- Ask students to use their own grids to find two more combinations of 100. Suggest that they shade the two sections of the grids with a different color and count to check that their combinations are correct.

3   Search for consistencies among the facts.

- Have students write an expression for the facts under each grid.

- Tell students to work with a partner. Ask them to look at all the number expressions they wrote to find an easy way to decide if two numbers equal 100. You may want to provide a hint that leads them to add the tens and add the ones in the numbers in each expression.

4   Conjecture about hundreds facts.

- Encourage students to conjecture about what they found and justify it using the grid. Students should recognize that the sum of the tens place is always 90 and the sum of the ones place is always 10. Show on the grid how one of the rows of ten is divided into two numbers that make a ten fact and the rest of the rows of ten are solid. Since one ten less than 100 is 90, the sum of those rows will always be 90.

5   Test the conjecture.

- Write the following expressions on the board: 32 + 68, 78 + 12, 47 + 53. Ask students which, if any of them, equals 100 and why.

- Challenge students to determine the number of hundreds facts there are and justify. [101]

©Curriculum Associates, LLC   Copying is not permitted.

AT A GLANCE

Students examine a break-apart model of three two-digit numbers. They add the numbers by combining each place value.

STEP BY STEP

- Have students read the problem at the top of the page. Ask students to restate the problem and describe what they are to find.

- Ask students to share their mental strategies for adding the tens and adding the ones. Discuss how finding numbers that are easy to add makes mental calculation more accurate.

- Tell students that breaking numbers apart is one way to add numbers. Discuss strategies that students may have for adding a series of numbers. Encourage students to devise their own methods of calculating and compare them to the methods explored in the lesson.

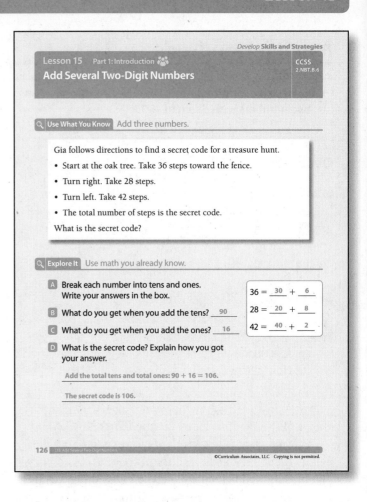

Develop **Skills and Strategies**

Lesson 15 Part 1: Introduction

Add Several Two-Digit Numbers

CCSS
2.NBT.B.6

Use What You Know Add three numbers.

Gia follows directions to find a secret code for a treasure hunt.
- Start at the oak tree. Take 36 steps toward the fence.
- Turn right. Take 28 steps.
- Turn left. Take 42 steps.
- The total number of steps is the secret code.

What is the secret code?

Explore It Use math you already know.

A Break each number into tens and ones. Write your answers in the box.

B What do you get when you add the tens? ___90___

C What do you get when you add the ones? ___16___

D What is the secret code? Explain how you got your answer.

Add the total tens and total ones: 90 + 16 = 106.

The secret code is 106.

$36 = \underline{30} + \underline{6}$
$28 = \underline{20} + \underline{8}$
$42 = \underline{40} + \underline{2}$

126 L15: Add Several Two-Digit Numbers

©Curriculum Associates, LLC   Copying is not permitted.

Concept Extension

- Write the numbers 20, 8, 30, 6, 40, and 2 on separate squares of paper.

- Project the numbers arranged with addition signs: 20 + 8 + 30 + 6 + 40 + 2. You may want to model each of the numbers with base-ten blocks. Make sure students are aware that these are the numbers shown in the Explore It box, but arranged horizontally instead of vertically.

- Ask: *Susan says that if we added 22, 38, and 46 we would get the same sum as the numbers on this page. What do you think about Susan's idea?*

- Allow students to share ideas and ask them to use the number sentence and/or models to justify. This is an extension of the commutative property of addition. Since addition is the process of combining groups, the order in which they are combined does not affect the sum.

Mathematical Discourse

- *How is adding three numbers like adding two numbers?*

  Students may respond that it makes it easier to see the place values in order to add hundreds to hundreds, tens to tens, and ones to ones.

©Curriculum Associates, LLC   Copying is not permitted.

AT A GLANCE

Students add two numbers in a series of three numbers and then add the third using the strategies of making tens and making hundreds.

STEP BY STEP

- Read Find Out More as a class. Ask students if this is a strategy any of them thought about on the previous page. When students are encouraged to devise their own strategies first, they take ownership of the strategy and then the text validates the strategy. Ask: *What must you remember to do when you add numbers by finding a ten in the ones place?* [You need to add an extra ten to the tens place.]

- Ask students to remember the opening activity as they examine the second strategy. Have them tell you how they know when two numbers equal 100. Follow up with the first Mathematical Discourse question.

- Have students work in pairs to complete the Reflect question.

- After students discuss and answer the Reflect question, ask the second Mathematical Discourse question. Have them think of numbers that may not be easy to add by making a ten or a hundred. Have students discuss strategies they could use in those situations. Listen for strategies such as count on by tens and then add the ones.

> **SMP Tip:** Exploring the strategies of breaking apart numbers and finding numbers whose sum is 100 reinforces the structure of the base-ten number system. *(SMP 7)*

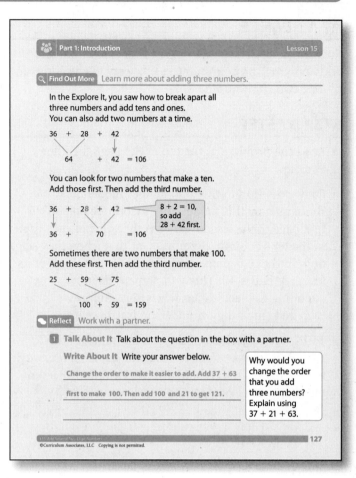

Mathematical Discourse

- *Why is it easy to add when you make a hundred first?*

   After you have a hundred, the other addend goes after the one so you have a hundred "something."

- *Do you think it is easier to break apart numbers or to add two numbers first and then the third one? Why?*

   Allow students to share personal preferences, listening for mathematical reasoning.

AT A GLANCE

Students apply strategies of breaking apart numbers and applying the commutative property to the addition of four two-digit numbers.

STEP BY STEP

- Read the problem at the top of the page together as a class.

- Draw attention to the first number model. Ask students how this model differs from the one on the first page of the lesson. Discuss the value of each digit in the tens column. Remind them that when they see a digit in the tens place, they should always think of its value; 4 tens is 40. This will prepare them for attending to place values when they multiply two- and three-digit numbers in future years.

- Tell students to look at the second model and ask: *Why does it make sense to group the numbers this way?* [9 + 1 makes ten, so add 41 and 39. It makes a ten number that is easy to add to other numbers.]

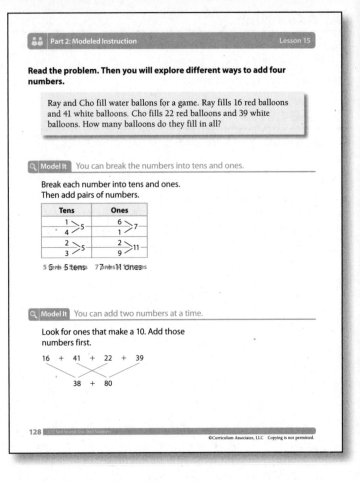

ELL Support

Engage your ELL students in sharing their mental strategies with the class. Students from other cultures may have learned strategies other than the ones presented. In some cases, specific vocabulary is used to describe a strategy such as: composing a ten to a higher place value. ELL students may fear calling attention to themselves by sharing different ways of thinking about or expressing their strategies. Provide a nonthreatening environment for them to do so and give them recognition for their ideas.

Mathematical Discourse

- *When would you want to use the make a ten or make a hundred strategy and when would it be easier to break numbers apart to add?*

  Students may respond that if they can see two digits whose sum is ten or two numbers whose sum is 100, use that strategy. If there aren't any of those combinations, it is easier to break apart the numbers.

SMP Tip: As students analyze strategies for adding numbers, they recognize the structure and regularity with which these structures occur. By generalizing and applying strategies to new situations, they gain fluency in mental computation. *(SMP 8)*

©Curriculum Associates, LLC   Copying is not permitted.

AT A GLANCE

Students revisit the problem on page 128, applying the strategies of breaking apart and grouping compatible numbers to add.

STEP BY STEP

- Read Connect It as a class. Make sure students understand that the questions refer to the problem on page 128.

- Have students share mental strategies they used to add the tens and the ones. They may notice that in the tens place 10 + 40 = 50 and 20 + 30 = 50. 50 + 50 = 100; or they may see that 30 + 40 = 70 and 20 + 10 = 30. 70 + 30 = 100. Expect students to see the 9 and 1 in the ones place and make a ten.

- After students complete the Try It section, ask them to share their calculations with the class. Make sure students recognize that there is more than one way to order and group the numbers, all resulting in the same sum.

Hands-On Activity

Model with base-ten blocks.

Materials: base-ten blocks, place value mat

- Have one student model the numbers shown on this page in terms of tens and ones on the place value mat. Tell the partner to model the numbers by putting them in groups of base-ten blocks.

- Ask students to combine their blocks in a way that is different from their partner and compare answers.

- Discuss how, when adding numbers, the order in which they are added or the way they are grouped to add will not affect the sum no matter what number of addends are used. Make sure they understand that place value position does matter. They can move the tens and ones around, but tens will still always be added to tens and ones will always be added to ones.

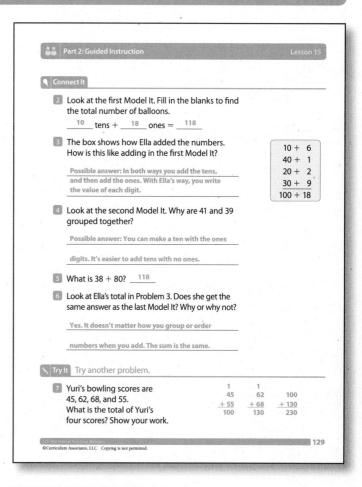

TRY IT SOLUTION

7 *Solution:* 230; Possible solution: 45 + 55 = 100; 662 + 68 = 130; 100 + 130 = 230. **(DOK 1)**

©Curriculum Associates, LLC   Copying is not permitted.

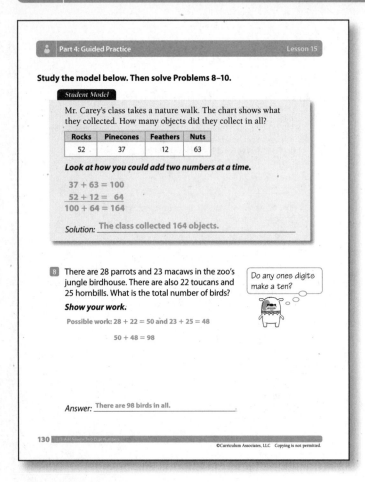

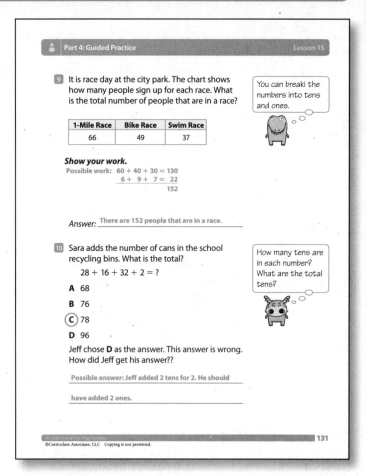

AT A GLANCE

Students interpret and solve word problems using strategies to add three and four two-digit numbers.

STEP BY STEP

- Ask students to solve the problems individually and show all their work. Review the sample problem together asking students to identify the strategy that was used. Remind them to try to practice the strategies they learned in this lesson when solving the remainder of the problems.

- When students have completed each problem, have them Pair/Share to discuss their solutions with a partner.

SOLUTIONS

Ex The strategy of finding and adding two numbers whose sum is 100, and then adding the remaining two numbers, and finally finding the sum is applied.

8 *Solution:* 98 birds; Students may add $28 + 22 = 50$, $23 + 25 = 48$, $50 + 48 = 98$. **(DOK 1)**

ERROR ALERT: Students who wrote 88 may have failed to include the composed ten when adding $28 + 22 = 40$.

9 *Solution:* 152; students may add $60 + 40 + 30 = 130$, $6 + 9 + 7 = 22$, $130 + 22 = 152$. **(DOK 2)**

10 *Solution:* **C**; $28 + 2 = 30$, $32 + 16 = 48$, $48 + 30 = 78$. **(DOK 3)**

Explain to students why the other two choices are not correct.

A is not correct because 1 ten was not added..

B is not correct because the 2 was not added.

©Curriculum Associates, LLC   Copying is not permitted.

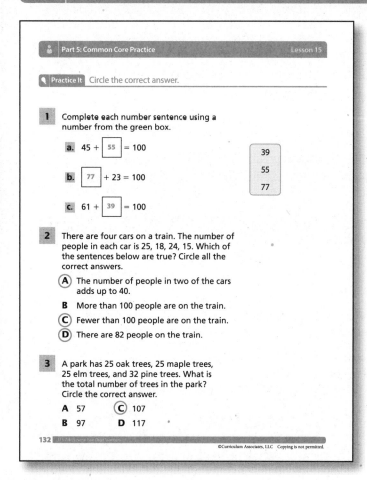

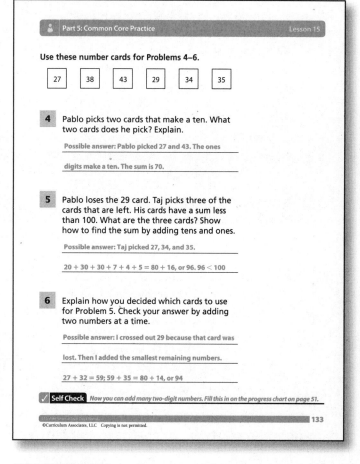

AT A GLANCE

Students solve two-digit addition problems involving three and four addends that might appear on a mathematics test.

STEP BY STEP

- First, tell students they will answer questions about adding three and four two-digit numbers. Then have students read the directions and answer the questions independently. Remind students to fill in the correct answer choices on the Answer Form.

- Make sure students understand that the number cards shown are used for all of the questions on that page.

- After students have completed the Common Core Practice problems, review and discuss correct answers. Have students record the number of correct answers in the box provided.

SOLUTIONS

1 *Solutions:* 55, 77, and 39; In each case, the sum of the ones place is ten and the sum of the tens place is 90. (**DOK 2**)

2 *Solutions:* **A**, **C**, and **D**; 25 + 15 = 40 (**A**); 25 + 18 + 24 + 15 = 82, 82 < 100 (**C**); sum is 82 (**D**). (**DOK 2**)

3 *Solution:* **C**; 25 + 25 + 25 + 32 = 107. (**DOK 1**)

4 *Solution:* 27 and 43; 7 + 3 = 10. (**DOK 2**)

5 *Solution:* Possible answer: 27, 34, and 35; 20 + 30 + 30 = 80, 7 + 2 + 5 = 14, 80 + 14 = 94. 94 < 100. (**DOK 2**)

6 *Solution:* Answers will vary. Possible answer shown above. (**DOK 3**)

Assessment and Remediation

- Ben read 37 minutes on Monday, 29 minutes on Tuesday, 35 minutes on Wednesday, and 13 minutes on Thursday. How many minutes did he record on his reading log that he turned in on Friday?
[114; 30 + 20 + 30 + 10 = 90; 7 + 9 + 5 + 3 = 24; 90 + 24 = 114]

- For students who are still struggling, use the chart below to guide remediation.

- After providing remediation, check students' understanding using the following problem: Joni threw 3 darts at a dartboard and hit the numbers 46, 25, 54. She added them to find the total. What was her score?
[125; 46 + 54 = 100; 100 + 25 = 125]

If the error is ...	Students may ...	To remediate ...
104	have added 37 + 13 and failed to add the regrouped ten.	Provide the student with base-ten blocks to model the addition, pointing out that the ten ones composed into a ten is added to the sum of the tens.
132	have inverted the 1 and 3 recording 13 as 31.	Have the student break each number into tens and ones and then compare them to the numbers that were added.
other answers	have miscalculated either the ones or the tens.	Have the student rework the problem utilizing a different strategy to check for accuracy.

Hands-On Activity

Understand strategies using base-ten blocks.

Materials: base-ten blocks, 10 × 10 grids that match the size of the base blocks (Activity Sheet 3, page 310), a set of 12 cards with two-digit numbers written on them for each student pair (Activity Sheet 8, pages 315–316)

- Give the materials to each student pair.

- The first student picks a card and models the number on the grid. The second student picks a card and decides if a ten or hundred can be made. If so, organize the blocks to make the ten or hundred. If not, model the number on the second grid. The first student picks a card and decides if a ten or hundred can be made with either of the numbers modeled. If so, make the ten or hundred and add the remaining blocks to the grid to find the sum. If a ten or hundred cannot be made, organize the ten rods on the grid and make tens with the unit cubes and then add the extra unit cubes to find the sum.

- Repeat using 3 or 4 addends until all the number cards are gone.

Challenge Activity

Generalize strategies to three-digit numbers.

Challenge students to generalize the strategies they learned in this lesson to adding a series of three-digit numbers and/or find a new strategy for adding three-digit numbers. Tell them to think of ways to add more than two three-digit numbers and record their ideas.

Students must do the following:

- Write the numbers you added.

- Tell the strategy you used to add them.

- Explain how the strategy works so that your classmates could use it.

- Show that it works every time by using it to add other numbers.

Tell students to follow this list for each strategy they find.

©Curriculum Associates, LLC   Copying is not permitted.

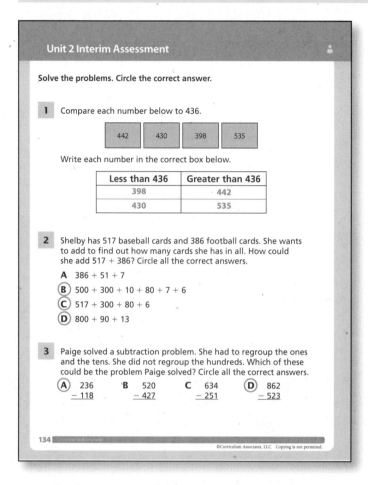

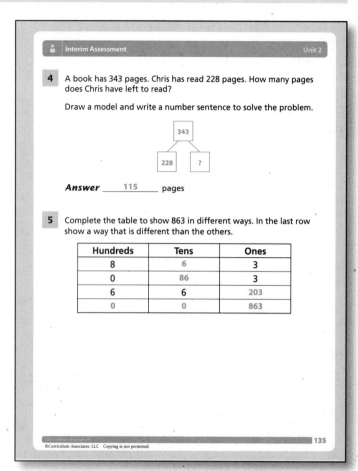

SCORING GUIDE AND ANSWER ANALYSIS

1 *Solution:* Less than 436: 398, 430; Greater than 436: 442, 535 **(DOK 1)**

2 *Solution:* **B**, **C**, **D**. To add 517 + 386, one can break apart both numbers by place value and add the parts: 500 + 300 + 10 + 80 + 7 + 6 (**B**) or 800 + 90 + 13 (**C**), or break up just one addend by place value: 517 + 300 + 80 + 6 (**D**) **(DOK 2)**

3 *Solution:* **A**, **D**. To subtract 236 − 118, regroup 3 tens as 2 tens 10 ones (**A**). To subtract 520 − 427, regroup 2 tens as 1 ten and 10 ones, and regroup 5 hundreds as 4 hundreds 10 tens (**B**). To subtract 634 − 251, regroup 6 hundreds as 5 hundreds 10 tens (**C**). To subtract 862 − 523, regroup 6 tens as 5 tens 10 ones (**D**). **(DOK 2)**

4 *Solution:* Models and number sentences will vary; 115. The problem situation involves a known whole and one part and one unknown part. Diagram should contain a total of 343 and a variable and the number 228 in the two parts, in either order. **(DOK 2)**

5 *Solution:* 6; 86; 203; Possible last row: 0; 0; 863; should show hundreds, tens, and ones with a combined value of 863. **(DOK 2)**

©Curriculum Associates, LLC Copying is not permitted.

PERFORMANCE TASK TEACHER NOTES

Common Core Standards: 2.OA.1, 2.NBT.1.a, 2. NBT.1.b, 2.NBT.3, 2.NBT.4, 2.NBT.5, 2.NBT.6, 2.NBT.7
Mathematical Practice Standards: SMP 2, 3, 4, 7
DOK: 3
Materials: (optional) base-ten blocks

About the Task

This task calls for students to read and write numbers using their understanding of place value. Students also will add and subtract to solve problems.

Getting Started

Read the problem out loud with your students. Be sure that students understand that stickers can be ordered in a group of 1, 10, or 100. Guide students to recognize the parallels between the number of stickers and the place value system. If students are having trouble understanding how many individual stickers some number of packs or sheets represents, you might have them model the number using base-ten models. **(SMP 4)**

Completing the Task

Students first need to find the total number of stickers each child wants to order. They should use place-value concepts to see the table as showing the number of hundreds, tens, and ones. Ask students why they cannot just add the numbers in the columns to find the total number of stickers. Have struggling students model the numbers with base-ten blocks. Ask which model they would use for each package of stickers. **(SMP 4, 7)**

The total number of stickers passed out by the children can be found by adding the four two-digit numbers. Students first should find the total themselves to determine whether Antoine's answer is correct. They should recognize that Antoine's answer is off by one ten, which could have resulted from his not regrouping ones. **(SMP 3)**

Extension

Have students try this problem:

The children buy 4 packs of 100 stickers and 18 sheets of 10 stickers. How many single stickers do they need to buy to have a total of 645?

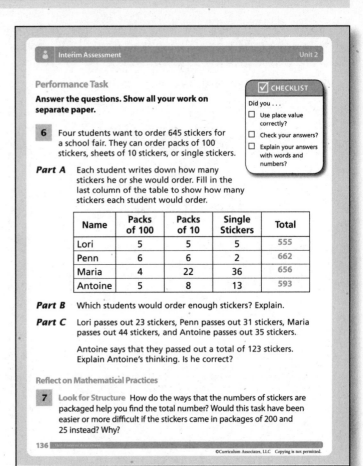

Within the image:

👤 Interim Assessment   Unit 2

Performance Task

Answer the questions. Show all your work on separate paper.

✓ CHECKLIST
Did you . . .
☐ Use place value correctly?
☐ Check your answers?
☐ Explain your answers with words and numbers?

6 Four students want to order 645 stickers for a school fair. They can order packs of 100 stickers, sheets of 10 stickers, or single stickers.

Part A Each student writes down how many stickers he or she would order. Fill in the last column of the table to show how many stickers each student would order.

Name	Packs of 100	Packs of 10	Single Stickers	Total
Lori	5	5	5	555
Penn	6	6	2	662
Maria	4	22	36	656
Antoine	5	8	13	593

Part B Which students would order enough stickers? Explain.

Part C Lori passes out 23 stickers, Penn passes out 31 stickers, Maria passes out 44 stickers, and Antoine passes out 35 stickers.

Antoine says that they passed out a total of 123 stickers. Explain Antoine's thinking. Is he correct?

Reflect on Mathematical Practices

7 Look for Structure How do the ways that the numbers of stickers are packaged help you find the total number? Would this task have been easier or more difficult if the stickers came in packages of 200 and 25 instead? Why?

136   Unit 2 Interim Assessment   ©Curriculum Associates, LLC   Copying is not permitted.

©Curriculum Associates, LLC   Copying is not permitted.

PERFORMANCE TASK SAMPLE RESPONSES AND RUBRIC

6 Sample 4-Point Solution

Part A

Name	Packs of 100	Sheets of 10	Single Stickers	Total
Lori	5	5	5	555
Penn	6	6	2	662
Maria	4	22	36	656
Antoine	5	8	13	593

Part B Penn and Maria; $662 > 645$ and $656 > 645$.

Part C Antoine is not correct. $23 + 31 + 44 + 35 = 133$, not 123. Antoine did not regroup 13 ones as 1 ten 3 ones.

REFLECT ON MATHEMATICAL PRACTICES

7 Possible Answer: The stickers come in groups of 1, 10 and 100, just like the place value in numbers. If the stickers came in packages of 200 and 25, the task would have been a little more difficult because I would have to add groups of 200 or 25 over and over again.

SCORING RUBRIC

4 points The student's response is accurate and complete. All calculations and comparisons are correct. All explanations are complete and correct and are supported with calculations or comparisons. Students show their work in arriving at their answers, including adding to find the total number of tickets passed out.

3 points Student has attempted all calculations and comparisons but has made limited minor errors. Explanations are correct, though some might not be complete. Student used the correct math to answer the questions but might not have interpreted the answer correctly.

2 points The student's response contains several mistakes in calculations and comparisons. The student might show knowledge of place value in numbers by completing the table but could not correctly solve the parts.

1 point The student's response contains an incorrect solution. The table is only partially correctly completed, and the student does not correctly solve the parts.

SOLUTION TO THE EXTENSION

Possible answer: They will need to buy 65 single stickers. 4 packs of 100 and 18 sheets of 10 is a total of $400 + 180 = 580$ stickers. $645 - 580 = 65$.

©Curriculum Associates, LLC   Copying is not permitted.

Unit 3: Measurement and Data

Which lessons are students building upon?

Grade 1, Lesson 31
Order Objects by Length
1.MD.A.1

Grade 1, Lesson 32
Compare Lengths
1.MD.A.1

Grade 1, Lesson 31
Order Objects by Length
1.MD.A.1

Grade 1, Lesson 32
Compare Lengths
1.MD.A.1

Grade 1, Lesson 33
Understand Length Measurement
1.MD.A.2

Grade 1, Lesson 33
Understand Length Measurement
1.MD.A.2

Grade 2, Lesson 16
Understand Length and
Measurement Tools
2.MD.A.1

Grade 2, Lesson 17
Measure Length
2.MD.A.1

Grade 1, Lesson 31
Order Objects by Length
1.MD.A.1

Grade 2, Lesson 16
Understand Length and
Measurement Tools
2.MD.A.1

Grade 2, Lesson 17
Measure Length
2.MD.A.1

Grade 1, Lesson 31
Order Objects by Length
1.MD.A.1

Grade 1, Lesson 32
Compare Lengths
1.MD.A.1

Grade 2, Lesson 19
Understand Estimating Length
2.MD.A.3

Grade 1, Lesson 33
Understand Length Measurement
1.MD.A.2

Grade 2, Lesson 17
Measure Length
2.MD.A.1

Grade 2, Lesson 20
Compare Lengths
2.MD.A.4

Grade 1, Lesson 29
Sort and Count
1.MD.C.4

Grade 1, Lesson 30
Compare Data
1.MD.C.4

©Curriculum Associates, LLC   Copying is not permitted.

Unit 3

Which lessons are students preparing for?

Lesson 16
Understand Length and Measurement Tools
2.MD.A.1

Grade 3, Lesson 22
Liquid Volume
3.MD.A.2

Grade 3, Lesson 23
Mass
3.MD.A.2

Lesson 17
Measure Length
2.MD.A.1

Grade 3, Lesson 22
Liquid Volume
3.MD.A.2

Grade 3, Lesson 23
Mass
3.MD.A.2

Lesson 18
Understand Measurement With Different Units
2.MD.A.2

Grade 3, Lesson 14
Understand What a Fraction Is
3.NF.A.1

Grade 3, Lesson 26
Measure Length and Plot Data on Line Plots
3.MD.B.4

Lesson 19
Understand Estimating Length
2.MD.A.3

Grade 3, Lesson 26
Measure Length and Plot Data on Line Plots
3.MD.B.4

Lesson 20
Compare Lengths
2.MD.A.4

Grade 3, Lesson 26
Measure Length and Plot Data on Line Plots
3.MD.B.4

Lesson 21
Add and Subtract Lengths
2.MD.B.5, 2.MD.B.6, 2.OA.A.1

Grade 3, Lesson 26
Measure Length and Plot Data on Line Plots
3.MD.B.4

Grade 3, Lesson 29
Add Areas
3.MD.C.7c, 3.MD.C.7d

Lesson 22
Understand Reading and Making Line Plots
2.MD.B.6, 2.MD.D.9

Grade 3, Lesson 26
Measure Length and Plot Data on Line Plots
3.MD.B.4

©Curriculum Associates, LLC   Copying is not permitted.

Which lessons are students building upon?

Grade 1, Lesson 29
Sort and Count
1.MD.C.4

Grade 1, Lesson 30
Compare Data
1.MD.C.4

Grade 1, Lesson 34
Tell Time
1.MD.B.3

©Curriculum Associates, LLC   Copying is not permitted.

Which lessons are students preparing for?

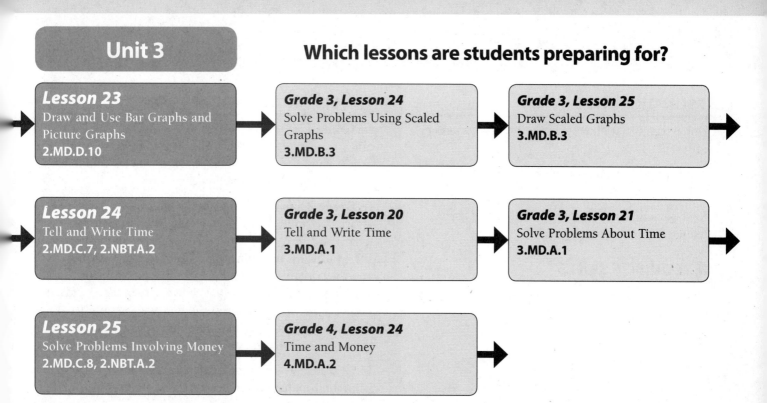

Lesson 23
Draw and Use Bar Graphs and Picture Graphs
2.MD.D.10

Grade 3, Lesson 24
Solve Problems Using Scaled Graphs
3.MD.B.3

Grade 3, Lesson 25
Draw Scaled Graphs
3.MD.B.3

Lesson 24
Tell and Write Time
2.MD.C.7, 2.NBT.A.2

Grade 3, Lesson 20
Tell and Write Time
3.MD.A.1

Grade 3, Lesson 21
Solve Problems About Time
3.MD.A.1

Lesson 25
Solve Problems Involving Money
2.MD.C.8, 2.NBT.A.2

Grade 4, Lesson 24
Time and Money
4.MD.A.2

©Curriculum Associates, LLC   Copying is not permitted.

Lesson 16 (Student Book pages 138–143)

Understand Length and Measurement Tools

LESSON OBJECTIVES

- Understand that objects can be measured using different units.
- Understand that measuring with standard units makes comparing lengths easier.
- Represent and measure the length of an object using tiles and rulers.

PREREQUISITE SKILLS

In order to be proficient with the concept/skills in this lesson, students should:

- Count fluently from 0 to 20.
- Understand that a model can represent a length.

VOCABULARY

standard unit: a commonly-used unit of measure, such as inch or centimeter

inch: the smallest unit for measuring length in the U.S. customary system

centimeter: a unit of length in the metric system

THE LEARNING PROGRESSION

In Grade 1, students compare the lengths of two objects directly, by placing the objects next to each other. They use words such as *taller, shorter,* and *longer* to compare and describe lengths.

In Grade 2, students measure the length of objects using a variety of tools. They learn about different units of length and compare and estimate lengths. Students also solve problems involving adding and subtracting lengths and they organize length data in a line plot. **In this lesson,** students investigate why we use standardized units for measuring lengths and why we use numbers to describe lengths. They use rulers and tiles to measure the lengths of objects to the nearest inch or centimeter.

In Grade 3, students measure objects more precisely, using half-inches and quarter-inches, when appropriate. They use what they know about length to solve problems involving perimeter and area. They also extend their use of standard units to measures of liquid volume and mass.

	Prerequisite Skills	2.MD.A.1
Ready Lessons	✓ ✓	✓
Tools for Instruction	✓	
Interactive Tutorials		✓ ✓

Ready *Teacher Toolbox* — *Teacher-Toolbox.com*

CCSS Focus

2.MD.A.1. Measure the length of an object by selecting and using appropriate tools such as rulers, yardsticks, meter sticks, and measuring tapes.

STANDARDS FOR MATHEMATICAL PRACTICE: SMP 5, 6 *(see page A9 for full text)*

©Curriculum Associates, LLC Copying is not permitted.

Measuring on Grid Paper

Objective: Experiment with measuring lengths.

Materials for each student:
• 1-inch grid paper (Activity Sheet 3, page 310)

Overview

Students are asked to find objects in the classroom that fit inside a rectangle.

Step by Step (20–30 minutes)

1 Describe the situation.

• Tell students that a company is designing a new pencil box that is 2 inches by 7 inches. Model how to draw a 2-inch by 7-inch rectangle on inch grid paper. Have students do the same on their own grid.

• Students need to find out which classroom objects will fit in the box.

2 Measure objects.

• Have students work in pairs.

• Ask each pair to find at least five different objects that fit in the box and one that does not fit.

3 Collect the data.

• As students find and measure the objects, have them keep a list of what fits in the box and what does not. They should also record the length and width of each object.

4 Discuss the results as a class.

• Invite students to show the objects they measured that will fit in the box.

• Ask: *How could you tell that an object will fit in the box?* Students might place the object on the grid paper, or place the grid paper on the object.

• Explain that you want to find the longest of all their objects that will fit in the box. Ask: *How can we tell that it is the longest object? What is the longest object?* Students might suggest putting two objects next to each other to see which is the longest.

• Ask: *Do you think that the company should make a pencil box this size? Do you have any suggestions about changing the shape or size of the box? Explain your choices.* Answers will vary.

©Curriculum Associates, LLC   Copying is not permitted.

AT A GLANCE

Students explore how to measure an object using paper clips.

STEP BY STEP

- Discuss the question at the top of the page. Ask students to describe different ways they have measured lengths in real life.

- Read the Think section together.

- Invite individual students to suggest why each of the four guidelines in the Think section must be followed when measuring an object.

- Use the Mathematical Discourse questions to be certain that students understand the importance of using the same unit and not a combination of units to measure an object.

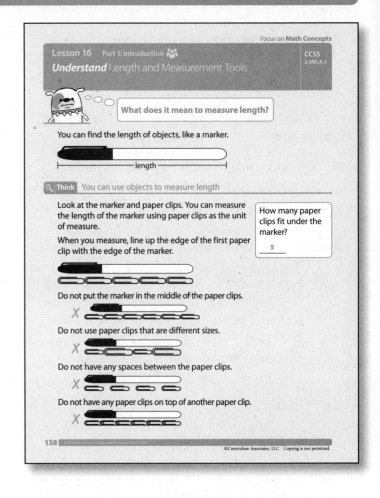

Mathematical Discourse

- *Suppose we had 3 big paper clips and 3 small paper clips and they fit under the marker exactly. Is it OK to say that the marker is 6 paper clips long? Why or why not?*

  Students' responses should indicate that to make an accurate measurement, all the paper clips need to be the same size.

- *Do you think that paper clips are good tools for measuring? Why or why not?*

  Students may point out that keeping the paper clips in a straight line could be difficult, or that we can't be sure that everyone uses paper clips of the same length.

Real-World Connection

Ask students to think of some examples of lengths that they know and use in their daily life.

Examples: how many blocks students travel to school, who is the tallest in the class, the length of a sport field, how deep a swimming pool is, how many miles to a grandparent's home, etc.

Students may describe lengths using comparisons: *I'm tall enough to stand up in the shallow end of the pool.* They might also use units: *It's four blocks from my house to my friend's house.* Listen for and talk about different types of units, both standard and non-standard.

©Curriculum Associates, LLC   Copying is not permitted.

AT A GLANCE

Students learn how to use standard units to measure length.

STEP BY STEP

- Give each student a ruler, and allow time for free exploration with the rulers. Read the Think section together. Have each student find both the inches and the centimeters on the rulers.

- Discuss with students how a ruler is similar to a number line. The left edge is 0. Each tick mark represents the distance from that mark to 0. The 0 should always line up with one side of whatever object is being measured.

- Read the Reflect question together. Ask students to discuss the question with a partner and then write their answer.

- Invite students to share their answers to the Reflect question with the class.

- Use the Mathematical Discourse questions to emphasize the importance of using standard tools and standard units.

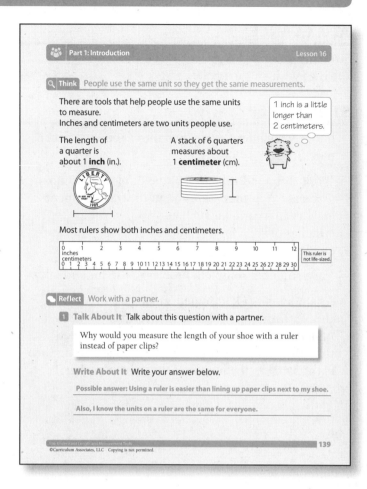

Note

The U.S. customary system and the metric system

Students may be familiar with the *U.S. customary system* of measurement (inches, feet, yards), the *metric system* (centimeters, meters, kilometers), or both. U.S. customary units are used in the United States. The metric system is used in most countries outside the United States. In the United States, it is used in the areas of science, medicine, and other industries.

ELL Support

ELL students may be more familiar with the metric system than with the U.S. customary system. Assure students that they will have many opportunities to practice measuring in both systems.

Mathematical Discourse

- *What if "one inch" meant "the length of your shortest toe"?*

  Students should understand that since our toes may be different lengths, a measurement such as "3 inches" would mean a different length to each person.

- *What if you use inches to measure your shoe, and your friend uses paper clips to measure her shoe? Can you compare the lengths of the two shoes?*

  Listen to be sure that students understand that if two people use different units, it is more difficult to compare lengths. They may suggest that if you know the length of a paper clip in inches, you could compare the lengths.

- *Why do we need a tool with standard units?*

  We need to use standard units so that we all agree on what a length such as "10 inches" means.

AT A GLANCE

Students measure length with inch tiles and line up the tiles with an inch ruler.

STEP BY STEP

- Give each student some inch tiles (Activity Sheet 3, page 310).

- Work through Problem 2 of the Explore It section as a class. You may want to put the measurement activity in a context, such as, "Audrey needs 4 inches of yarn for a craft project. Does she have enough yarn?"

- Have students complete Problems 4–6 individually.

- As students work, circulate among them. Use the Mathematical Discourse questions to check understanding. Make sure students understand that the number of tiles needed to measure the yarn is the same as the length of the yarn in inches.

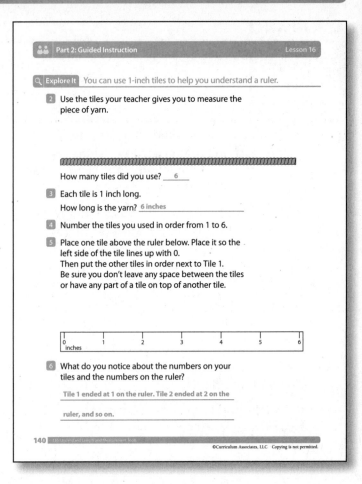

Hands-On Activity

Practice measuring with inch tiles.

Materials: inch tiles, assorted common objects or parts of the classroom

Have students work in pairs. Ask them to measure items in the classroom with the inch tiles. Each student in the pair should measure the same object and agree on the length. Have them keep track of their results in a table like the one below.

Object	Length (in inches)
Short side of notebook	8

After students have measured several objects, discuss the results. What is the longest length they found? What is the shortest? What are some drawbacks to measuring with inch tiles?

Mathematical Discourse

- *How do you know where to put the first tile when you measure the yarn?*

  It is important to line up one edge of the tile with one end of the yarn.

- *If you put your inch tiles in a different order, would you still need the same number of tiles?*

  Yes, the order of the tiles does not matter.

SMP Tip: Students use appropriate tools (*SMP 5*) as they measure. Encourage students to think about how using tiles and using a ruler are similar, and about how they could measure if neither one were available.

©Curriculum Associates, LLC   Copying is not permitted.

AT A GLANCE

Students analyze the measurements they made in the activity on the previous page. They then measure the length of yarn in centimeters.

STEP BY STEP

- Have students work with a partner to complete the Talk About It questions.

- Some students may think that they should line up the end of their yarn with the tick mark at 1 on the ruler, instead of at 0 (Problem 9). Remind the class that the number 1 at the first tick mark represents a distance of 1 inch from the 0 edge of the ruler. It is not a starting point.

- Direct the group's attention to Try It Another Way. Make sure that all students have centimeter tiles (Activity Sheet 4, page 311). Have students complete the question individually, then compare their results with a partner.

> **SMP Tip:** When lining up the inch tiles and counting them, students attend to precision. (*SMP 6*) They should apply the same precision to measuring with rulers.

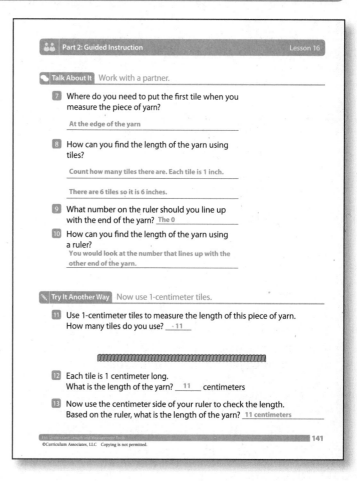

Real-World Connection

Share with students some ways in which measurements are used in different careers. For example, a surveyor measures land. A biologist might use a stage micrometer (a microscope slide with a scale on it) to make very small measurements. A carpenter uses a tape measure to measure and cut pieces of wood.

Mathematical Discourse

- *Will you get the same result if you measure the yarn with inch tiles or a ruler?*

  Yes, the result should be the same.

- *Which tool do you think is easier to use for measuring, the inch tiles or the ruler?*

  Students may suggest that the ruler is easier to handle, more accurate, and is better for measuring an object that is vertical.

- *Do you think it is easier to measure in inches or in centimeters?*

  Answers will vary. Students may prefer inches because the tiles are bigger and easier to handle, or centimeters because they seem more accurate.

©Curriculum Associates, LLC   Copying is not permitted.

AT A GLANCE

Students demonstrate their understanding of measuring tools.

STEP BY STEP

- Discuss each Connect It problem as a class using the discussion points outlined below.

Create:

- This problem focuses on the concept that measuring a length with a ruler corresponds to counting the number of tiles that align with the length.

- As students share their completed rulers, ask questions like: *What does the number 4 represent on the ruler?* Listen for responses that demonstrate that students recognize that each number on a ruler represents the distance from the 0 point of the ruler to the corresponding mark on the ruler.

Compare:

- This problem asks students to notice that the units on a ruler must be equal in size.

- Ask: *Could you use a ruler that is made with a mixture of inch tiles and centimeter tiles?* Students should recognize that the units on a ruler are either all inches or all centimeters.

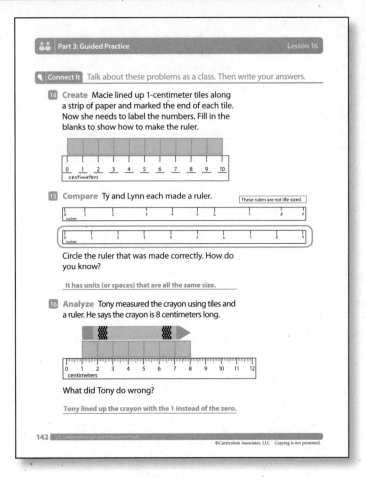

Analyze:

- As students analyze the error, ask them to look at where the ruler and the tiles line up with the crayon.

- Ask: *Why do you think Tony made the error he did?* Students may suggest that it seems natural to start a sequence at 1 rather than 0. Remind them of the result of the first Connect It problem: The mark at the number 1 represents a distance of 1 unit from the 0 mark.

©Curriculum Associates, LLC   Copying is not permitted.

AT A GLANCE

Students demonstrate their understanding of length and measurement tools by creating rulers in both inches and centimeters.

STEP BY STEP

- Direct students to complete the Put It Together task on their own.

- Read the directions with students and make sure they understand each part of the task before proceeding.

- As students work on their own, walk around to assess their progress and understanding, to answer their questions, and to give additional support, if needed.

- If time permits, ask students to share the rulers they created and explain why they are good measurement tools.

SCORING RUBRICS

A

Points	Expectations
2	The student lines up the inch tiles starting at the edge of the box. The ends of the tiles are marked and numbered correctly.
1	The student is partially correct. The completed ruler may have some gaps between the spaces or be numbered incorrectly.
0	The student was not able to create the ruler.

B

Points	Expectations
2	The student lines up the centimeter tiles starting at the edge of the box. The ends of the tiles are marked and numbered correctly.
1	The student is partially correct. The completed ruler may have some gaps between the spaces or be numbered incorrectly.
0	The student was not able to create the ruler.

Part 4: Common Core Performance Task Lesson 16

🔍 **Put It Together** Use what you have learned to complete this task.

17 For this task, you will need 1-inch tiles and 1-centimeter tiles.

A Use your 1-inch tiles to make an inch ruler.

| 0 | 1 | 2 | 3 | 4 | 5 | 6 |
| inches | | | | | | |

How long is your ruler? 6 inches

B Use your 1-centimeter tiles to make a centimeter ruler.

| 0 1 2 3 4 5 6 7 8 9 10 11 12 13 14 15 |
| centimeters |

How long is your ruler? 15 centimeters

C Explain the steps you took to make the rulers.

First I lined up the tiles above the paper strip right

next to each other. Then I marked the end of each

tile. Then I numbered the marks.

L16: Understand Length and Measurement Tools 143
©Curriculum Associates, LLC Copying is not permitted.

C

Points	Expectations
2	The student's response accurately describes all steps the student took to make the ruler.
1	The student's response omits one or more steps used to create the ruler.
0	The student was not able to describe how the ruler was made.

©Curriculum Associates, LLC Copying is not permitted.

Intervention Activity

Model rulers with grid paper.

Materials: Inch grid paper (Activity Sheet 3, page 310) and centimeter grid paper (Activity Sheet 4, page 311), objects to measure, crayons or markers, scissors

- Tell students to number 10 squares in a row on the inch grid paper. They can use different colors for the numbers, but square number 1 should be black.

- Have students cut out and use this homemade ruler to measure several different objects. If possible, choose objects with dimensions that are whole inches. Tell students to make sure that the black square always lines up with the left edge of the object they are measuring.

- Repeat the activity using 20 squares on centimeter grid paper and a different set of objects, if necessary.

On-Level Activity

Measure lengths of feet.

Materials: Rulers

- Have students work in groups of 3 or 4.

- Tell students they will measure the length of each person's foot in their group, to the nearest inch.

- Have each student trace around his or her own foot on a piece of paper. Then use a ruler to measure the longest possible length on the tracing, to the nearest inch. Have another student in the group check the measurement.

- Record each student's name and foot length. When all the groups are finished, compare all the lengths. Who has the longest foot?

Challenge Activity

Model proportional reasoning.

Materials: At least 10 of the same measureable object, such as unused crayons, index or playing cards, or pieces of paper; yardstick or meter stick

- Measure the length of one crayon, to the nearest inch or centimeter, and record the length in a table like the one below. Put two crayons end to end and measure the total length. Add a third crayon to the chain and measure the total length again.

Number of crayons	Total length (inches)
1	
2	

- Continue adding crayons, measuring, and recording until the chain of crayons is longer than the yardstick or meter stick.

- Ask students to look for patterns in the lengths they recorded. Can they predict the length of a line of 100 crayons? Ask them to explain their reasoning using diagrams or words.

©Curriculum Associates, LLC   Copying is not permitted.

Lesson 17 (Student Book pages 148–157)

Measure Length

LESSON OBJECTIVES

- Learn about rulers, yardsticks, meter sticks, and tape measures.
- Measure lengths using different tools.
- Learn how to use a ruler repeatedly to measure a length.
- Choose a tool for measuring the length of a given object.

PREREQUISITE SKILLS

- Understand that objects can be measured with different units.
- Add multiples of 30.

VOCABULARY

There is no new vocabulary in this lesson.

THE LEARNING PROGRESSION

In the previous lesson, students began using standardized units to measure lengths. They discovered that standard units are useful for comparing and recording measurements.

In this lesson, students practice measuring with different tools, such as rulers, yard sticks, and measuring tapes. They learn how to choose which tool to use, and how to measure an object longer than a ruler by using the ruler repeatedly.

In the next lesson, students will compare measuring in different types of unit. They will find that the smaller the unit, the greater the number needed to measure an object.

▇ Ready *Teacher Toolbox*   Teacher-Toolbox.com

	Prerequisite Skills	2.MD.A.1
Ready Lessons	✓ ✓ ✓	✓
Tools for Instruction	✓	
Interactive Tutorials	✓	✓ ✓

CCSS Focus

2.MD.A.1 Measure the length of an object by selecting and using appropriate tools such as rulers, yardsticks, meter sticks, and measuring tapes.

ADDITIONAL STANDARDS: **2.NBT.5** *(see page A42 for full text)*

STANDARDS FOR MATHEMATICAL PRACTICE: **SMP 3, 4, 5, 6, 7** *(see page A9 for full text)*

©Curriculum Associates, LLC   Copying is not permitted.

Measuring Paths on a Grid

Objective: Practice measuring in inches.	**Materials for each student:** • 1-inch grid paper (Activity Sheet 3, pages 310) • colored pencils • ruler

Overview

Students will experiment with finding and measuring different paths between two locations on grid paper.

Step by Step (15–20 minutes)

1 Present the situation.

• Have students draw a rectangle that is 3 inches by 4 inches on their grid paper. Then have them draw two opposite points labeled "Home" and "School" at two vertices of the rectangle.

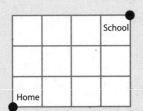

• Tell students that they are going to find the lengths of different paths from a teacher's home to her school. The paths have to stay on the grid lines and cannot go outside the 3 × 4 rectangle.

2 Sketch some possible paths.

• On the board, draw some examples of paths that the teacher might take.

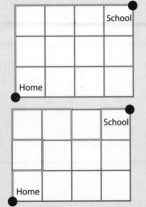

This is one path the teacher could take from home to school. Its length is 7.

This is a longer path that the teacher could take from home to school. Its length is 11.

• Give students time to find at least 6 different paths that the teacher could take. They may prefer to use different colors to draw the paths, or draw more rectangles. As they finish each path, have them find its length in inches. They can use rulers to confirm the lengths.

3 Share results.

• After students have finished, compile their path lengths. What is the shortest path length they could find? What is the longest? Did anyone find a path that is 8 inches long? Did any path cross itself, or hit an intersection twice?

4 Extend the problem.

• Have students measure directly from the point labeled "Home" to the point labeled "School," along the diagonal of the rectangle. [5 inches]

• Ask students to suppose that each grid square represents 10 blocks. How could you find how many blocks long any of the paths are? [Find how long the path is in inches. Count by 10 that many times.]

©Curriculum Associates, LLC   Copying is not permitted.

AT A GLANCE

Students review measuring with a centimeter ruler.

STEP BY STEP

- Tell students that this page models measuring in centimeters with a ruler.

- If students are using rulers that have centimeters on one edge and inches on the other, make sure they use the side with centimeters.

- Let students know that they have time to answer the Explore It questions on their own.

- As students work, circulate among them to assess understanding and address any misconceptions about aligning a ruler correctly. Use the Mathematical Discourse questions to advance understanding of using a centimeter ruler and ensure accuracy.

- Once students have completed the questions, go through the results with the class.

- Draw different lengths on the board, and ask pairs of students to measure them in centimeters. One student can hold the ruler, the other can read the measurement.

SMP Tip: Throughout this lesson, students use tiles, rulers, yardsticks, and meter sticks to measure. This gives them the opportunity to practice using appropriate tools strategically. *(SMP 5)*

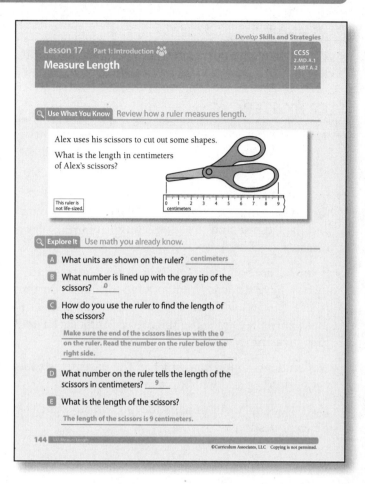

Mathematical Discourse

- *What do you notice about how the ruler is lined up with the scissors?*

   Students should know that the 0 mark on the ruler is correctly placed to align with one end of the scissors. Also, students should recognize that the ruler is lined up to measure the longest possible length of the scissors.

- *How did you decide that the scissors are 9 centimeters long instead of 8 centimeters or 10 centimeters?*

   Answers may vary, but students should know that the tip of the scissors is closest to the 9 centimeter mark on the ruler.

AT A GLANCE

Students learn about different types of measuring tools, including yard sticks and meter sticks.

STEP BY STEP

- Read Find Out More as a class. Have rulers, yardsticks, meter sticks, and tape measures, if possible, available for students to use.

- Have students examine each type of tool used in the classroom to see if there is a gap between its end and the 0 mark, and to see which type of units they measure.

- If your classroom rulers have both centimeters and inches, have students find both types of units on the rulers. Discuss with students how they can check to make sure they are using the correct units each time they measure.

- Ask students to tell you which of the measuring tools is the shortest and which is the longest.

- Have students work in pairs to read and answer the Reflect question.

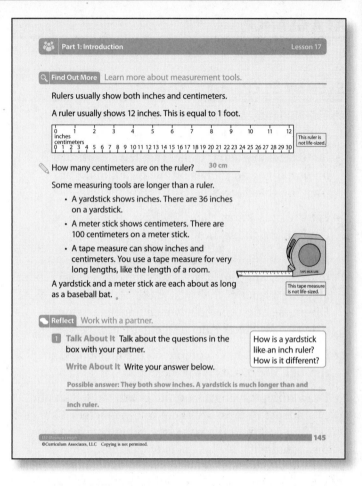

Visual Model

Create a representation of your measuring tools.

- On the board or on a large sheet of paper, have different pairs of students trace and label each of the measuring tools that you have in the classroom. One student can hold the tool while the other traces.

  ☐ Inch ruler

  ☐ Centimeter ruler

  ☐ Yard stick

- If possible, leave this diagram on the board throughout the measurement lessons.

ELL Support

Discuss with students that the word "foot" has two different meanings, the unit of measure and the part of your body that is below the ankle. Students may find it helpful to know that the unit of measure was originally based on the length of an adult's foot.

Real-World Connection

Discuss with students what type of workers might use the measuring tools seen in this lesson. They may have noticed measuring tapes being used by plumbers, or architects, or in fabric stores. Point out that measuring lengths is a very common use of mathematics in everyday life.

©Curriculum Associates, LLC   Copying is not permitted.

AT A GLANCE

Students compare measuring with inch tiles and measuring with rulers.

STEP BY STEP

- Read the problem at the top of the page as a class. Make sure that students have inch tiles, centimeter tiles (Activity Sheets 3 and 4, pages 310–311), rulers, and paper available.

- Draw students' attention to the first Measure It. Have students align their inch tiles with the paper as shown in the diagram.

- Draw students' attention to the second Measure It. Have them line up their rulers with the paper.

- Point out that students can use centimeters to measure the paper instead of inches. When they align centimeter tiles, note that the last tile does not align with the right edge of the paper. Tell students that we say the paper is "almost 28 centimeters long" in this case.

> **SMP Tip:** Lining up the 0 mark of a measuring tool correctly is a good opportunity for students to attend to precision. *(SMP 6)*

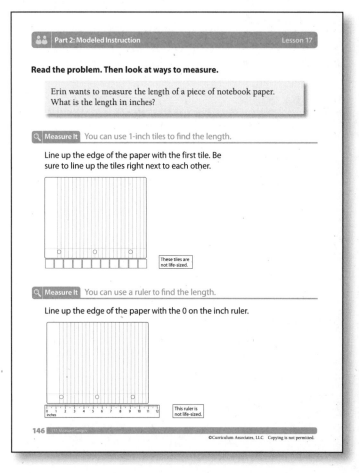

Mathematical Discourse

- *How do you know that the inch tiles and ruler are lined up with the paper correctly?*

  When measuring with inch tiles, one edge of a tile should line up with one edge of the paper. When measuring with a ruler, the 0 mark on the ruler should line up with the edge of the paper.

- *What do the two methods of measuring shown on this page have in common? How are they different?*

  They both use inches. The ruler is in one piece, the tiles are many pieces.

- *What do you predict would happen if you measured a different side of the paper?*

  Answers will vary. Students may reply that the side opposite the one they are measuring is the same length, and the other two sides are shorter.

AT A GLANCE

Students revisit and complete the problem on page 150. They then use centimeters to measure a key.

STEP BY STEP

- Read the first two Connect It problems as a class. Make sure students understand that the questions follow up on the problem on page 146.

- Ask students to answer the first three questions on their own. Invite individual students to share their answers to Problem 4.

- For Problem 5, have students work in pairs. Ask them to think about the type of units they see on a yardstick. Have yardsticks available for students to look at if they are unsure about the units.

- For the Try It questions, have students work in pairs. Use the Mathematical Discourse question to check understanding.

ELL Support

Pair English language learners with proficient readers for the Talk About It and Try It questions. Have yardsticks, meter sticks, and centimeter tiles available for all students.

Hands-On Activity

Materials: Rulers or meter sticks, common objects such as books, folders, pencils

- Have students measure and record the lengths of a variety of objects in the classroom with the rulers.

- Then give them target lengths such as 10 centimeters, 20 centimeters, or 100 centimeters, that are different from the lengths of the objects. Ask students to find objects or parts of the classroom of those lengths.

- Encourage students to share their results. Do they agree on the lengths of the objects you gave them? Were they able to find objects with the given lengths?

Part 2: Guided Instruction — Lesson 17

Connect It Understand and use the models to solve the problem.

2 Look at the first Measure It. How many inch tiles are used? __11__

3 Look at the second Measure It. What is the length of the paper? __11 inches__

4 If you could measure with 1-inch tiles or an inch ruler, which would you choose? Why?

Answers will vary. Students might choose the ruler

because there is only one thing to line up.

5 **Talk About It** Talk about the questions in the green box with a partner.
Write About It Write your answer below.

Possible answer: The length would be the same

number of inches. A yardstick shows inches, too.

> Would the length of the paper be the same if you measured it using a yardstick? Why or why not?

Try It Measure the key using centimeters.

6 Use centimeter tiles. The key has a length of __5__ centimeters.

7 Use a centimeter ruler. The key has a length of __5__ centimeters.

8 What would the length of the key be if you measured it with a meter stick? __5__ centimeters

L17 Measure Length

147

©Curriculum Associates, LLC   Copying is not permitted.

Mathematical Discourse

- *What would you happen if you used a mix of inch tiles and centimeter tiles to measure the key or the piece of paper?*

   Students should recognize that combining customary and metric units to measure any object is not workable.

TRY IT SOLUTIONS

6 *Solution:* 5

7 *Solution:* 5

8 *Solution:* 5

ERROR ALERT: Students who say that the length is 4 centimeters may be lining up the edge of the key with the 1 rather than the 0 on the ruler.

©Curriculum Associates, LLC   Copying is not permitted.

AT A GLANCE

Students explore measuring with a centimeter ruler and a meter stick.

STEP BY STEP

- Read the problem at the top of the page as a class. Tell students that they will practice measuring an object that is longer than a ruler.

- Draw students' attention to the Picture It section.

- Give students lengths of string that are 90 centimeters long, and draw a line segment on the board that is also 90 centimeters long. Tell students they will practice using a ruler to measure a length longer than the ruler.

- Align a centimeter ruler at the left end of the segment on the board, and draw a tick mark at the 30 centimeter mark. Have students do the same thing with the string, holding an index finger in place instead of drawing a tick mark. Move the ruler so the 0 mark aligns with the tick mark or index finger. Repeat the marking and moving to measure the segment.

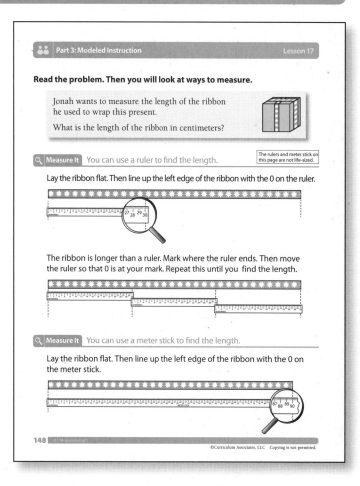

Concept Extension

Using string to measure.

Materials: small boxes or books, meter sticks, string

- Have students work in small groups. Give each group one box, a meter stick, and a long length of string.

- Show students how to measure around a box: Wrap the string around the box, mark the point where the end of the string meets the string, unwrap the string and measure it on the meter stick.

- Have students measure their boxes, then trade boxes with other groups to measure again.

Mathematical Discourse

- *Why is it important to lay the ribbon flat when measuring it?*

    Students may say that since the rulers are flat, the ribbon must be also. If we are using a paper or fabric tape measure, we could leave the ribbon on the package and wrap the tape measure around it.

- *Can you think of another way to measure the ribbon when it is flat?*

    We could use a tape measure or several rulers put together.

L17: Measure Length **183**
©Curriculum Associates, LLC   Copying is not permitted.

AT A GLANCE

Students learn how to add ruler lengths to find measures, and compare using a centimeter ruler to using a meter stick.

STEP BY STEP

- Tell students that this page will help them find lengths of objects that are longer than one ruler's length.

- Work through the Connect It section as a class.

- For Problem 12, have students work with a partner. You may want to have students mimic what is shown on the student page and measure an actual 90-centimeter piece of string with a meter stick.

- After students complete the Try it question, ask how many underlined "this book" and how many circled it. Ask individuals from each group to defend their choice.

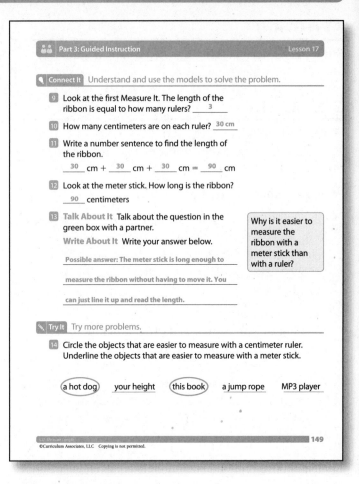

©Curriculum Associates, LLC Copying is not permitted.

149

L17: Measure Length

Part 3: Guided Instruction   Lesson 17

ELL Support

Pair English language learners with proficient readers for Problem 12. Before students begin the Try It question, demonstrate circling and underlining words on the board.

SMP Tips: In Problems 9 and 10, when students progress from "three ruler lengths" to "30 + 30 + 30," they are modeling a situation with a number sentence. (SMP 4)

In Problem 13, defending their choice of the ruler or meter stick and understanding other students' choices is a chance for students to construct arguments and critique reasoning. (SMP 3)

TRY IT SOLUTIONS

14 *Solution:* Circled terms: "hot dog" and "MP3 player." Underlined terms: "your height" and "jump rope." "This book" may be either underlined or circled. See "Step by Step" for discussion of this result.

Hands-On Activity

Materials: centimeter rulers

- Draw several line segments on the board, or put several lengths of painter's tape or strips of paper on the floor. Use lengths that are multiples of the length of your centimeter rulers, such as 30 centimeters, 60 centimeters, and 150 centimeters.

- Have students work in small groups to measure the lengths of the segments. Make sure that they write the number sentence they are using to find the total length of each segment.

- When they are done, have them share the results. Write the complete number sentence for the length on the board or on each piece of tape or paper.

©Curriculum Associates, LLC   Copying is not permitted.

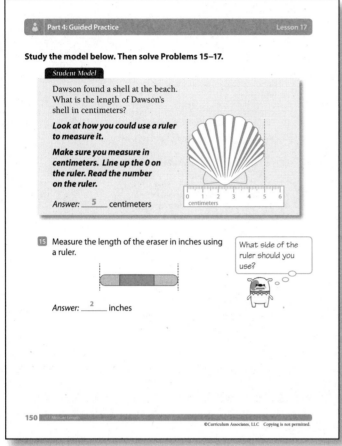

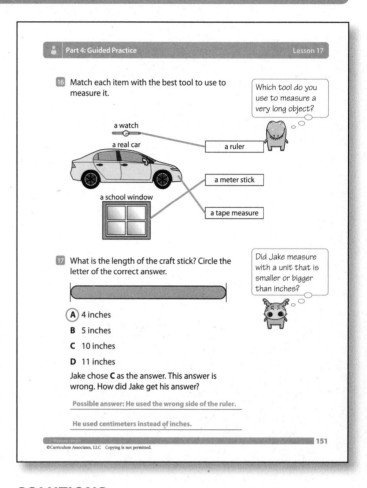

AT A GLANCE

Students practice measuring.

STEP BY STEP

• Read the student model as a class. Have students confirm that the ruler is aligned properly.

• Ask students to measure the eraser. Check their results and address any misconceptions.

SOLUTIONS

Ex A centimeter ruler is used to find the length of the shell in centimeters by aligning one side with 0 on the ruler.

15 *Solution:* 2 inches. **(DOK 1)**

16 *Solution:*
Watch : ruler
Car : tape measure
Large window : meter stick. **(DOK 2)**

17 *Solution:* **A**; Possible response: Jake measured the stick using centimeters instead of inches.

Explain to students why the other two choices are not correct:

If a student chose **B**, make sure the student is measuring from 0 on the ruler, not 1.

If a student chose **D**, make sure that the student uses inches and aligns the ruler correctly. **(DOK 3)**

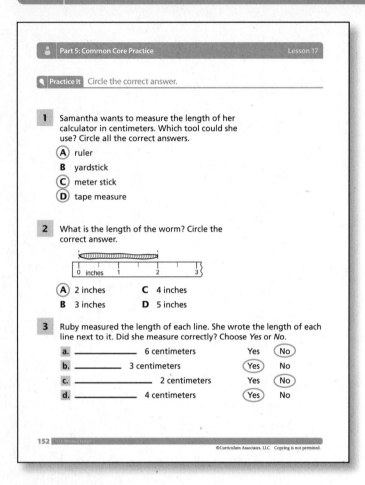

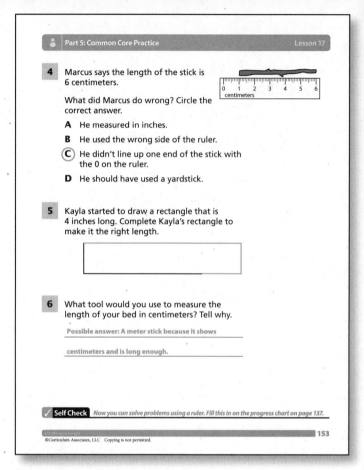

AT A GLANCE

Students solve measurement problems that might appear on a mathematics test.

STEP BY STEP

- First, tell students they will use addition and subtraction to solve one-step word problems. Then have students read the directions and answer the questions independently.

- After students have completed the Common Core Practice problems, review and discuss correct answers.

SOLUTIONS

1 *Solution:* **A**, **C**, and **D**; all of these measuring tools except the yardstick (**B**) can be used to measure the calculator. *(DOK 2)*

2 *Solution:* **A**; 2 inches. *(DOK 1)*

3 *Solution:* No; Yes; No; Yes. *(DOK 1)*

4 *Solution:* **C**. *(DOK 2)*

5 *Solution:* Check students' drawings. *(DOK 2)*

6 *Solution:* Meter stick, tape measure, or centimeter ruler; because they all measure with centimeters. *(DOK 2)*

©Curriculum Associates, LLC   Copying is not permitted.

Assessment and Remediation

- Draw a line segment 10 inches long and ask students to measure it in inches. [10]
- For students who are still struggling, use the chart below to guide remediation.
- After providing remediation, check students' understanding by drawing a line segment of a different length and having them measure its length.

If the error is . . .	Students may . . .	To remediate . . .
11 inches	have started measuring from 1 on the ruler instead of from 0.	Have students find one inch on the ruler, then measure a line segment one inch long. Repeat with two inches, then three inches.
25 inches	have used centimeters instead of inches.	Have students find the side of the ruler with inches on it, and the side with centimeters.
any other number	read the ruler incorrectly.	Have students align the ruler with the line segment correctly, then place one finger at each end of the segment. One finger should be at 0 and the other should be at 10.

Hands-On Activity

Estimate measurements.

Materials: bean bags; yardstick, meter stick, or tape measure

- Students should work in pairs or small groups.
- One student will guess how far he or she can (gently) toss a bean bag, and then toss it.
- Students work together to measure the length of the toss.
- Repeat until each student in the group has had a chance to guess, toss, and measure at least two times.
- Ask the following questions: *Who had the longest toss? Who had the toss that was closest to his or her guess? Did you change your guess before you tossed the bean bag the second time?*

Challenge Activity

Find a length indirectly.

Cut four strips of paper whose lengths are multiples of 8, such as 32, 40, 56, and 72 centimeters, or 16, 24, 32, and 48 inches.

Fold two of the strips in half three times, so they are one-eighth of their original length.

Give students the other two strips. Have students measure the strip, fold it in half, measure the folded length, and then record the folded length. Repeat the folding and measuring until it has been folded in eighths. Ask what they notice about the lengths they recorded, and if they see a pattern.

Give students the strips you folded, and have them measure the folded length. Can they predict the length of the strips when they are completely unfolded?

©Curriculum Associates, LLC   Copying is not permitted.

Lesson 18 (Student Book pages 154–159)

Understand Measurement with Different Units

LESSON OBJECTIVES

- Compare lengths measured in different units.

- Understand the relationship between feet and inches.

- Understand the relationship between centimeters and meters.

- Explore how the number of units used to measure is related to the size of the units used.

PREREQUISITE SKILLS

In order to be proficient with the concept/skills in this lesson, students should:

- Measure lengths in inches and centimeters.

VOCABULARY

There is no new vocabulary in this lesson.

THE LEARNING PROGRESSION

In Grade 1, students developed their understanding of measuring in different units, using nonstandard units. They compared lengths directly and put lengths in order without using formal units such as inches or centimeters.

In Grade 2, students extend their knowledge of measuring lengths to the use of standard units, focusing on inches and centimeters. **In this lesson,** students compare measurements made in inches and feet, inches and centimeters, and other units. For example, students measure an object in both feet and inches, and learn that more inches are needed to measure the object than feet.

In Grade 3, choosing an appropriate unit will continue to be important as students begin to measure volumes in weights in addition to lengths. Students will apply what they know about measuring lengths to problems involving perimeters and areas.

■ **Ready** *Teacher Toolbox*		*Teacher-Toolbox.com*
	Prerequisite Skills	2.MD.A.2
Ready Lessons	✓	✓
Tools for Instruction	✓	
Interactive Tutorials	✓ ✓	

CCSS Focus

2.MD.A.2 Measure the length of an object twice, using length units of different lengths for the two measurements; describe how the two measurements relate to the size of the unit chosen.

STANDARDS FOR MATHEMATICAL PRACTICE: SMP 2, 5, 6 *(see page A9 for full text)*

©Curriculum Associates, LLC Copying is not permitted.

Comparing Measurements

Objective: Review measuring in centimeters and inches; compare measurements of the same objects using different units.	**Materials for each student:** • rulers • copies of Activity Sheet 9, page 317

Overview

Students measure lengths using inches and centimeters. They then compare the measurements and look for a pattern.

Step by Step (20–30 minutes)

1 **Activate students' knowledge about measuring lengths.**

- Draw a line segment on the board. Ask students to describe all the different ways they could use to find out how long it is. [use a ruler, a tape measure, a yardstick, a meter stick]

- Ask students what units are on each of the measuring tools they just described.

2 **Take some measurements.**

- Give each student a copy of Activity Sheet 9.

- *Option 1:* Each student can measure each object twice, once in inches and once in centimeters.

- *Option 2:* Half the students can use inches to measure the objects and half can use centimeters.

- Remind students to find the lengths to the nearest inch or nearest centimeter. Record the lengths the students find on the board in a table like this one:

Object	Length in inches	Length in centimeters
Seedling		
Slanted side of triangle		
Pen		
Bug		

3 **Talk about the results.**

Ask questions about the lengths that the students measured:

- *What do you notice about the lengths we found?* [For each object, the number in the inch column is different from the number in the centimeter column; students may also notice that the numbers in the centimeter column are bigger than the ones in the inch column.]

- *Does changing the units change how big or how small the object is?* [No, the objects stay the same.]

©Curriculum Associates, LLC   Copying is not permitted.

AT A GLANCE

Students compare measuring in inches with measuring in feet.

STEP BY STEP

- Tell students they will learn about measuring an object in two different ways.

- Introduce the problem at the top of the page.

- Have students find 24 inches and 2 feet on a yard stick or tape measure, and compare the two lengths.

- Read and complete the Think section as a class.

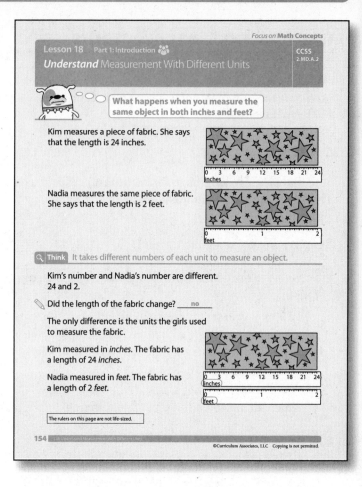

Hands-On Activity

Measure other objects in feet and inches.

Materials: yard sticks or rulers, common large classroom objects such as tables and chairs

- Have students work in small groups. Give each group a yard stick or a ruler.

- Make a list of large objects in the classroom on the board, such as a student's table, the teacher's desk, or the base of a window. If possible, choose things that are taller or longer than 2 feet.

- Have students work together to measure each of the objects in inches and in feet.

- Record the lengths they measured on the board, with inches in one column and feet in the other.

- Have students put each column of lengths in order from shortest to longest. Ask: *Is the order the same for the measurements in inches and in feet?*

Mathematical Discourse

- *Can you think of other ways to measure the pillow?*

  Students may suggest using centimeters to measure the pillow, or using inch tiles or centimeter tiles instead of a yard stick.

- *How does using a different unit change the measurement?*

  Switching from inches to feet means that the number changes, although the size of the pillow does not.

- *Why is it important to say what units you are using when you measure something?*

  If you just say, "The pillow is 2," no one knows if it is 2 inches long or 2 feet long.

©Curriculum Associates, LLC   Copying is not permitted.

AT A GLANCE

Students find out more about the relationship between feet and inches, then examine the relationship between centimeters and meters.

STEP BY STEP

- Tell students that they will learn more about how inches are related to feet.

- Have students find 1 foot and 12 inches on the yard sticks or tape measures as you read the Think section together.

- Write "1 foot = 12 inches" and "2 feet = 24 inches" on the board, and have students line up 12 one-inch tiles next to a customary ruler.

- Read and complete the Think section as a class.

- To prepare for the Reflect question, have students find 100 centimeters and 1 meter on a meter stick. Invite a student to read the Reflect question to the class, then have students work with a partner to answer the question.

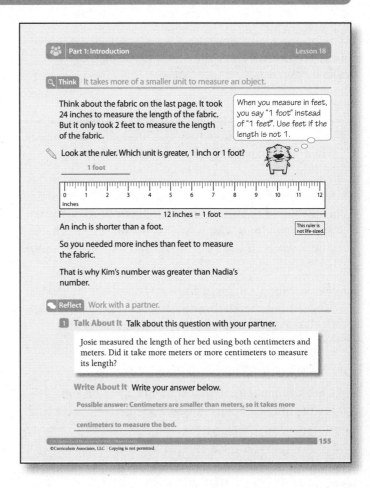

Visual Model

Draw a ruler on the board showing 12 inches. Under the ruler write "1 foot." Ask students: *Which is bigger, 1 foot or 12 inches?* [They are the same.] Then ask: *Which measurement uses more units, 1 foot or 12 inches?* [12 inches has a greater number of units than 1 foot does.]

ELL Support

- ELL students may be more familiar with centimeters than with inches. Provide support for students learning both types of units by having meter sticks and yard sticks available when needed.

- Pair ELL students with strong readers for the Reflect question.

Mathematical Discourse

- *Why would you measure something in feet instead of inches?*

  You might use feet to measure something very large, like a building. It would be easier than measuring it in inches.

- *Why would you measure something in inches instead of feet?*

  You might choose inches to measure more accurately, or to measure a smaller object, like a coin.

Misconception Error

Students may assume that using a bigger unit leads to using a bigger *number* of units. In this lesson, they learn that the opposite is actually true: measuring with a bigger unit means the number of units needed is smaller.

AT A GLANCE

Students use rulers to compare measuring in inches with measuring in centimeters.

STEP BY STEP

- Tell students that now they will look at what happens when you measure an object in both inches and centimeters.

- Make sure students have centimeter and inch rulers available for use. Have students identify which ruler is for inches and which is for centimeters, or which side is which if the classroom rulers have both units on them.

- Work through the first Explore It problem as a class. Model good measuring skills: Check the units, align the 0 correctly, and measure to the nearest unit.

- Have students work together in small groups to complete the second Explore It problem.

- Check to make sure that students agree on the results of the Explore It questions before continuing.

SMP Tip: When students measure objects on this page with inches and centimeters, they are using appropriate mathematical tools strategically (SMP 5). Encourage students to attend to precision (SMP 6) when they measure the objects.

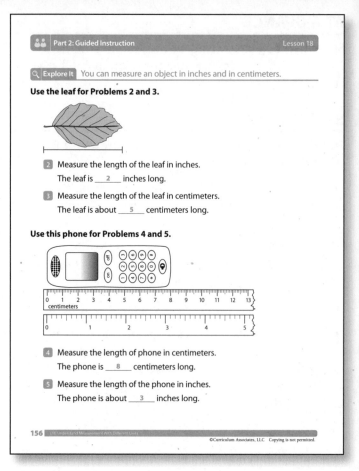

Mathematical Discourse

- *Can the measurement in inches and the measurement in centimeters both be accurate, even though they are not the same number?*

  Yes, the number of inches should be different from the number of centimeters because the units are not the same size.

- *Can you explain why you should say whether the measurement is in inches or centimeters?*

  Saying that the phone is "13" doesn't tell other people whether it is a big phone (13 inches) or a normally sized one (13 centimeters).

©Curriculum Associates, LLC Copying is not permitted.

AT A GLANCE

Students revisit the questions on the previous page. They describe the relationship between the size of a unit and the number of units needed to measure an object.

STEP BY STEP

- Work through the first Talk About it question as a class.

- Have students work with a partner for the rest of the Talk About It questions.

- Check students' understanding with questions such as: *If you have some very small units, do you need many of them or just a few of them to measure an object? If you have larger units, do you need many or just a few to measure the same object?*

- Read the Try It Another Way questions as a class, then have students answer them individually.

> **SMP Tip:** In the Try It Another Way questions, students must decide whether it take more or less of a smaller unit to measure an object. Doing this without using concrete measurement tools is an opportunity for students to reason abstractly and quantitatively. *(SMP 2)*

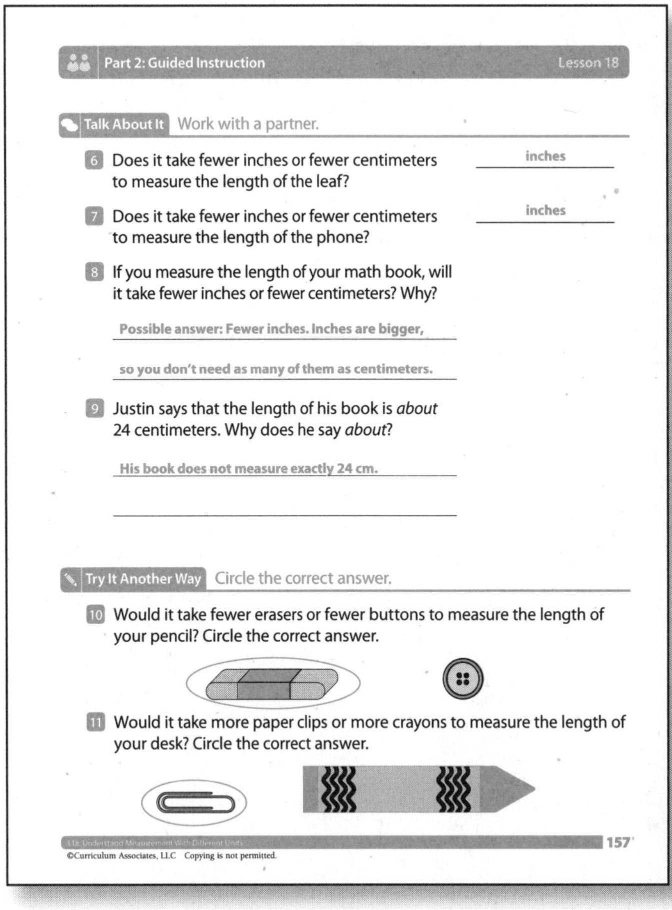

The following reproduces the student page shown at right:

> **Part 2: Guided Instruction** Lesson 18
>
> **Talk About It** Work with a partner.
>
> **6** Does it take fewer inches or fewer centimeters to measure the length of the leaf? _____ inches
>
> **7** Does it take fewer inches or fewer centimeters to measure the length of the phone? _____ inches
>
> **8** If you measure the length of your math book, will it take fewer inches or fewer centimeters? Why?
>
> Possible answer: Fewer inches. Inches are bigger,
>
> so you don't need as many of them as centimeters.
>
> **9** Justin says that the length of his book is *about* 24 centimeters. Why does he say *about*?
>
> His book does not measure exactly 24 cm.
>
> **Try It Another Way** Circle the correct answer.
>
> **10** Would it take fewer erasers or fewer buttons to measure the length of your pencil? Circle the correct answer.
>
> **11** Would it take more paper clips or more crayons to measure the length of your desk? Circle the correct answer.
>
> L18: Understand Measurement With Different Units
> ©Curriculum Associates, LLC Copying is not permitted. 157

Hands On Activity

Compare measurements with nonstandard units.

Materials: Connecting cubes and paper clips

- Have students measure one connecting cube. Is it longer or shorter than one inch? Next, predict whether more or fewer connecting cubes than inches will be needed to measure the leaf and the phone shown in Problems 4 and 5. Check your prediction by measuring the leaf and the phone with the connecting cubes.

- Repeat this using a different nonstandard measuring device, a paper clip. Is it longer or shorter than one inch? Will it take more or fewer paper clips than inches to measure the leaf and the phone?

Mathematical Discourse

- *In Problem 6, how did you decide that it takes fewer inches than centimeters to measure the book?*

  Students may reply that they followed the pattern they noticed in measuring the leaf and the phone.

- *How could you check whether your answer to Problem 6 is correct?*

  We could measure the book in inches and in centimeters, and then see whether more inches or centimeters were needed.

ELL Support

Discuss with students that word "fewer" means "less than." Write a short sentence such as "There are *fewer* ○s than □s" on the board and draw a picture with, for example, 4 circles and 8 squares.

AT A GLANCE

Students demonstrate what they have learned about how the size of a unit affects the number of units needed to measure an object.

STEP BY STEP

- Read the Connect It questions with the students, or have student volunteers read them. Discuss the problems as a class, using the discussion points below.

Analyze:

- Have students work with a partner to discuss which unit goes with which number.

- Ask students to share their responses with the class. Listen for responses that show that students either decided that a larger number of the smaller-sized units are needed to measure the picture, or that students visualized measuring the picture with the given units.

Compare:

- Ask students to describe how they decided that more feet are needed to measure the bedroom than yards.

- Ask: *How could you find out if your answer is correct?* Students may respond that they could measure the bedroom in feet, or make a model showing three feet for each yard.

Explain:

- Have students discuss the problem and their responses with a partner.

- Ask students to draw diagrams, using rulers if they like, to support their answers. The diagrams should show that 12 inches are longer than 12 centimeters.

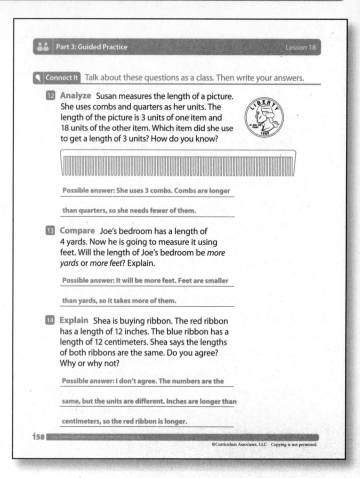

Part 3: Guided Practice   Lesson 18

Connect It Talk about these questions as a class. Then write your answers.

12 **Analyze** Susan measures the length of a picture. She uses combs and quarters as her units. The length of the picture is 3 units of one item and 18 units of the other item. Which item did she use to get a length of 3 units? How do you know?

Possible answer: She uses 3 combs. Combs are longer than quarters, so she needs fewer of them.

13 **Compare** Joe's bedroom has a length of 4 yards. Now he is going to measure it using feet. Will the length of Joe's bedroom be *more yards* or *more feet*? Explain.

Possible answer: It will be more feet. Feet are smaller than yards, so it takes more of them.

14 **Explain** Shea is buying ribbon. The red ribbon has a length of 12 inches. The blue ribbon has a length of 12 centimeters. Shea says the lengths of both ribbons are the same. Do you agree? Why or why not?

Possible answer: I don't agree. The numbers are the same, but the units are different. Inches are longer than centimeters, so the red ribbon is longer.

158   L18: Understand Measurement with Different Units   ©Curriculum Associates, LLC   Copying is not permitted.

©Curriculum Associates, LLC   Copying is not permitted.

AT A GLANCE

Students demonstrate their understanding of measuring in different units.

STEP BY STEP

- Tell students they will complete the Put It Together task on their own.

- Read the directions and the four parts to the question before the students begin.

- Have rulers and yardsticks available for students to use if they want them.

- As students work on their own, walk around to assess their progress and understanding, to answer their questions, and to give additional support, if needed.

- If time permits, ask students to share the numbers they chose and justify their choices.

SCORING RUBRIC

A–D

Points	Expectations
2	The student completes the measurements and the unit choices correctly.
1	Either the measurements or unit choices are correct, but not both.
0	Neither the measurements nor the unit choices are correct.

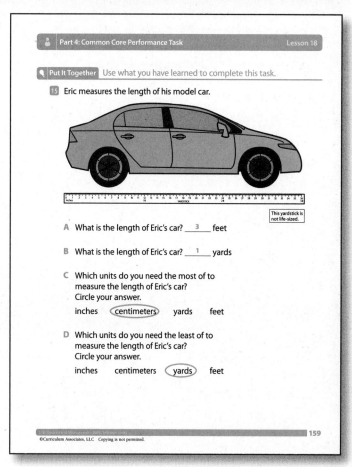

Intervention Activity

Measure objects and compare units.

Materials: rulers

- Provide students with rulers that show both inches and centimeters, or two rulers.

- Have students use the rulers to draw line segments that are the following lengths:

     2 inches
     6 inches
     10 inches
     12 inches

- Help students measure each of the segments in centimeters, and have them record the lengths. [5 cm, 15 cm, 25 cm, and 30 cm]

- Ask students which is longer, 2 inches or 5 centimeters? [They are the same.] Which uses more units, 2 inches or 5 centimeters? [5 centimeters] Which uses a bigger unit, 2 inches or 5 centimeters? [2 inches]

- Repeat the questions using the other lengths.

On-Level Activity

Measure objects and choose the units.

Materials: common classroom objects, rulers or yard sticks or meter sticks

- Have students work in small groups.

- Before beginning the activity, make a list of about 6 objects in the room that students can measure. Include some larger objects, such as the length of one side of the room, and some smaller ones, such as a paperclip.

- Students decide which unit to use to measure each object on the list. They work together to measure the objects and record the lengths. For example, they might choose feet to measure the length of one side of the room, and centimeters to measure the paperclip.

- Students record the lengths and explain why they chose the units in each case.

Challenge Activity

Materials: hundreds charts (Activity Sheet 2, page 309), small objects to use as counters, paper and pencil

- Students have now had practice measuring lengths using the U.S. customary system, which is based on 1 foot equaling 12 inches, and the metric system, which is based on 1 meter equaling 100 centimeters. Ask students to make up a measurement system of their own, based on a number different from 12 or 10. The invented measurement system should include at least two different units, and students can decide how big the units are, how they are related, and what their names are.

- Have students make a chart showing the units they have invented, their approximate size, and how they are related to each other. Have them include "benchmark" measurements, giving the lengths of three common objects in their invented units. Have them present their new measurement systems to the class.

©Curriculum Associates, LLC   Copying is not permitted.

Lesson 19 (Student Book pages 160–165)

Understand Estimating Length

LESSON OBJECTIVES

- Estimate lengths in inches, centimeters, feet, and meters.
- Use benchmark objects when estimating.

PREREQUISITE SKILLS

In order to be proficient with the concept/skills in this lesson, students should:

- Measure lengths in inches and centimeters.
- Add numbers less than 10.

VOCABULARY

estimate: use math to make a close guess

THE LEARNING PROGRESSION

In Grade 1, students developed their understanding of measuring in different units, using nonstandard units. This prepares them to make reasonable estimates of lengths in different units.

In Grade 2, students learn more about measuring in standard units. Being able to estimate lengths, as they learn in this lesson, is good practice for estimating answers to many types of math problems.

In Grade 3, estimating in appropriate units will continue to be important as students begin to measure volume and weight in addition to length. Students will apply what they know about measuring lengths to problems involving perimeters and areas. Students will extend their estimation skills by estimating volume, mass, and intervals of time.

◼ Ready *Teacher Toolbox*

Teacher-Toolbox.com

	Prerequisite Skills	2.MD.A.3
Ready Lessons	✓	✓
Tools for Instruction		✓
Interactive Tutorials	✓	✓

CCSS Focus

2.MD.A.3 Estimate lengths using units of inches, feet, centimeters, and meters.

STANDARDS FOR MATHEMATICAL PRACTICE: *SMP 1, 3, 4, 5 (see page A9 for full text)*

©Curriculum Associates, LLC Copying is not permitted.

One-Unit Scavenger Hunt

Objective: Find "benchmark" objects that can be used as estimates for some common unit measures.

Materials for each student:
- rulers
- common classroom objects

Overview

Students estimate the length of a variety of objects in order to find objects that measure about one inch, one centimeter, one foot, and one meter.

Step by Step (15–20 minutes)

1 Activate students' knowledge about standard units.

- Have students use rulers to draw lengths of one inch, one centimeter, and one foot. (A length of one foot can be drawn diagonally on a regular sheet of notebook paper.) Draw a length of one meter on the board.

- Have students guess at some objects or distances that are about the length of each of the units they drew.

2 Hunt for objects.

- Tell students that they are going to search for things that are close to the length of each of the units. They can use objects or groups of objects, such as a book or two connecting cubes, or distances, such as the height of a doorknob. They should not use anything temporary, such as the length of a classmate's ponytail.

- Give students time to guess, measure, and guess again until they find objects in the classroom to match all four units.

- Record the objects the students find on the board:

Unit	Objects
One centimeter	
One inch	
One foot	
One meter	

3 Check the results.

- Have students check the lengths of each other's suggested benchmark objects. Discuss which ones are closest to the unit measures.

©Curriculum Associates, LLC   Copying is not permitted.

AT A GLANCE

Students explore what it means to estimate a length.

STEP BY STEP

- Tell students they will learn about estimating length.

- Read the introductory text as a class.

- Use the Mathematical Discourse questions to begin a discussion of items that might be used to estimate length.

- Read the Think section as a class. Talk with students about how estimates are not exact. On this page, for example, a quarter is not exactly one inch at its widest part, and the toy car is not exactly the same length as three quarters.

- Have students measure the toy car with a ruler. Tell them that following up each estimate with a measurement will help them become better estimators.

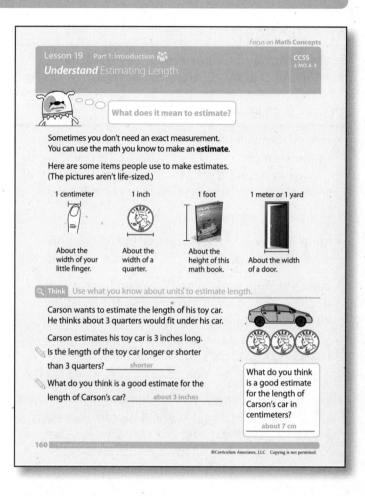

ELL Support

Discuss the difference between an *exact* measurement and an *estimated* measurement. Tell students that for an exact measurement, they will use a measuring tool such as a ruler, yard stick, or meter stick. For an estimated measurement, they will not use a measuring tool. Point out that in this lesson, students will follow up each estimate with a measure.

Mathematical Discourse

- *Can you think of why we might estimate a length instead of measuring it directly?*

  Students may point out that we don't always have a ruler available, or that we can't always handle an object to measure it, or that we might not need to know the exact length.

- *What other items could Carson use to estimate the length of the toy car?*

  Students may suggest using the benchmark for one inch that they found in the Opening Activity, or they may have another way of estimating one inch.

©Curriculum Associates, LLC   Copying is not permitted.

AT A GLANCE

Students find out how to estimate lengths using benchmarks that are not equal to one unit.

STEP BY STEP

- Have students look at the diagram of the pencil box in the Think section. Discuss how Julia could use the marker to estimate the pencil box's length and invite students to give their best estimates of this length.

- Read the Think section together.

- Make sure students measure the pencil box with a centimeter ruler.

- Have students work in pairs to complete the Reflect question. Invite a volunteer to read the question aloud before students begin.

Visual Support

Encourage students to make and label simple diagrams that compare the length they are estimating to a length they already know. For example, if they are estimating that a book is about as long as three pencil lengths, sketch three pencils in a row and write the pencil's length next to each one. This will help students visualize both the length and the addition problem they have generated.

ELL Support

Pair ELL students with proficient readers to work on the Reflect question together.

Real-World Connection

Ask students if they can think of any jobs in which estimates of lengths might be made. A truck driver might estimate how far he or she can drive in one day, and a mover might estimate how big a truck is needed to deliver a large piece of furniture. List the jobs that students suggest, and then ask what type of units each type of worker might use.

SMP Tip: When students measure the lengths of the pencil box on this page and the toy car on the previous page, they are using appropriate tools strategically. (SMP 5)

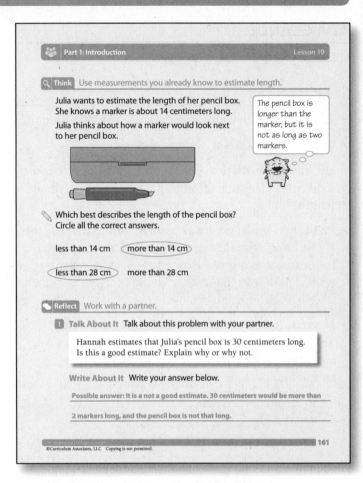

Mathematical Discourse

- *What are some other reasonable estimates for the length of the pencil box?*

  Students' answers should be greater than 14 centimeters, but less than 28 centimeters, since the pencil box is not as long as two markers put end to end.

- *How is using the marker to estimate different from using three quarters, the way Carson did in the problem on the previous page?*

  The marker is 14 units long, and the quarter is only 1 unit long. Instead of thinking about lining up the marker two or three times, as Carson did with the quarter, Julia is deciding if the box is longer or shorter than the marker.

- *What are some other items we could use to help us make good estimates?*

  Students may suggest common objects that are reliably all the same length, such as unused crayons or playing cards.

©Curriculum Associates, LLC   Copying is not permitted.

AT A GLANCE

Students practice estimating lengths in inches and centimeters.

STEP BY STEP

- Tell students that they can become good estimators by practicing estimating lengths in both inches and centimeters.

- Work through the Explore It section with the class. Students can measure the width of their own little fingers to see how they compare to one centimeter.

- Reinforce that an estimate of a length does not have to equal the exact length. However, the estimate should not be a random guess.

Hands-On Activity

Materials: rulers, common classroom objects

- Have students work in pairs. Give each pair a list of about 4 common classroom objects such as a table, 10 connecting cubes, the height of a bulletin board, and a stapler.

- Students estimate the length of each object, using benchmark objects if they like. They then measure each object and compare the estimate with the actual length. They can record the name of the object, the estimate, and the actual length in a table.

- After they are finished, compare the results as a class. Ask: *Can you describe how you made your estimates? Did your estimates improve during this activity?*

Misconception Error

When students are working on the Reflect question, they may think that an estimate must be close to the actual measurement. Encourage them to recognize that identifying or supporting the reasoning behind an estimate is more important than making a "perfect" estimate.

Part 2: Guided Instruction   Lesson 19

Explore It   Use different units to help you estimate length.

Use the stamp to answer Problems 2–4.

2. Use the width of your little finger to help you estimate the length of the stamp.

   The stamp is about ____3____ cm long.

3. Use a centimeter ruler to measure the length of the stamp.

   What is the actual length? ____3____ cm long

Use the hair clip and ribbon to answer Problems 4 and 5.

|← 2 inches →|

4. Estimate the length of the ribbon.

   The ribbon is about ____4____ inches long.

5. Use an inch ruler to measure the length of the ribbon.

   What is the actual length? ____5____ inches long

162   L19 Understand Estimating Length   ©Curriculum Associates, LLC Copying is not permitted.

Mathematical Discourse

- *What do you notice about the estimate in Problem 4 and the measured length in Problem 5?*

  They are not the same. An estimate and an exact length do not have to be equal.

- *Can you explain why you should tell what units you are using when you estimate?*

  If I just say that the stamp is 3, without saying whether it is 3 inches or 3 centimeters, other people won't know if it is a reasonable estimate.

Concept Extension

If students are comfortable with the idea of lengths of measured fractions of an inch, encourage them to measure to the nearest half-inch or quarter-inch in Problem 5.

©Curriculum Associates, LLC   Copying is not permitted.

AT A GLANCE

Students examine how a reasonable estimate is developed.

STEP BY STEP

- Have students work in small groups for Talk About It Problems 6 through 9.

- After students have completed Problem 9, discuss as a class why an estimate and the actual measure might be very different numbers.

- Have students work in pairs to complete Problem 10.

- For the Try It Another Way questions, have tape measures, yard sticks, or meter sticks available. Have all students make both estimates, then have one student measure the desk, and another measure the wall. Record the actual lengths as a class.

- Check with students to see how close their estimates were to the exact measurements. Discuss with students that if an estimate is very far from the actual measure, it may mean that they made a mistake in either measuring or estimating.

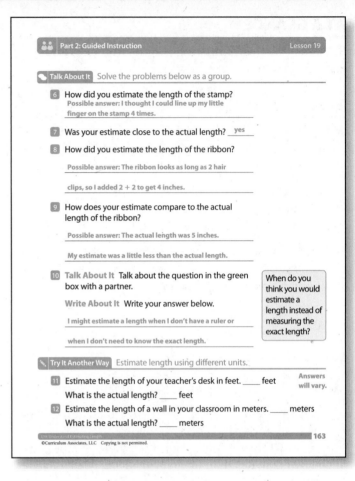

ELL Support

Pair ELL students with proficient readers for the Talk About It questions.

SMP Tip: In Problem 8, students move from the idea that the ribbon is as long as two hair clips to writing a number sentence to represent the two lengths. This is an example of modeling a real-life math situation with a number sentence. (SMP 4)

Mathematical Discourse

- *Can you think of other ways to estimate the lengths?*

  Students may suggest using the technique described on page 160, imagining how many quarters could line up below the ribbon.

- *Some teachers say that "an estimate is a guess with a method behind it." What do you think that means, and do you agree?*

  Answers will vary, but listen for evidence that students recognize that an estimate of an object's length should include some thought, such as comparing it to a known length, or imagining how many unit lengths would be needed to cover the object.

©Curriculum Associates, LLC   Copying is not permitted.

AT A GLANCE

Students demonstrate their understanding of estimating lengths. They explain their estimation methods, and analyze a method that is described.

STEP BY STEP

- Read the Connect It questions with the students, or have student volunteers read them aloud. Discuss the problems as a class, using the discussion points below.

Explain:

- Have students answer the questions individually.

- Ask students to share their responses with the class. Students may have valid reasons to choose inches or centimeters instead of feet, so listen for responses that show they compared their arm lengths to a known length to make their estimates.

Analyze:

- Encourage students to talk with a partner about the error Erik may have made. Have rulers with both inches and centimeters available for students to use.

- Point out to students that Erik's estimate and his measurement are very different. Ask: *Do you think that 10 inches is a reasonable length for a crayon?* Students should recognize that crayons are shorter than 10 inches, and that the measurement must be incorrect. Ask: *How could Erik have measured 10 instead of 4?* Students can look at the rulers to see that 4 inches is about the same length as 10 centimeters.

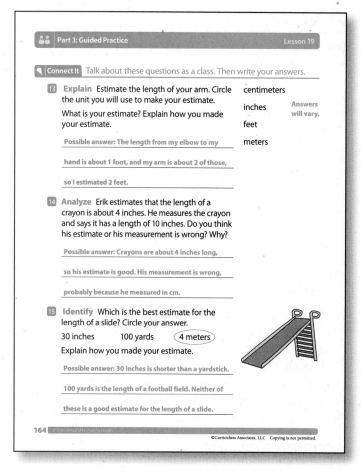

Identify:

- Have students discuss the problem and their responses with a partner.

- Ask: *What would be a good way to estimate the length of a slide?* Encourage students to think of how a slide compares to their own heights, or to the height of an adult.

SMP Tips: In Problem 14, students are asked to critique another's reasoning (*SMP 3*). Problem 15 asks students to make sense and persevere in solving problems. (*SMP 1*)

ELL Support

Make sure students know that they can choose either metric or U.S. customary units, unless the problem specifies one or the other.

AT A GLANCE

Students demonstrate their understanding of making reasonable estimates.

STEP BY STEP

- Read the directions and the four parts of the Put It Together question before students begin. Have rulers, yard sticks, and meter sticks available for part C.

- Have students complete parts A and B on their own.

- As students work, walk around to assess their progress and understanding, to answer questions, and to give additional support, if needed.

- For part C, have individuals measure their chosen objects.

- Have students complete part D on their own. If their estimates do not seem reasonable, encourage students to think about whether they might have measured incorrectly or made a mistake in the estimate. It's important that they try to identify their error, but it's not really necessary to correct it for this activity.

Part 4: Common Core Performance Task   Lesson 19

Put It Together Use what you have learned to complete the task.

16 Mrs. Chen made this list of lengths.

Item	Length
unsharpened pencil	19 centimeters
sticky note	3 inches
egg carton	1 foot
height of door	2 meters

Answers will vary.
Possible answers:

A Estimate the length of something in your classroom. Use an item from Mrs. Chen's list to make your estimate. Record your choices at the right.

Object: ___math book___

Item used
for estimate: ___pencil___

B Explain how you found your estimate.

Estimate: ___30 cm___

Possible answer: My math book is longer than a

pencil, but not as long as 2 pencils, so I estimated

30 cm.

C Use a ruler, a yardstick, or a meter stick to measure the actual length of your object.

Actual length of object: ___about 28 cm___

D How does the actual length compare to your estimate?

Possible answer: The actual length was a little less

than my estimate. The estimate and actual length

are close, so my answer makes sense.

L19 Understand Estimating Length   165
©Curriculum Associates, LLC   Copying is not permitted.

SCORING RUBRICS

A

Points	Expectations
2	The student makes a reasonable estimate of the length.
1	The estimate is reasonable, but the units are incorrect.
0	The estimate is obviously a guess, or not completed.

B

Points	Expectations
2	The explanation is clear and makes sense.
1	Some part of the explanation is not clear.
0	The explanation is not clear or is missing.

C

Points	Expectations
2	The student completes the measurement and uses an appropriate unit.
1	Either the measurement or unit choice is correct, but not both.
0	Neither the measurement nor the unit choice is correct.

D

Points	Expectations
2	The student compares the estimate and the actual length correctly. If they are very different, the student identifies whether the estimate or the measurement is incorrect.
1	The student compares the estimate and the actual length incorrectly, or does not identify whether the estimate or the measurement is incorrect (if applicable).
0	The student does not compare the estimate to the actual length.

©Curriculum Associates, LLC   Copying is not permitted.

Intervention Activity

Measure objects and compare units.

Materials: Rulers, strips of paper cut to different lengths

• Have students estimate the length of one of the strips of paper in inches. Then the student should measure the paper and write its actual length on the paper.

• Use the first strip of paper to estimate the length of another strip of paper. Measure the second strip and write its length on it.

• Continue estimating, measuring, and recording with all the strips of paper. If time allows, turn the strips of paper over and repeat the activity using centimeters instead of inches.

• When all the strips of paper have been labeled, ask, *How did this help you make reasonable estimates?*

On-Level Activity

Find an object with a given measure.

Materials: cards with different measurements on them, rulers or yard sticks or meter sticks, common classroom objects

• Have students work in pairs or small groups.

• Before beginning the activity, prepare a set of cards with different measurements on them, such as "8 inches," "30 centimeters," "4 feet," "2 meters," and "6 yards."

• One student in the group shuffles the cards and selects one card at random. The student uses estimation to find an object in the classroom whose length is about the same as the one on the card.

• The students measure the object they chose to see how close their estimate was. Students can discuss whether the actual length is "close enough" to the length on the card.

• The next student selects a card and repeats the process.

• When all the cards have been used, ask, *How did this help you make reasonable estimates?*

Challenge Activity

Estimate a familiar distance.

Have students estimate the length of a round trip from their home to school. Include diagrams that explain how students made the estimate. You can suggest that they start by measuring the length of their stride, then counting how many strides are in one block. For an extra challenge, ask students to make the estimate in two different units, such as feet and meters.

©Curriculum Associates, LLC   Copying is not permitted.

Lesson 20 (Student Book pages 166–175)

Compare Lengths

LESSON OBJECTIVES

- Compare the lengths of objects by determining which measure is greater than or less than the other.
- Use addition and subtraction to compare lengths finding how much greater or less the measure of one object is than the other.

PREREQUISITE SKILLS

- Add and subtract within 20.
- Measure in standard units of measure.
- Use measuring tools to measure to the nearest unit.

VOCABULARY

There is no new vocabulary.

THE LEARNING PROGRESSION

In Grade 1, students explored measurement as the process of comparing lengths one to another and to a length of iterated units.

In Grade 2, students expand on the concept of unit of measure as they measure the length of an object using two different units of measure in whole number units. At this level they use tools to measure standard units, estimate lengths and determine the appropriate tool to use in measuring. **In this lesson,** students compare lengths of objects within a specific unit and use addition and subtraction to find the differences in length.

In Grade 3, students increase accuracy by measuring lengths in fractions of an inch. They recognize that the length of a side of a figure can be measured in units and combined to find the perimeter of the figure.

Ready *Teacher Toolbox*		*Teacher-Toolbox.com*
	Prerequisite Skills	*2.MD.A.4*
Ready Lessons	✓ ✓	✓
Tools for Instruction	✓	
Interactive Tutorials	✓	

CCSS Focus

2.MD.A.4 Measure to determine how much longer one object is than another, expressing the length difference in terms of a standard unit of measure.

STANDARDS FOR MATHEMATICAL PRACTICE: **SMP 1, 2, 3, 4, 5, 6** *(see page A9 for full text)*

©Curriculum Associates, LLC   Copying is not permitted.

Use a Benchmark to Compare Lengths

Objective: Explore comparing lengths by comparing objects to a benchmark.

Materials for each student:
• different-colored counters

Overview

Students find objects that are longer than and shorter than a benchmark. They then compare a length in a different orientation to a benchmark and devise a strategy for comparison.

Step by Step (15–20 minutes)

1　Establish a benchmark.

• Ask students if they see something in the room that is longer than their desktop; shorter than their desktop. Listen to several responses, making sure students understand what it means to be longer or shorter and that they are all using the same side of the desk as the benchmark length.

• Tell students that they will work with a partner to find things in the room that they think are longer or shorter than their desktop.

2　Record comparisons.

• Demonstrate how to make a table to record their observations.

• Have students look around the room and find at least 10 **different** objects that fit each category and record them in the table.

Longer than a desk	Shorter than a desk

3　Share comparisons.

• Invite students to share their ideas with the class. Ask them what they did—or could do—if they weren't certain how an object's length compared to their desk's length. Listen for suggestions that refer to direct comparison such as: "We could lay the object on the desk to see which one is longer."

• Show students an object, such as a lamp or potted plant, that has a height close to the length of a desk and ask: *Do you think this is taller or shorter than the length of a desk?* You may want to point out the height to make sure students understand the measure you are referring to.

• Allow students to discuss the situation and offer suggestions of how they know it is longer or shorter. They may suggest tipping it over to compare or measuring both objects.

4　Devise a strategy.

• Ask students to think of a strategy that would allow them to compare these objects quickly without using a direct comparison or measurement.

• Suggest using something like a string or piece of yarn if no one else does. Invite a volunteer to measure a desk using a piece of string or yarn and another student to measure the height of the other object. Tape the two lengths of string on the board to compare. Discuss how these objects were more difficult to compare because of their orientation.

• Ask: *How much longer (or shorter) is (the object) than your desk? How could you know for sure?* Tell students that this lesson will help them use measuring to compare and find out how much longer or shorter one object is than another.

©Curriculum Associates, LLC　　Copying is not permitted.

AT A GLANCE

Students measure pictures of objects in centimeters, record and compare the measures.

STEP BY STEP

- Tell students that this page will help them review measuring with a ruler.

- Have students read the problem at the top of the page. Remind students where the centimeters are on their ruler.

- Work through the Explore It questions as a class. Make sure students are counting the number of centimeter intervals that determine the length of the spoon and fork.

- Following Problem C, ask the Mathematical Discourse question.

- For Problem D, make sure students are attending to the measurements recorded in Problems A and B and not relying on visual comparisons.

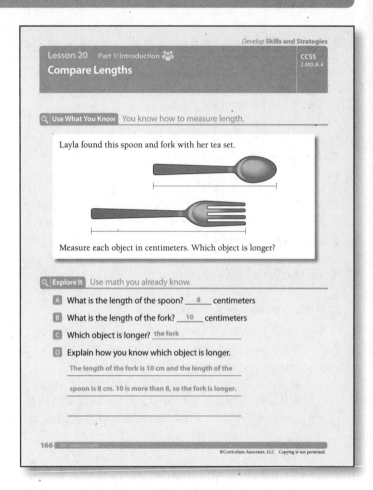

Hands-On Activity

Materials: centimeter cubes

- Have students line the cubes up next to the picture of the spoon and fork on this page. Make sure the cubes span the entire length of each object.

- Ask: *How does the number of cubes you used compare to the number of centimeters you measured? Why?* The numerical measures are the same. Students should remember from a previous lesson that each cube is one centimeter in length and each interval on the ruler is the same length as one centimeter cube.

SMP Tip: Throughout this lesson, emphasize the importance of precision in measurements. If one measure is inaccurate, the comparison is also inaccurate. (*SMP 6*)

Mathematical Discourse

- *Why do you think it is a good idea to compare lengths using centimeters rather than just by looking at the objects?*

  Students should respond that when objects aren't lined up exactly, it might be difficult to tell which one is longer. Measuring gives numbers to compare.

ELL Support

ELL students may be more familiar with the metric system than the U.S. customary system of measure. Encourage them to share what they know about the metric system and be the "experts" in the class. Help them to see that comparing in the U.S. customary system is the same as comparing in the metric system.

©Curriculum Associates, LLC   Copying is not permitted.

AT A GLANCE

Students use subtraction to compare lengths.

STEP BY STEP

- Ask students to look at the objects and measurements in Find Out More. Ask: *How can you tell that the fork is 2 centimeters longer than the spoon?* Students should recognize that when comparing measurements, they can use subtraction or addition to find out the difference.

- Ask the Mathematical Discourse question to connect the process used when comparing lengths to fact families.

- Have students complete and discuss Talk About It.

Concept Extension

Materials: centimeter cubes

- Provide students with an easy to measure small object, such as a toothpick or length of a drinking straw.

- Instruct students to arrange centimeter cubes one next to the other along the object. Then use the centimeter side of their ruler to measure. Make sure the two measurements are the same.

- Model and ask students to move the ruler so that the left side of the object is lined up with the number 2 on the ruler. Ask: *How long is the object you measured?* Discuss how the size of the object hasn't changed. Point out that the *distance between the 2 and the number lined up on the right side of the object is the measure.* Make sure they understand that measurement is a comparison of an object to a set of iterated units, either physical units or intervals on a ruler.

- Ask: *Would it be possible to measure starting at any number on the ruler? Explain.* Students should recognize that they could by counting the total number of units that extend along the length of the object.

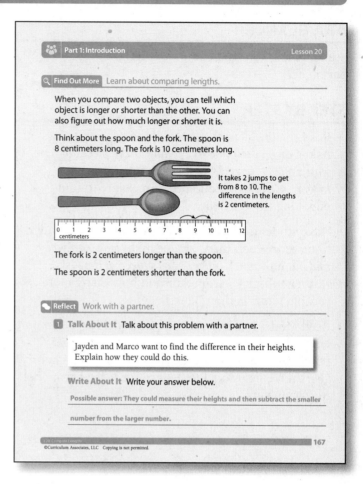

Mathematical Discourse

- *How is comparing lengths like working with fact families?*

  Students should respond that the longer length is like the whole. If you subtract the shorter length you get the difference. Those are like the parts. If you add the difference and the shorter length, you get the longer length. If you subtract the difference from the longer length, you get the shorter length.

AT A GLANCE

Students measure and compare lengths using a bar model.

STEP BY STEP

- Read the problem at the top of the page as a class. Ask: *Can you tell just by looking at the pieces of tape which one is longer?* [Yes] *Can you tell how much longer? Why?* [No. You need to measure to find how long they each are.]

- Have students use the centimeter side of their ruler to measure each piece of tape. Ask: *How can you find out how much longer Nate's piece of tape is?* [Either subtract 3 from 8 or find how many more centimeters 8 is than 3.]

- Read Model It. Ask how the bar model helps compare lengths. Students should recognize that the bar model is a way to represent numbers in a fact family. Use the Visual Model to help connect the bar model to centimeters.

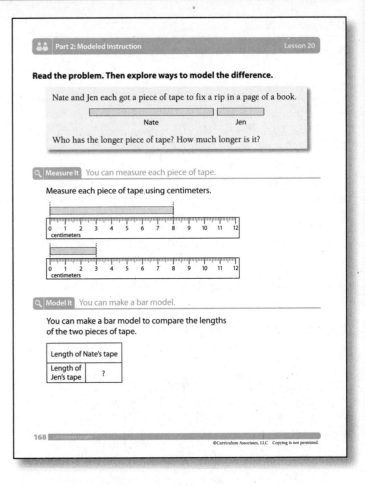

Visual Model

Materials: centimeter grid paper cut into 2-row sections (Activity Sheet 4, pages 311)

- Have students color a row of 8 bars to represent a piece of tape. They should then use a different color to represent the 3 cm piece of tape. Instruct them to cut off the excess grid squares.

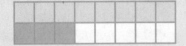

- Discuss that the part of the grid that is uncolored is the difference between the two lengths.

Real-World Connection

On this page, students see how comparing measurements are used in daily life. Discuss how the tape shown on this page would need to be compared to the length of the rip in the paper to decide which one was the best to use for repairing it.

Discuss that sometimes just looking at objects to compare is good enough such as knowing that one person is taller than the other. At other times it is important to be able to tell how much longer or taller one object is than another such as if you have an 18 inch piece of ribbon for a craft you are making. The craft only requires 13 inches of ribbon. You need to know how much longer your piece of ribbon is to know how much to cut off.

©Curriculum Associates, LLC   Copying is not permitted.

AT A GLANCE

Students model the difference between two lengths by writing number sentences.

STEP BY STEP

- Read Connect It as a class. Remind students that the questions refer to the tape they measured on page 168.

- Invite students to share ideas of ways they could know which piece of tape is longer. Encourage them to include ideas such as: just by looking at them; seeing that one is longer on a bar model; knowing that 8 is greater than 2, etc. For this question it is not necessary to include the numerical difference.

- Have students discuss the number sentences they wrote in Problem 6. Reinforce the idea that the difference can be found using either number sentence. Ask: *Do you need to write a number sentence to find the differences? Why?* [No. I know my facts for 8.] *When would it be important to write a number sentence?* [When the difference between the two numbers is very large.]

- Tell students that for Try It, they may use a bar model to compare, but should try to write a number sentence or explain how they know the difference. You may want to provide them with centimeter grid paper, if necessary.

> **SMP Tip:** Encourage students to make connections to mental strategies they have learned to help them solve the comparison problems. This reinforces the concept of the relationship between number and measurement. A measurement is the comparison of an object to a set of iterated units that are counted. Therefore they can be compared in the same way other quantities are compared. *(SMP 2)*

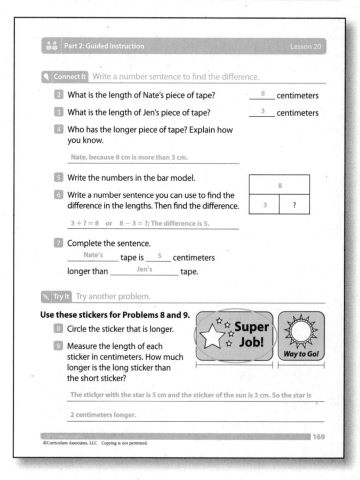

TRY IT SOLUTIONS

8 *Solution:* The sun sticker is longer so it should be circled. **(DOK 1)**

9 *Solution:* The sun is 2 cm longer. $5 - 3 = 2$. **(DOK 2)**

©Curriculum Associates, LLC   Copying is not permitted.

AT A GLANCE

Students model a difference in length by measuring each object or by measuring the difference.

STEP BY STEP

- Ask students how the question on this page is different from the questions on the previous pages. They should notice that they are asked to find how much shorter rather than how much longer one object is than another.

- Have students describe what they must do to answer the question. Make sure they recognize that they can use addition or subtraction in the same way that they did when finding how much longer one was than the other.

- Discuss what the difference is in finding which object is shorter or longer than the other. Help students recognize that the procedure is the same, that is they find the difference in length. The comparison statement they make is different. Ask students how they can reword the problem and answer to find which is the longer object.

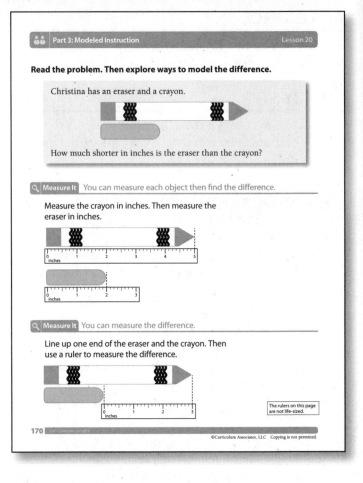

Hands-On Activity

Materials: 1-inch square tiles (Activity Sheet 3, pages 310)

- Ask students to find two books that are different heights.

- Have them compare the books by placing them next to each other.

- Ask: *If your books were a bar model, what would tell you the difference in their heights?* [The distance from the shortest to the longest book.]

- Instruct students to lay their tiles one next to another to extend from the shortest book to the longest. Have them tell the difference between the books in inches.

- Have students measure the difference with their ruler to see that the measures are the same.

Mathematical Discourse

- *Do you think it is easier to find the difference by subtracting or by measuring it? Why?*

  Answers will depend on student preferences, but some may respond that when measuring the difference, only one measurement is made.

- *Sarah asks, "Why does it matter if I am finding which one is longer or which one is shorter since the answer is the same for both of them?" What should I tell her?*

  The difference between them is the same, but if the question asks how much shorter one is than the other, you have to write down the name of the shorter object not the name of the longer object.

©Curriculum Associates, LLC   Copying is not permitted.

AT A GLANCE

Students revisit the problem on page 170, comparing lengths by measuring each object or by measuring the difference.

STEP BY STEP

- Tell students that Connect It will help them explore ways to find the difference between the chalk and the crayon shown on page 170.

- Discuss Talk About It as a group. Use the Hands-On Activity to explore a situation in which lining up lengths may be difficult. Have students share ideas of when lining up to compare works and when it may be difficult to use.

Hands-On Activity

Materials: a 6 × 9 inch piece of construction paper, rulers, 1-inch square tiles (Activity Sheet 3, pages 310)

- Give each student a piece of construction paper and ask them to compare the side lengths.

- Ask: *How might you find out how much longer one side is than the other?* Students may suggest that they can measure. *Would it make sense to measure the difference in the lengths? Explain.* [It would not make sense since the sides are not lined up next to each other.] Ask students if they could think of a way to use the strategy of measuring the difference in this situation. They may suggest comparing their piece of paper to their partner's measuring the difference, or using tiles to extend along each length and then repositioning them next to each other to find the difference.

- Allow students to use the inch side of a ruler to measure each side of the paper using subtraction to compare and then use one of the other strategies. Share results.

- Discuss which strategy makes more sense to use in this situation and why.

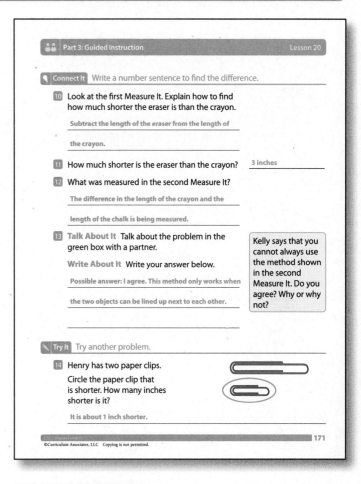

TRY IT SOLUTION

14 *Solution:* Students should circle the shorter paper clip and respond that it is 1 inch shorter. **(DOK 2)**

©Curriculum Associates, LLC   Copying is not permitted.

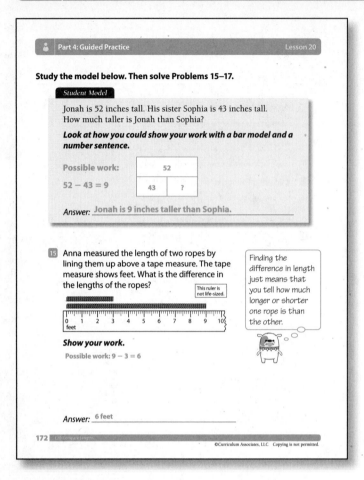

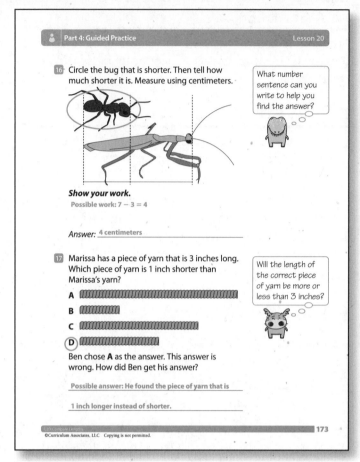

AT A GLANCE

Students model and determine the difference between two measures.

STEP BY STEP

- Ask students to solve the problems individually and show all their work, including the number sentences they wrote. Remind students to pay attention to whether they are to find which object is longer or shorter.

- For Problem 16, make sure students understand that they are finding a length of yarn that is shorter than the one Marissa has.

- When students have completed each problem, have them Pair/Share to discuss their solutions with a partner.

SOLUTIONS

Ex A bar model and a number sentence are used to model the difference between two given measures.

15 *Solution:* 6 feet; $9 - 3 = 6$. **(DOK 1)**

16 *Solution:* 4 cm; $7 - 3 = 4$. Check that the shorter bug is circled. **(DOK 2)**

17 *Solution:* **D**; 2 inches is 1 inch less than 3 inches.

Explain to students why the other two choices are not correct:

B is not correct because 1 in. is the difference, not the length of the yarn.

C is not correct because 3 inches is equal to Marissa's yarn, not shorter. **(DOK 3)**

©Curriculum Associates, LLC　Copying is not permitted.

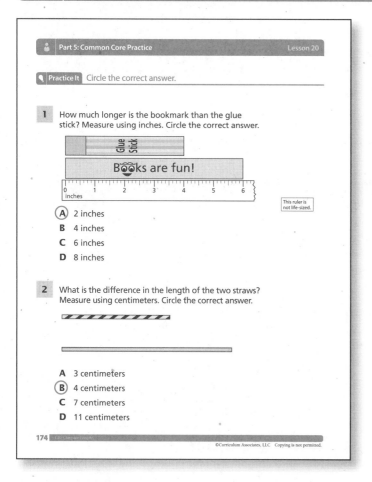

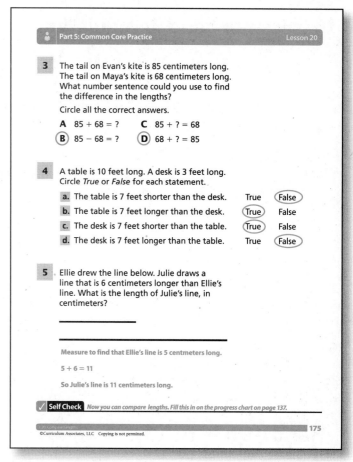

AT A GLANCE

Students measure and model the difference between two measures that might appear on a mathematics test.

STEP BY STEP

- First, tell students they will measure objects and compare lengths in order to answer the questions on the next two pages. Then have students read the directions and answer the questions independently.

- Draw students' attention to Problem 5. Tell them that there are several things they will need to do to complete the problem. Tell them to make sure they complete all the parts.

- After students have completed the Common Core Practice problems, review and discuss correct answers.

SOLUTIONS

1 *Solution:* **A**; 6 − 4 = 2. (*DOK 2*)

2 *Solution:* **B**. (*DOK 2*)

3 *Solution:* **B** and **D**; The number sentences are part of the same family. (*DOK 2*)

4 *Solution:* False, The table is 7 feet longer than the desk; True; True; False, The desk is shorter than the table. (*DOK 2*)

5 *Solution:* Students should draw an 11-cm line; 11 − 5 = 6 or 5 + 6 = 11. (*DOK 3*)

Assessment and Remediation

- Give students two strips of paper; one 12 cm and one 7 cm long. Have students measure in centimeters to compare lengths and tell how much longer one is than the other. [5 cm]

- For students who are still struggling, use the chart below to guide remediation.

- After providing remediation, check students' understanding by giving them an unused pencil and a new crayon to measure and compare.

If the error is . . .	Students may . . .	To remediate . . .
19 cm	have added the lengths rather than subtracted.	Provide students with centimeter cubes. Ask them to identify where the difference between the paper strips is shown. Have them place centimeter cubes along the side of the longer strip to find the difference.
4 cm	have measured or subtracted incorrectly.	Have students measure the paper strips again to ensure they measured accurately. Then have them use addition rather than subtraction to find the difference. Remind them of the importance of precision and care when measuring.

Hands-On Activity

Materials: string, scissors, ruler or yardstick for each student pair

- Have students work in pairs to compare the measures of their body parts.

- Make a list of the body parts students may want to compare such as the length of an arm, leg, foot, hand, finger, neck, head, and torso.

- Instruct students to measure two different body parts of their partner using the string. Then measure the lengths of string in inches and find the difference in lengths.

- Tell students to record their findings on paper labeled as shown.

Body parts	Difference
hand to foot	

- Have students compare the differences in the measure of their body parts to that of their partner. They should find that they are fairly consistent.

Challenge Activity

Compare units of measure.

Materials: rulers and meter sticks

- Have students measure at least ten different objects in both inches and centimeters.

- Tell them to record their measurements in a table.

Object	Inches	Centimeters

- Instruct them to compare the measurement in inches and centimeters to see if they could find a way to estimate the centimeter length of an object if they only knew the length in inches. (They should find that the number of centimeters is a little less than 3 times the number of inches.)

- Have them test their strategy and share it with their peers.

©Curriculum Associates, LLC ·Copying is not permitted.

Lesson 21 (Student Book pages 176–185)

Add and Subtract Lengths

LESSON OBJECTIVES

- Use addition and subtraction to solve problems involving lengths.

- Recognize the importance of working within a single unit when adding or subtracting.

- Interpret and apply models that represent measurement problems involving addition and subtraction.

PREREQUISITE SKILLS

- Add and subtract within 100.

- Apply concepts of fact families.

- Understand addition and subtraction situations involving adding to, taking from, putting together, taking apart, and comparing.

- Measure in centimeters and inches.

VOCABULARY

There is no new vocabulary.

THE LEARNING PROGRESSION

In Grade 1, students compare lengths of objects by iterating units. They develop the understanding that the length of an object is determined by the number of iterated units that are used to compare.

In Grade 2, students measure and compare objects using more than one unit of measure. They recognize the need for comparing within a single unit and estimate lengths based on an understanding of units of measure. **In this lesson,** students apply what they have learned about measuring to solving problems involving measurements. They use models to represent a problem and devise strategies to organize the information that leads to a solution.

In Grade 3 and beyond, students will apply these skills to problems involving additional units of measure such as miles and kilometers, to fractions of units, and to problems involving area and perimeter.

Ready *Teacher Toolbox*		Teacher-Toolbox.com
	Prerequisite Skills	2.MD.B.5, 2.MD.B.6, 2.OA.A.1
Ready Lessons	✓	✓
Tools for Instruction	✓ ✓	✓
Interactive Tutorials	✓ ✓	

CCSS Focus

2.MD.B.5 Use addition and subtraction within 100 to solve word problems involving lengths that are given in the same units, e.g., by using drawings (such as drawings of rulers) and equations with a symbol for the unknown number to represent the problem.

2.MD.B.6 Represent whole number as lengths from 0 on a number line diagram with equally spaced points corresponding to the number 0, 1, 2, … and represent whole number sums and differences within 100 on a number line diagram.

2.OA.A.1 Use addition and subtraction within 100 to solve one- and two-step word problems involving situations of adding to, taking from, putting together, taking apart, and comparing, with unknowns in all positions, e.g., by using drawings and equations with a symbol for the unknown number to represent the problem.

STANDARDS FOR MATHEMATICAL PRACTICE: SMP 1, 2, 3, 4, 5, 6 (see page A9 for full text)

©Curriculum Associates, LLC   Copying is not permitted.

Add and Subtract Lengths

Objective: Explore addition and subtraction of lengths.

Materials for each student:
- $\frac{1}{2}$ inch. grid paper cut into lengths of 6, 8, 9, 10, 12, 14, 15, and 16 squares (preferably each a different color)
- 12-inch length of string (Activity Sheet 10, page 318)

Overview

Students find lengths of units that can be combined to equal a length of string. They devise and compare strategies to find the appropriate lengths.

Step by Step (20–30 minutes)

1 Pose the problem.
- Provide student pairs with grid paper strips and a 12-inch length of string. You may want them to tape each end of the string to their desk to keep it from moving.
- Tell students they need to find lengths of grid paper that, when combined, are exactly the same length as the string. Have them record each combination on a piece of paper in number sentence form.

2 Explore the concept.
- As students work through the problem, circulate the room asking questions such as: *How did you know that you needed a length of 8 units to add to a length of 16 units? Can you find 3 lengths that equal the length of the string? What do you need to do to decide? What can you do if there are not the right lengths you need to equal the length of the string?*

3 Share strategies.
- Invite students to share the strategies they used to find lengths such as subtracting a length from 24; thinking of what length is needed to get to 24; trying different lengths until finding ones that work (guess and check).
- Ask: *If you put an 8 and a 6 together, what other length would you need to use to equal the length of the string?* [10 squares] Listen for strategies such as add 8 + 6 then subtract the sum from 24. Ask students to explain each strategy and tell how they know they are correct.

4 Connect the concept.
- Ask students to think about other problems they have done that use the strategies they used to solve these problems. Discuss with them that these are like solving one- and two-step problems they did earlier in the year. Tell them they will be solving this kind of problem in the lesson.

©Curriculum Associates, LLC   Copying is not permitted.

AT A GLANCE

Students solve a problem involving measurement by using subtraction.

STEP BY STEP

- Have students read the problem at the top of the page. Ask a volunteer to tell what they know based on the information given and what they need to find out.

- Work through Explore It as a class. Ask the Mathematical Discourse questions to engage student thinking about how to use addition or subtraction.

- Discuss how this problem resembles the problems from the previous lesson where they compared lengths to find which object was shorter. Point out that in this problem, they are given the difference to use to find a missing length rather than finding the difference as in the previous lesson.

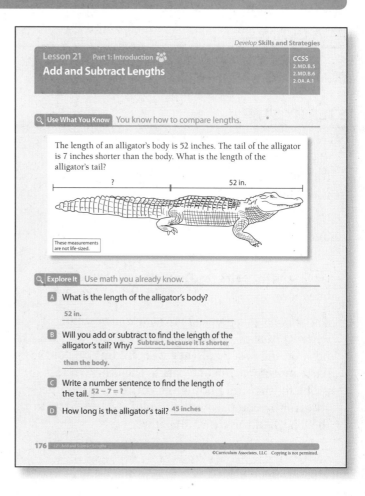

Visual Model

Relate the problem on this page to a number bond model from Lesson 2.

Tell students that in this problem the length of the alligator's tail is being compared to the alligator's body.

Ask students which part is longer. Since the body is the greater of the two, it can be considered the whole.

Show the top of the following model.

alligator body	
tail	7

Ask students to tell what they know about the tail. It is 7 inches shorter. Ask: *How can that help us find the length of the tail?* [add the length of the tail to 7 and it will equal the length of the body]

Add the bottom portion of the model and discuss how this model relates the problem.

Mathematical Discourse

- *Why doesn't it make sense to add 52 and 7 for this problem?*

  The problem says that the tail is shorter than the body. If we added, the tail would be longer than the body.

- *How might you use addition to think about this problem?*

  Since the tail is 7 inches shorter than the body, you can think of what you need to add to 7 to get 52.

- *Do you think it is easier to add or subtract? Why?*

  Students may respond that subtraction is easier since the difference is so great.

AT A GLANCE

Students add lengths to solve a problem and compare the result to a whole length.

STEP BY STEP

- Ask students to look at the pictures in Find Out More. Ask: *What are the parts in the first picture?* [the alligator body and tail] *What is the whole?* [the whole alligator]

- Use the Concept Extension to help students understand the importance of working within a single unit.

- Have student pairs read and discuss the Reflect question.

- Ask: *How is this problem the same and how is it different from the problem on the first page?* Discuss how, on the first page, they were finding one of the parts by comparing one part to the other. In this problem, they are finding the entire length of the alligator by comparing the sum of the two parts to the length of the entire alligator.

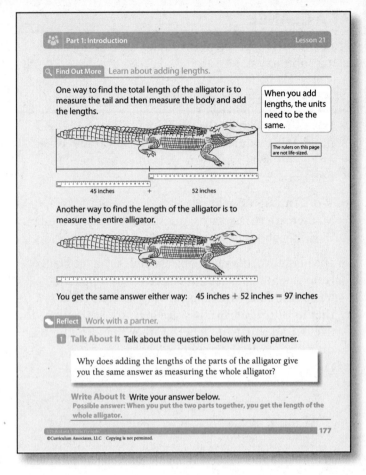

Concept Extension

Materials: one-inch tiles (Activity Sheet 3, pages 310), centimeter cubes, marker, crayon

Ask students measure a marker with tiles and record the length in inches.

Have students measure the crayon with centimeter cubes and record the length in centimeters.

Show students how to lay the marker and crayon next to each other end to end. Ask: *If the marker is the length of a lizard and the crayon is the length of the lizard's tail, how long is the lizard?* Discuss with students how difficult it is to describe the length because each part is measured in two different units. Ask: *Would it make sense to add the two lengths? Explain.* Students should respond that it would not make sense. There is no common name for the unit.

Remind them that in adding lengths the unit used must be the same.

Mathematical Discourse

Discuss with students times in their lives when they have added or subtracted lengths. If students have no ideas, suggest a situation such as building a model train track. The track comes in pieces of different lengths. You have to add the lengths to know how many track pieces will fit across the table top on which you are building it.

©Curriculum Associates, LLC   Copying is not permitted.

AT A GLANCE

Students explore how a picture, number line, and bar model can be used in solving a one-step problem involving measurement.

STEP BY STEP

- Read the problem at the top of the page as a class. Ask students to tell if this is like a "find the total", "find the part", or "find the start" question and why. Students should recognize that when 8 centimeters are cut off, only part of the whole necklace is left. If they add the part that is left to the part that was cut off, they will have the length of the entire necklace.

- Draw students' attention to Picture It. Ask how drawing a picture can help solve the problem. Guide students to see that a picture helps make sense of the problem and leads to a strategy to use.

- Ask: *Does it matter which end the 8 centimeters is cut from? Explain.* [No, it doesn't matter. It is still 8 centimeters shorter than at first.] You may want to demonstrate this situation using 2 equal lengths of string or yarn. Project the yarn so the students can watch as you measure. Cut a piece off of one end and measure the new length. Repeat for the second length of yarn, cutting the same size piece from the other end of the yarn.

- Discuss with students how the bar model shown on this page resembles the visual model they explored earlier in the lesson.

- Draw attention to the second Model It. Ask the Mathematical Discourse questions to remind students how they might use a number line to mentally solve a problem.

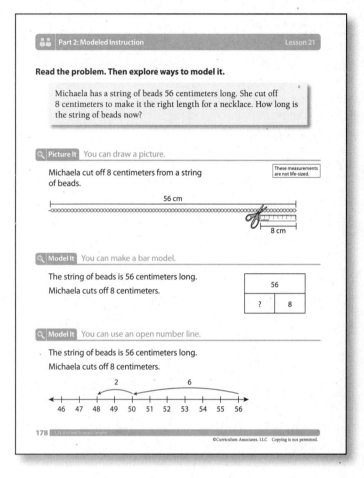

Mathematical Discourse

- *Why does it make sense to jump backwards 6 units and then 2 more units on the number line?*

    When you jump backwards 6 units, you get to 50. Then it is easy to take away 2 more.

- *Would it make sense to use addition instead of subtraction for this problem? Explain.*

    If you think: What number can I add 8 to for a sum of 56, it makes sense.

SMP Tip: Discuss with students how the models on this page help them make sense of a problem and lead to a number sentence. Make sure to emphasize these connections as students work through problems on the next page. (*SMP 4*)

©Curriculum Associates, LLC   Copying is not permitted.

AT A GLANCE

Students revisit the problem on page 178 by writing number sentences to represent what is shown in the models. They then solve measurement problems involving addition and subtraction.

STEP BY STEP

• Read and work through the Connect It questions as a class. Make sure students understand that the questions refer to the problem on page 178.

• For Problem 6, have students share the strategies they used to solve the problem. Guide students to see how the models shown on the previous page can be applied to this and similar problem situations.

• Have students use the information in Problem 6 to formulate a question that asks how much longer one string of beads is than the other. They should ask: *How much longer is a string of beads that is 56 centimeters long than a string that is 34 centimeters long?* Remind them that the number answer is the same, but the way they are comparing is different.

• Tell students that they may use a picture or other model to help in thinking about the Try It problems. Have students explain the thinking they used in solving the problems, sharing strategies and/or number sentences.

ELL Support

Make sure students understand the vocabulary used in Problem 8. Tell them that *farther* means longer or more feet. Rephrase the problem to say: Jesse measured 59 feet for his throw. Owen measured 15 more feet than Jesse for his throw. How far did Owen throw the ball?

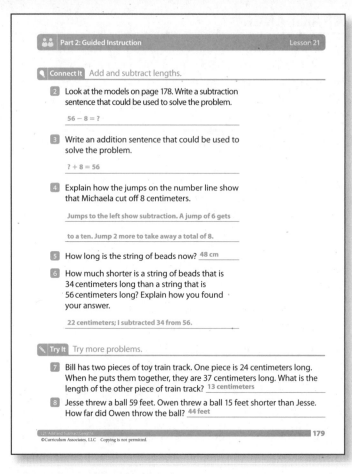

TRY IT SOLUTIONS

7 *Solution:* 13 cm; $37 - 24 = 13$ or $24 + ? = 37$ **(DOK 2)**

ERROR ALERT: Students who wrote $24 + 37 = 61$ added the numbers shown in the problem to find a whole rather than finding an unknown part.

8 *Solution:* 44 feet; $59 - 15 = 44$ **(DOK 2)**

SMP Tip: As students complete the problems on this page, emphasize the importance of accuracy. Encourage them to look back at the problem and the model they used after they have solved it to make sure the answer makes sense in the context of the problem. *(SMP 1)*

©Curriculum Associates, LLC Copying is not permitted.

AT A GLANCE

Students model a multi-step word problem involving measurement using a picture, number line, and bar model.

STEP BY STEP

- Read the problem at the top of the page as a class. Have students describe what they know and what they need to find out to solve the problem.

- Relate this problem to the two-step problems they solved in Unit 1. Ask what makes it a two-step problem. They should remember that they need to do more than add or subtract one set of numbers to solve.

- Ask students to explain Picture It. Ask: *When you find the sum, have you finished the problem? Why?* Make sure students recognize that once the sum is found, it still needs to be compared to 50 in order to determine whether there is enough border to cover the bottom of the poster board.

- Have students compare the number line and the bar model with a partner. Discuss as a class how each model can be used to think about the problem.

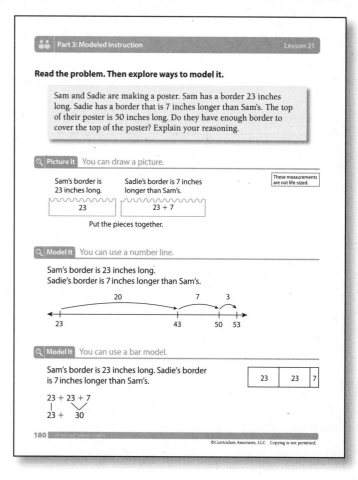

Concept Extension

Materials: one-inch tiles, centimeter cubes

Have students **attempt** to model the situation on this page using tiles. Discuss that the difficulty in modeling with tiles is that there are too many of them to fit across the desk.

Ask: *What do you think would happen if we used centimeter cubes instead of tiles?* The students may respond that they would fit the desk, but the unit is different.

Have students model with centimeter cubes. Discuss how, even though the centimeter cubes don't show the exact length, they produce the same numerical answer. Their small size makes modeling easier.

Mathematical Discourse

- *How do the models on this page help you make sense of the problem?*

  Students should recognize that the models help organize the information so they can easily see what information they have and what they need to find.

- *Which model do you think is easier to use? Why?*

  Students will express personal preferences. Encourage them to justify using reasons that express how the model helps them organize and make sense of the problem rather than reasons such as: It is easier.

AT A GLANCE

Students revisit the problem on page 180, writing number sentences to model the situation. Then students solve a two-step word problem involving measurement.

STEP BY STEP

- Tell students that Connect It will help them learn how to write number sentences for the problem on page 180.

- Work through Connect It together as a class.

- For Problem 12, engage students in a discussion of the misunderstanding Ethan has about adding units of measure. Remind students of the Concept Extension from the Introduction. Complete the Concept Extension activity on this page to explore the relationship between feet and inches.

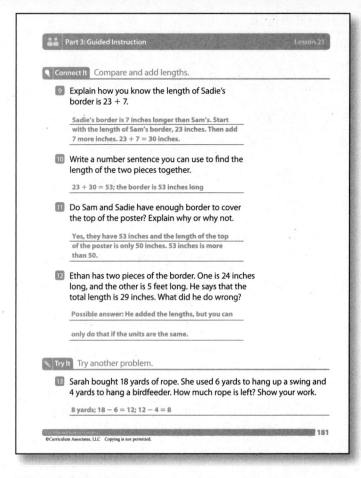

Part 3: Guided Instruction — Lesson 21

Connect It Compare and add lengths.

9. Explain how you know the length of Sadie's border is 23 + 7.

   Sadie's border is 7 inches longer than Sam's. Start with the length of Sam's border, 23 inches. Then add 7 more inches. 23 + 7 = 30 inches.

10. Write a number sentence you can use to find the length of the two pieces together.

    23 + 30 = 53; the border is 53 inches long

11. Do Sam and Sadie have enough border to cover the top of the poster? Explain why or why not.

    Yes, they have 53 inches and the length of the top of the poster is only 50 inches. 53 inches is more than 50.

12. Ethan has two pieces of the border. One is 24 inches long, and the other is 5 feet long. He says that the total length is 29 inches. What did he do wrong?

    Possible answer: He added the lengths, but you can only do that if the units are the same.

Try It Try another problem.

13. Sarah bought 18 yards of rope. She used 6 yards to hang up a swing and 4 yards to hang a birdfeeder. How much rope is left? Show your work.

    8 yards; 18 − 6 = 12; 12 − 4 = 8

L21: Add and Subtract Lengths
©Curriculum Associates, LLC   Copying is not permitted.   181

Concept Extension

- Ask: *How do you think we might find out how many inches are equal to 5 feet?* Listen to student suggestions. A student may suggest adding the inches in each foot.

  Show students a ruler and draw the following model on the board.

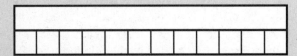

  Write "1" in each of the small squares. Tell students they are inches.

- Ask: *If one foot is equal to 12 inches, how many inches do you think are equal to 2 feet? How do you know?* Students should respond that 12 + 12 = 24 so 24 inches equals 2 feet.

- Add another model like the one above next to it. Ask: *How can we find the number of inches that equal 5 feet?* [add 12 inches together 5 times] Draw 3 more of the above model end to end on the board for a total of 5 feet/inches. Add on 3 groups of 12 to 24 to get a total of 60 inches. Ask: *How much border did Ethan have?* [84 inches]

TRY IT SOLUTION

13 *Solution:* 8 yards; 18 − 6 = 12; 12 − 4 = 8 (**DOK 2**)

ERROR ALERT: Students who answer 10 yards added the yarn used, but failed to subtract from, 18.

©Curriculum Associates, LLC   Copying is not permitted.

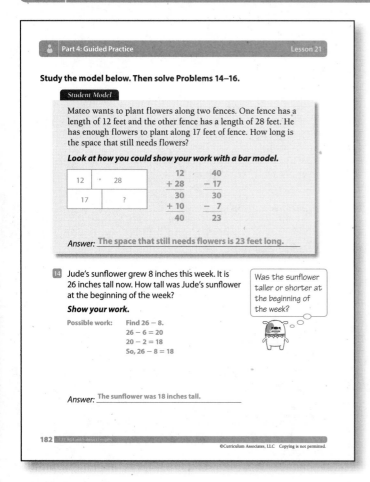

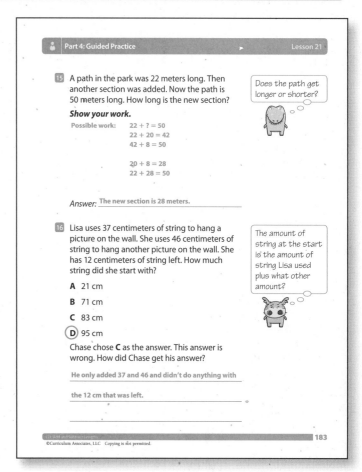

AT A GLANCE

Students model and solve one-step problems involving addition and subtraction.

STEP BY STEP

Ask students to solve the problems individually and show all their work, including the number sentences they wrote.

- Draw a picture and/or create a number line on the board to show students other ways to represent the modeled item.

- When students have completed each problem, have them Pair/Share to discuss their solutions with a partner.

SOLUTIONS

Ex A bar model and number sentences are used as examples for solving this problem.

14 *Solution:* 18-inches tall; $26 - 6 = 20$; $20 - 2 = 18$; so $26 - 8 = 18$. (**DOK 2**)

15 *Solution:* The new section is 28 meters; $22 + 8 = 30$; $30 + 20 = 50$; $8 + 20 = 28$. (**DOK 2**)

16 *Solution:* **D**; $37 + 46 + 12$

Explain to students why the other two choices are not correct:

A is not correct because you need to find $37 + 46 + 12$, not $46 - 37 + 12$.

B is not correct because you need to find $37 + 46 + 12$. not $37 + 46 - 12$. (**DOK 3**)

©Curriculum Associates, LLC   Copying is not permitted.

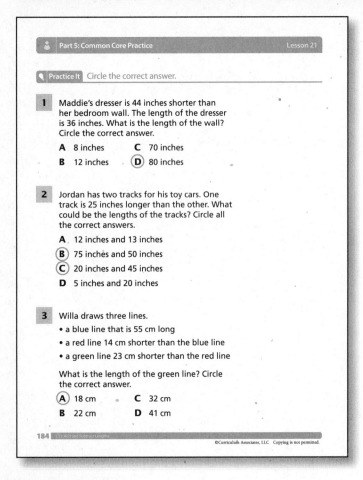

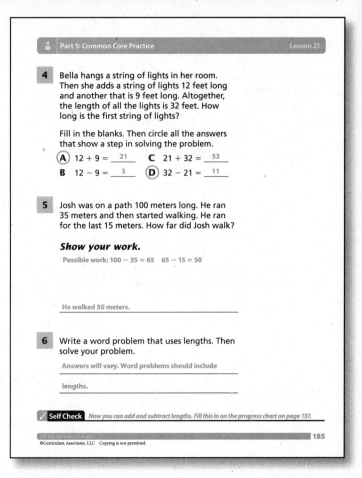

AT A GLANCE

Students use addition and subtraction to solve one-step word problems that might appear on a mathematics test.

STEP BY STEP

• First, tell students they will use addition and subtraction to solve one-step word problems. Then have students read the directions and answer the questions independently.

• After students have completed the Common Core Practice problems, review and discuss correct answers.

SOLUTIONS

1 *Solution:* **D**; Add 44 inches to the length of the dresser to find the length of the wall; $44 + 36 = 80$. **(DOK 2)**

2 *Solution:* **B** and **C**; These number pairs have a difference of 25. **(DOK 2)**

3 *Solution:* **A**; The red line is $55 - 14$, or 41 inches and the green line is $41 - 23$, or 18 inches. **(DOK 2)**

4 *Solution:* **A** and **D**; Add 12 and 9 to find the length of two strings, then subtract the sum (21) from the total length. **(DOK 3)**

5 *Solution:* Josh walked 50 meters. Subtract the distance he ran $(35 + 15)$ from the total length of the path $(100 - 50 = 50)$. **(DOK 2)**

6 *Solution:* Answers will vary. Possible answer: Rita's pet snake is 48 centimeters long. Josh's pet snake is 61 centimeters long. How much longer is Josh's pet snake? $61 - 48 = 13$; Josh's pet snake is 13 centimeters longer than Rita's pet snake. **(DOK 3)**

©Curriculum Associates, LLC   Copying is not permitted.

Assessment and Remediation

- The directions for making a number chart say: Make the first 9 inches of the chart one color. Make the rest a different color 6 inches longer than the first part. How long is the chart? [25 in.]

- For students who are still struggling, use the chart below to guide remediation.

- After providing remediation, check students' understanding using the following problem: The back bed of a pickup truck is 6 feet long. The front part of the truck is 2 feet longer. How long is the truck? [14 feet]

If the error is . . .	Students may . . .	To remediate . . .
15 inches	have added the given numbers	Ask students what "longer than" means. Draw a number bond model to help students see that 15 inches represents only one part of the chart.
3 inches	have subtracted the given numbers	Ask students if their answer makes sense. Read each sentence and model with blocks to see that there are two parts of the chart that need to be combined.

Hands-On Activity

Materials: strips of unit squares cut from half-inch grid paper (Activity Sheet 10, page 318)

- Pose the problem: Mr. Jones is setting up tables for a big dinner. He has tables that are 4 feet, 6 feet, and 8 feet long. He sets up an 8-foot and a 6-foot table to make one long table. He needs to make the long table 30 feet long. What other tables can he set up to finish his job?

- Write the table sizes on the board. Tell students to color and cut the grid paper to show the 8-foot and the 6-foot tables.

- Instruct students to cut the other paper strips into groups of 4, 6, and 8 units to show the tables Mr. Jones has. Tell them to use those to show what other table or tables he needs to make a 30-foot long table.

- Have students record their solution and strategy on a paper with the headings: My answer is: This is how I found it.

Challenge Activity

Materials: strips of unit squares cut from half-inch grid paper (Activity Sheet 10, page 318)

Challenge students to complete the problem on the left finding all the possible combinations of tables Mr. Jones could use.

Encourage students to organize their information and tell how they know they have found all the possibilities.

Extend the challenge by having students find the number of **yards** that equals the 30-foot table. Make sure they show their strategy and explain how they solved the problem.

©Curriculum Associates, LLC   Copying is not permitted.

Lesson 22 (Student Book pages 186–191)

Understand Reading and Making Line Plots

LESSON OBJECTIVES

- Represent data on a line plot.
- Understand that the numbers on a ruler or number line can be used to represent a given length.
- Interpret marks on a line plot as groups of data.

PREREQUISITE SKILLS

In order to be proficient with the concept/skills in this lesson, students should:

- Know how to measure in inches, feet, centimeters, and meters.
- Differentiate among and compare lengths in inches, feet, centimeters, and meters.
- Understand that a number line is a series of intervals organized on a line.

VOCABULARY

There is no new vocabulary.

THE LEARNING PROGRESSION

In grade 1, students organize and interpret data within categories. They compare lengths to analyze data determining whether a length is greater than or less than the others.

In grade 2, students represent lengths and whole number sums on a number line. They measure to the whole number unit and represent and interpret data. **In this lesson,** students organize lengths on a line plot. They read charts, represent, and interpret the data. They recognize that a number line and ruler can be used as tool for organizing information where the number on the ruler represents a length rather than an iteration of units.

In grade 3, students measure in the fractions of an inch and create line plots using fractional values. Line plots are seen as one of many ways to display data. Beyond grade 3, students will explore applications of line plots other than to record measurements and extend the concept of creating scale.

▪ **Ready** *Teacher Toolbox*		*Teacher-Toolbox.com*
	Prerequisite Skills	2.MD.B.6, 2.MD.D.9
Ready Lessons	✓ ✓	✓
Tools for Instruction	✓	✓
Interactive Tutorials		✓

CCSS Focus

2.MD.B.6 Represent whole numbers as lengths from 0 on a number line diagram with equally spaced points corresponding to the numbers 0, 1, 2, …, and represent whole-number sums and differences within 100 on a number line.

2.MD.D.9 Generate measurement data by measuring lengths of several objects to the nearest whole unit, or by making repeated measurements of the same object. Show the measurements by making a line plot, where the horizontal scale is marked off in whole-number units.

STANDARDS FOR MATHEMATICAL PRACTICE: SMP 1, 2, 3, 6 *(see page A9 for full text)*

©Curriculum Associates, LLC   Copying is not permitted.

Explore a Number Line

Objective: Develop the concept of a number line.

Materials for each student:
- blank piece of unlined paper
- pencil
- ruler
- $\frac{1}{2}$-inch strip of heavy paper or tag board

Overview

Students connect the number line used for recording data in a line plot to an open number line and create a number line with equally spaced intervals.

Step by Step (20–30 minutes)

1 Interpret an open number line.

- Draw a horizontal line on the board and ask students how they would make an open number line to solve the addition 8 + 7. Have students use white boards to model, if desired.

- Invite a volunteer to the board to model the addition on the number line.

- Ask: *Why did you start at 8?* Point to the left of the 8 and ask: *What is on this side of the 8?* Students may reply that nothing is there. If so, ask what numbers come before 8 when counting. Ask: *Why didn't you show those numbers?* [It isn't necessary since 8 is the first number used in the addition.] Make sure students understand that even though they aren't recorded, they still exist.

- Discuss what the jump from 8 to 15 on the number line represents. Ask: *How do you know there are 7 spaces between 8 and 15?* [The 7 above the curved arrow tells you.]

2 Create a number line.

- Demonstrate and have students follow as you use a ruler to draw a horizontal line across the paper the long way. Place an arrowhead at each end of the line. Tell students that the arrows mean that the line keeps going in both directions, but we only have room on the paper for some of it.

- Use the paper strip to make a hash mark on the far left side of the line. Have students do the same. Show students how to make hash marks every $\frac{1}{2}$ inch by marking the right side of the strip and then continuing to move and mark the right side of the strip along the length of the line.

- Tell students to write a 0 under the first mark and then write numbers in sequence under each of the remainder of the marks.

3 Add on the number line.

- Tell students to show the addition 8 + 7 on this number line using an arrow like on the open number line.

- Ask: *How is adding on this number line like adding on an open number line? How is it different?* Students should notice that they can use an arrow like on the open number line, but this line shows all the numbers before, after, and in between that the open number line does not.

4 Analyze

- Cover the 0–7 and 16–22 and ask: *Could you still solve the addition if these numbers weren't shown? Explain. Would it make sense to leave out one of the numbers between 8 and 15 on this number line? Why?* Students should recognize that the numbers on either side of the 8 and 15 don't affect their ability to solve, however, since the numbers in between are in sequence, they are necessary.

©Curriculum Associates, LLC   Copying is not permitted.

AT A GLANCE

Students explore the concept of a number line used in creating line plots by comparing it to a tape measure.

STEP BY STEP

- Read the Study Buddy question and answer at the top of the page.

- Ask students to recall ways they organized data and the kinds of data they looked at. They may recall bar graphs displaying kinds of pets, ways to come to school, colors of balloons, types of leaves, etc.

- Tell students that this lesson will help them explore a way to organize measurements (numerical data). Have them generate ideas of the kinds of things one might measure (height, weight, distance, temperature, money, etc.).

- Observe the heights listed. Ask questions such as: *What is the height of the tallest friend? The shortest friend? What are the heights of friends who are the same height?*

- Draw attention to the tape measure and number line in Think. Ask students what the numbers on the tape measure represent.

- Invite a volunteer to come to the front of the class to be measured. Use a retractable measuring tape to measure the student's height, hold it in place, mark it with masking tape, and turn the measuring tape horizontally to show the marked height. Make sure students understand that the tape measure indicates height whether positioned vertically or horizontally.

- Have students compare the visual representations of the tape measure and the number line as the comparisons are read in Think.

- Ask the Mathematical Discourse questions. Following the second question, extend the retractable tape measure and discuss that a tape measure includes numbers greater than and less than those shown on this page.

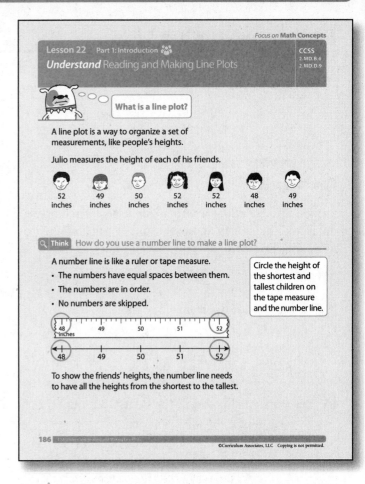

Mathematical Discourse

- *How is the number line shown here like an open number line? How is it different?*

  Students may note that numbers are organized on a line from least to greatest, but this number line shows each number in sequence where the open number line showed large intervals from one number to the next.

- *Why do you think only some of the numbers on the measuring tape and number line are shown?*

  Students should respond that the other numbers are not needed, since there are no heights greater than 52 inches or less than 48 inches. Make it clear that more numbers *could be* shown in the scale, but the book uses only the numbers that are needed in order to fit them all on the page.

©Curriculum Associates, LLC   Copying is not permitted.

AT A GLANCE

Students explore the structure of a line plot.

STEP BY STEP

- Draw student's attention to Think. Discuss the function of each part of the plot as described.

- Complete the Hands-On Activity to reinforce the concept of a line plot.

- Have students complete Talk About It and share their responses with the group.

Hands-On Activity

Build a line plot.

Materials: each student needs: a ruler, ten straws in varying lengths (at least 3 the same length), ten small counters such as beans, paper and pencil

- Instruct students to measure each straw to the nearest inch and record it on their paper.

- Tell students to organize the straws from smallest to largest.

- Have them lay the ruler in front of them horizontally and use the counters to indicate the length of each straw by placing a counter above the number that shows the length on the ruler.

- Discuss how the plot they made compares to the way they ordered the straws. Ask: *What does the line plot tell you that the grouped straws does not?* [The size of the straws and the exact difference in inches between them.]

- Use the data from one student to make a line plot. Record the data set on the board and draw a line near it. As students describe the scale and how to label it, add to the line drawn. Allow students to instruct you in marking the lengths of straws on the plot (mark incorrectly once or twice to keep students engaged and nurture self-correction).

- Ask: *What could we name this plot?* Lead students to write a title that reflects the plot such as: Lengths of Straws.

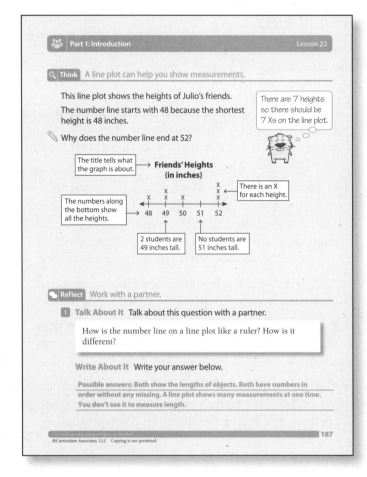

Mathematical Discourse

- Why is it important to include a title and label for a line plot?

  Students should understand that the title lets anyone who sees the graph know what the data represents. The label tells that they were measured in inches and not feet or centimeters.

- Paige asks, *"Why do you have to put the 51 on the plot when no one is 51 inches, but you don't have to put 53 on the plot since no one is 53 inches? What could you tell her?"*

  Listen for responses that indicate that students understand that numbers greater or less than those in the data set don't need to be included to keep the line plot from being too long. Those that are in the plot must include all the numbers in sequence since they represent measurements. If the 51 was not included, it would appear that there was only one inch between 50 and 52 instead of 2 inches.

AT A GLANCE

Students construct a line plot by recording lengths they measure.

STEP BY STEP

- Discuss Explore It with the class. Tell students to make sure and use the centimeter side of their ruler when measuring.

- Discuss possible strategies for measuring and recording data on the line plot. Ask the first Mathematical Discourse question. Make sure students know that both strategies are acceptable. They need to use the way that works best for them.

- Ask the second Mathematical Discourse question as students are measuring.

- Provide students time to work individually on the rest of the Explore It problems on this page and then share their responses in groups.

- Watch for students who are still having difficulty. See if their understanding progresses as they work in their groups during the next part of the lesson.

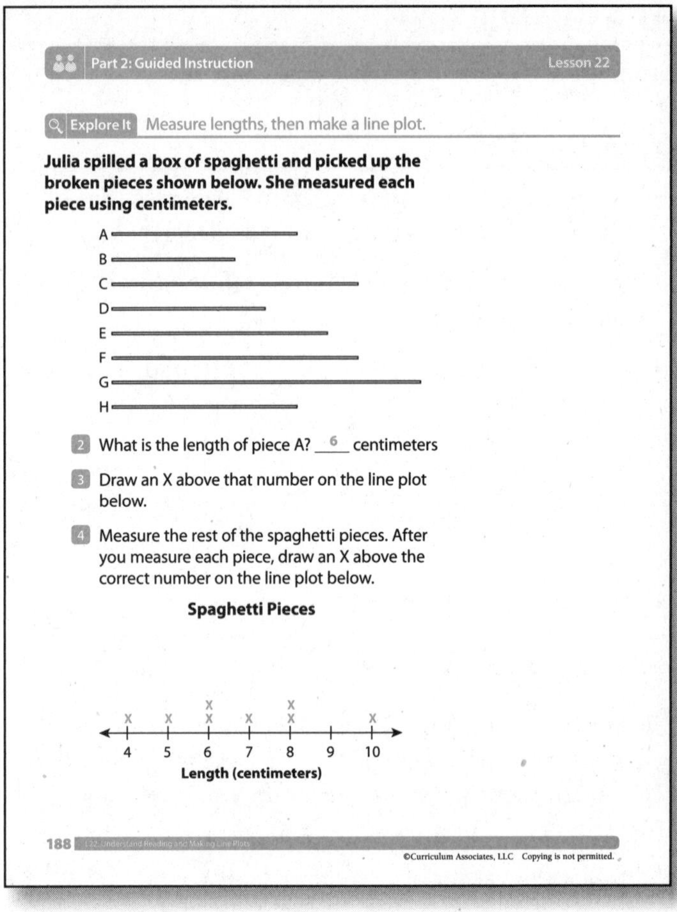

Explore It Measure lengths, then make a line plot.

Julia spilled a box of spaghetti and picked up the broken pieces shown below. She measured each piece using centimeters.

> A ———————
> B ————
> C ——————————
> D ————————
> E ——————
> F ——————————
> G ———————————
> H ——————

2 What is the length of piece A? __6__ centimeters

3 Draw an X above that number on the line plot below.

4 Measure the rest of the spaghetti pieces. After you measure each piece, draw an X above the correct number on the line plot below.

Spaghetti Pieces

```
                    X
          X         X         X
  X       X    X    X    X
  |---|---|---|---|---|---|---|
  4   5   6   7   8   9   10
       Length (centimeters)
```

188 L22: Understand Reading and Making Line Plots

©Curriculum Associates, LLC Copying is not permitted.

Hands-On Activity

Materials: $\frac{1}{4}$-inch paper strips cut into lengths of 4 cm, 5 cm, 6 cm, 6 cm, 7 cm, 8 cm, 8 cm, 10 cm; ruler for each student pair

- Have students compare the lengths of the strips of paper to the lengths of the spaghetti shown on this page to see that they correspond to each other.

- Demonstrate and have students follow as you line the paper strips up along the centimeter side of the ruler from shortest to longest, one above the other.

- Compare the strips lined up on the ruler to the line plot. Discuss how there is one X above each number on the plot corresponding to a strip along the ruler and two X's where there are two strips.

Mathematical Discourse

- *Why might it be easier to record each piece of spaghetti on the line plot as you measure?*

  Students may respond that if they record each one as they measure, it doesn't take as much time as writing measures first and then plotting.

- *How does the care you take in measuring affect your line plot?*

  Students should respond that if they don't measure correctly, they might put a mark on the plot in the wrong place.

SMP Tip: Encourage students to take care when measuring the pieces of spaghetti on this page. Remind them of the importance of lining up one end of the ruler to one end of the spaghetti to measure. (*SMP 6*)

©Curriculum Associates, LLC Copying is not permitted.

AT A GLANCE

Students analyze the line plot made on page 188.

STEP BY STEP

- Instruct students to work in pairs to complete Problems 5–9. Walk around to each group, listen to, and join in on discussions at different points.

- As students work on Problem 8, remind them that 0, 1, 2, 3 could be shown on the plot, but are not necessary since there are no lengths shorter than 4 cm.

- For Problems 10–13, make sure students use the data on the line plot to answer the questions.

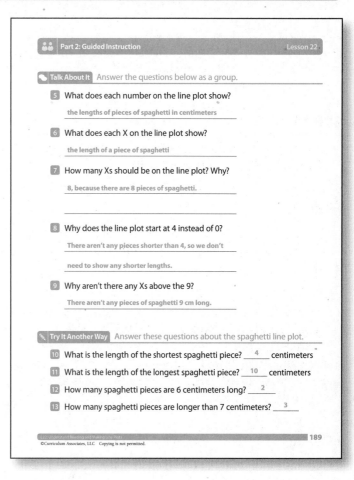

Concept Extension

Compare lengths in a line plot.

- Draw and display a completed line plot from this page.

- Ask: *How much longer is the longest piece of spaghetti than the shortest piece?* [5 centimeters] *How can you tell?* Students may suggest subtracting 4 from 9.

- Erase or cover the scale on the line plot and ask students if they could still find the difference between lengths of the spaghetti.

- Discuss that since units used in measurement are represented by the intervals between numbers, the number of intervals between each length tells how much longer one piece is from another.

- Have students find the difference between two pieces of spaghetti that you indicate on the plot.

Mathematical Discourse

- *How would the line plot change if there was a piece of spaghetti 14 cm long in this group?*

  Students should respond that the line would be longer and would have to include at least 11, 12, 13, and 14.

SMP Tip: Focusing on the *unit* as an interval reinforces the concept of the accumulation of distance. A measure is the quantity of a collection of iterated units. *(SMP 2)* Therefore a measure could be taken from any starting point on a ruler.

AT A GLANCE

Students demonstrate their understanding of a line plot by examining the situations posed and answering related questions.

STEP BY STEP

- Discuss each Connect It problem as a class using the discussion points outlined below.

Identify:

- Allow students to work with a partner to share ideas. Encourage them to explain and justify their thinking.

- As students share their ideas with the class, make sure they have ordered the lengths from least to greatest and included all values between and including 6 and 11. Reinforce the idea that these are the values that MUST be included, however, it would be acceptable to create a scale that includes all the numbers from 0 to 11 or greater.

Explain:

- Ask: *What do the X's on the line plot represent?* [the number of children who jump each distance]

- Tell students that it is easy to misunderstand what a graph is saying. Discuss the importance of accuracy in creating a graph so that others can read it easily and the importance of understanding what graphs mean so that they are read properly.

- Have students generate ideas of ways to make sure the line plot they create is clear so someone like Nate doesn't misinterpret it.

- You may want students to draw this line plot on whiteboards with X's all the same size so it could not be misread.

Analyze:

- Ask: *What part of the line plot tells the distance Bo ran each day?* [the scale]

- Discuss why Tia might make the mistake of reading the three X's as the farthest Bo runs.

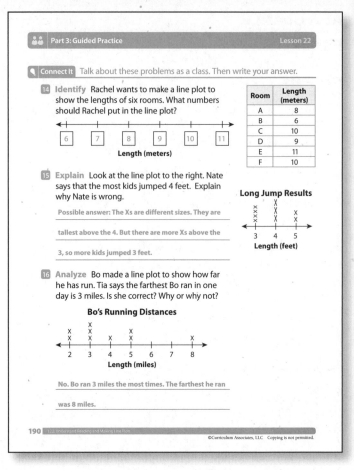

- Ask: *How might the line plot be read if Bo forgot to include a label for the scale?* [No one would know if he was running in meters, feet, yards, or miles. It also might make someone like Tia misunderstand what the numbers and marks represent.]

Concept Extension

Why do we graph?

- Discuss with students that organizing information on a display helps us understand the data so we can use it to make decisions.

- Ask: *What kinds of things can Bo tell about his running just by looking at the line plot?* [He can see how far he ran on different days; He can tell just by looking how many times he ran each distance; He can tell what distances he did not run.] *What might he decide to do by looking at the plot?* [He might try to run farther; He might decide that he likes running 3 miles best and so only run that far all the time; He might decide if he wants to run a marathon or a half marathon.]

©Curriculum Associates, LLC   Copying is not permitted.

AT A GLANCE

Students demonstrate their understanding of line plots by creating a line plot and then analyzing it.

STEP BY STEP

- Direct students to complete the Put It Together task on their own.

- Read the directions with students and make sure they understand each part of the task before proceeding.

- Copy and distribute Activity Sheet 11, page 319, to students.

- As students work on their own, walk around to assess their progress and understanding, to answer their questions, and to give additional support, if needed.

- If time permits, ask students to share the line plots they made. You may want students to share other observations they make from the line plots such as: There are no shells 5 or 6 inches; There are two more 2-inch shells than 4-inch shells.

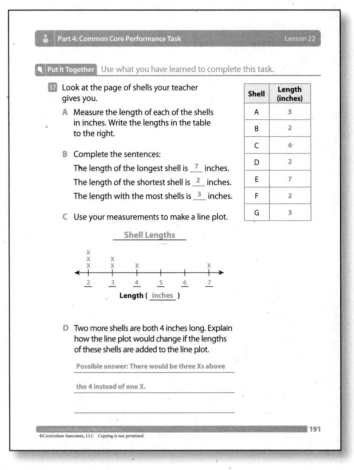

SCORING RUBRICS

A

Points	Expectations
2	The student accurately measures each shell and records the measure in the chart.
1	The student may measure with some accuracy, however is inconsistent. The chart may or may not be completed.
0	The student does not accurately measure nor complete the table.

B

Points	Expectations
2	The student creates a line plot that includes all the elements and data that is accurately displayed.
1	The student completes some of the line plot, but omits parts and attempts to display the data. Some may be accurate and some may not.
0	The student does not create an accurate line plot nor display data.

C

Points	Expectations
2	All responses are accurate.
1	Some responses are accurate.
0	No responses are accurate.

D

Points	Expectations
2	The student responds that four X's would be above the 3.
1	The student may know there are more 3's to display, but does not articulate how.
0	The student does not articulate a reason or solution.

Intervention Activity

Materials: for each student: paper with a portion of a ruler (0–10 in.) printed on it the long way and a number line below it marked with one-inch intervals (leave room between ruler and number line for recording), a set of used colored pencils (10–12 inch), $\frac{1}{2}$-inch squares of paper (Activity Sheet 10, page 318), glue

- Tell students they are to measure each pencil to the nearest inch using the ruler printed on the paper. Have them glue a paper square above the closest inch (if necessary, cut squares from colored paper matching the colors of pencils). If more than one pencil is the same length, glue another paper square above the one(s) recorded.

- Once students have completed measuring the pencils, have them number the number line to match the inches shown on the ruler.

- Have students use an X to represent each of the pencils measured. They should replicate the placement of the paper squares on the ruler with X's on the number line.

- When finished, have students compare the graphs articulating similarities between them. Students should notice that the number line plot represents the lengths of pencils that were recorded on the ruler.

On-Level Activity

Materials: for each student: a copy of a number line divided into 10 unlabeled intervals (Activity Sheet 12, page 320), 10–12 used colored crayons, ruler

- Have students measure each crayon to the nearest centimeter and record the length on a separate piece of paper or white board.

- Tell students to examine all the measurements and then decide what number to start with on the scale. Number each interval on the scale in numerical order.

- Instruct students to mark an X above each mark on the number line that corresponds to the length of a crayon.

- Tell students to make sure and label the scale and include a title.

- Have them write three observations they make from the data.

- Tell students to measure an unused crayon and compare its length to those on the line plot. Ask: *What does the line plot tell you about the way you have used your crayons this year?* [It may indicate that they have been used a lot or that generally, they have not been used much.]

Challenge Activity

Materials: 10–12 books from the classroom, ruler, yard stick, plain paper, pencil

- Select books for students to measure. Make sure some of them are the same height.

- Have students measure the height of each book and create a line plot to display their results. Tell them to make sure they have all the parts labeled and have included a title.

- Once complete, have students write observations they make from the line plot and then think of how the information in the line plot might help someone make a decision. What might they decide to do?

©Curriculum Associates, LLC   Copying is not permitted.

Lesson 23 (Student Book pages 192–201)

Draw and Use Bar Graphs and Picture Graphs

LESSON OBJECTIVES

- Compare data in a tally chart, table, picture graph, and bar graph.
- Interpret graphs by reading the data shown in the graph.
- Analyze bar graphs by comparing data in each category.
- Create a bar graph from a given set of data.

PREREQUISITE SKILLS

- Represent and interpret simple graphs.
- Identify how many more and how many less.
- Measure intervals.

VOCABULARY

picture graph: A data display in which pictures are used to display the number of data in each category.

bar graph: A data display in which bars are used to represent the number of data in each category.

data: A set of collected information.

THE LEARNING PROGRESSION

In Grade 1, students organized data into three categories. They represented the data in a bar graph and interpreted it by comparing the data from one category to another.

In Grade 2, students organize and represent data in more than one way, recognizing the kinds of data that are best represented in a line plot and those organized into categories and best represented in a bar graph.
In this lesson, students organize data into a tally chart and table in order to use it for a graph. They represent the data in both a picture graph and bar graph using a scale in a one-to-one correspondence with the data. Students recognize the relationship of the two forms of graphs and how the shape of the data is consistent when in either form.

In Grade 3, students expand on their understanding of scale as they represent data in a graph where the scale is in intervals of twos, fives, etc. They organize data and represent it in a bar, determine an appropriate scale and use the data to solve one- and two-step problems.

◼ **Ready** *Teacher Toolbox*		*Teacher-Toolbox.com*
	Prerequisite Skills	*2.MD.D.10*
Ready Lessons	✓ ✓	✓
Tools for Instruction	✓	✓
Interactive Tutorials	✓	✓ ✓

CCSS Focus

2.MD.D.10 Draw a picture graph and bar graph (with single unit scale) to represent a data set with up to four categories. Solve simple put-together, take-apart and compare problems using information presented in a bar graph.

STANDARDS FOR MATHEMATICAL PRACTICE: **SMP 1, 2, 3, 4, 6** *(see page A9 for full text)*

©Curriculum Associates, LLC   Copying is not permitted.

Organize Data

Objective: Collect and organize data.	**Materials for each student:** • a 3 in. square piece of paper

Overview

Students explore the purpose for organizing, displaying, and interpreting data by representing the results of a quick classroom survey in a scatter plot and bar graph.

Step by Step (15–20 minutes)

1 **Collect the data.**

• Divide the board into 4 large sections and label each one with the types of books students like to read such as: Adventure/Mysteries; Animal Stories; Fantasy (Make Believe) Stories; Biographies (stories about the lives of real people), etc. Make sure you limit it to 4 categories.

• Distribute a square piece of paper to each student. Have them write their name on the paper.

• Ask students to decide which type of story listed is their favorite kind of book to read. Have them come to the board and tape their square piece of paper randomly in the appropriate section.

2 **Organize the data.**

• If students organized the squares in the form of a bar graph, ask them to explain why they organized them in that way. If not, discuss how they might compare the number of students' names that appear in each group. They should notice that they need to count the number of squares in each group. Ask: *How might we organize the squares so that it is easy to compare the number in each group?* They should see that by aligning them side-by-side, it is easy to compare the data. Show how to arrange the squares in a vertical bar.

• Students should have some experience with bar graphs. If so, ask where the labels you wrote should be placed. Write the labels under the bars they represent. Ask: *What do each of the squares of paper stand for?* [A person in the class who likes that kind of book.] Ask: *How do you know the number of students who like each kind of book?* [Count the number of squares.] *What could we do to show others how many are in each group so they don't have to count?* Lead students to see that they can write a number on the board to the left of the "bars" that corresponds with each paper square.

3 **Purpose for displaying data.**

• Tell students that data or information is collected, organized, and displayed for a reason. The information is used to make decisions.

• Ask: *Who might be interested in this information?* [A teacher or librarian might be interested.]

How might they use this information to make a decision? [It can help a teacher know what kinds of books to use in the classroom. It might help a librarian decide the kind of books to buy most and least of for the library.] *Do you think this graph would be the same if we asked another second grade class to tell their favorite kinds of stories? Why?* Discuss that the data may be completely different for students in another class, however, generally second graders like many of the same kinds of stories. So, on the other hand, it would not be unlikely that another class would have the same results.

©Curriculum Associates, LLC   Copying is not permitted.

AT A GLANCE

Students read a picture graph, answer questions, and write number sentences about it.

STEP BY STEP

- Draw students' attention to the picture graph at the top of the page. Ask students what they think a picture graph is. Discuss that a picture graph is a display of information using a picture of each piece of data to show the totals in each category or group.

- Ask: *What vegetables do you see listed in this graph?* [carrots, beans, broccoli, corn] Compare the numbers for each category on the graph and ask the first Mathematical Discourse question. Discuss with students that, although we can't be sure the next person surveyed will choose carrots, graphs are often used to make predictions. The predictions then help them make decisions. Ask: *If you sold vegetables at a Farmer's Market, how might this information help you make decisions?* [You might plant more carrots and not as much corn or beans.]

- Work through the Explore It questions as a class. Discuss the difference between the questions in parts C and D. Ask the second discourse question.

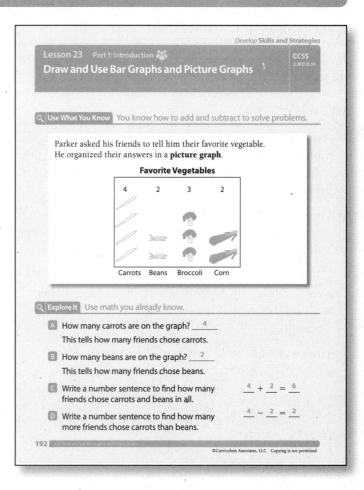

Lesson 23   Part 1: Introduction

Draw and Use Bar Graphs and Picture Graphs

CCSS 2.MD.D.10

Develop Skills and Strategies

🔍 **Use What You Know**   You know how to add and subtract to solve problems.

Parker asked his friends to tell him their favorite vegetable. He organized their answers in a **picture graph**.

Favorite Vegetables

| 4 | 2 | 3 | 2 |

Carrots   Beans   Broccoli   Corn

🔍 **Explore It**   Use math you already know.

A   How many carrots are on the graph?   4
This tells how many friends chose carrots.

B   How many beans are on the graph?   2
This tells how many friends chose beans.

C   Write a number sentence to find how many friends chose carrots and beans in all. $4 + 2 = 6$

D   Write a number sentence to find how many more friends chose carrots than beans. $4 - 2 = 2$

192   L23: Draw and Use Bar Graphs and Picture Graphs   ©Curriculum Associates, LLC   Copying is not permitted.

Mathematical Discourse

- *If Parker asked one more of his friends to tell their favorite vegetable, what do you think it would be? Why?*

  Answers may vary, but students should recognize that since carrots were chosen most often there is a good possibility the next student surveyed will choose carrots.

- *How might you write Problem D as an addition problem? Explain.*

  Students should respond that $2 + ? = 4$ could be used to solve. Starting at the number of beans and counting up to the number of carrots gives the difference.

Real-World Connection

- Find samples of graphs in the newspaper or magazines. Discuss how those who make graphs use them to help make decisions.

- Provide real-life scenarios such as: An ice cream shop makes a graph of the flavors of ice cream they sell each day for a month. What kinds of decisions might they make? The city graphs the number of cars that drive on 4 different streets in a week. How might that help them make a decision about road repair?

- If possible, have community members or school personnel such as a principal, secretary, janitor, cook, librarian, etc. come to the classroom and show/tell how they use graphs to help them make decisions.

©Curriculum Associates, LLC   Copying is not permitted.

AT A GLANCE

Students build a bar graph to display the data shown on page 192.

STEP BY STEP

- Ask students to read Find Out More. Discuss that in a **bar graph**, a bar (rectangle) is used to represent the information from the picture graph. The information gathered is called **data**.

- Discuss each part of the graph shown. Ask students to describe what the numbers on the graph tell them. Compare the parts of the bar graph to the parts of a line plot.

- Remind students of the way they used labels when making line plots. Ask the Mathematical Discourse question.

- Have students complete the Reflect questions in pairs. Discuss observations as a class.

Concept Extension

Different data displays.

- Draw students' attention to the two data displays shown on these pages and ask: *Would it make sense to put this data on a line plot? Explain.* [Listen to student responses and justifications, reserving judgment.]

- Have students draw a number line on white boards or plain paper with at least 6 intervals and number them. Then have students attempt to mark the data on the line plot.

- Ask: *Does the line plot give you information about the vegetables students chose? Explain.* [No. There is one X above each number, but you don't know what they mean.]

- Discuss how some graphs display data better than others. Some data can be displayed on more than one kind of graph such as the distances Bo ran each day, but other kinds of data are better shown on a certain kind of graph. That is why we learn about different types of displays.

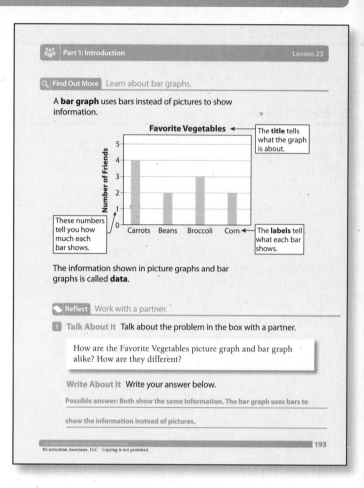

Mathematical Discourse

- *What might happen if there were no labels on this graph?*

  No one would know what the numbers mean. They might represent hundreds of people. And you wouldn't know which vegetable each of the bars represents.

©Curriculum Associates, LLC   Copying is not permitted.

AT A GLANCE

Students organize data in a chart and then use it to make a picture graph and a bar graph.

STEP BY STEP

- Read the problem at the top of the page as a class. Ask students what the tally marks in the chart represent. Make sure students know how to read tally marks. Have them write the corresponding number under each set of marks.

- Draw students' attention to Picture It. Ask them to describe what the picture graph shows. They should recognize that it is displaying the data from the chart using a picture rather than a tally mark to show each response. Ask the first Mathematical Discourse question.

- Discuss with students how to read the bar graph shown in Model It. Make sure they either visually line up the bars with a numerical value or use a piece of paper or ruler to line them up.

- Have students compare the bar graph to the picture graph. Discuss how both graphs display the same data. In the picture graph, pictures of sports balls represent the number of students who selected each sport. The bar graph is more abstract—the bars represent a student who has selected a sport, but the bars don't look like the student or the sport. Ask the second Mathematical Discourse question.

SMP Tip: Discuss with students how each bar in a bar graph represents a quantity. Have them notice that the scale is drawn in intervals. Each interval in this graph represents one classmate. When lining up the bar to the number on the scale, they are finding the number of intervals (or students) calculated. *(SMP 2)*

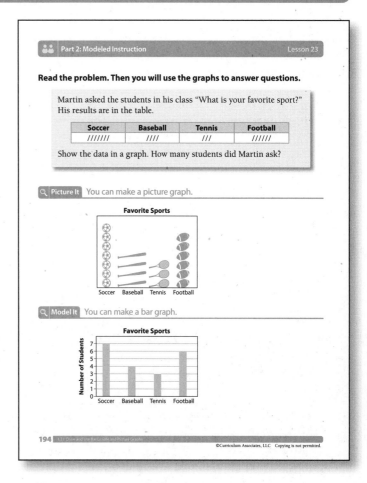

Mathematical Discourse

- *Why would it make sense for Martin to collect his data in a chart rather than in a picture graph?*

  To make a picture graph, he would either have to have pictures of balls and glue with him or take time to draw the pictures on the graph. It would take a longer time to gather his information than by making tally marks.

- *Why does the bar graph include a scale and the picture graph does not?*

  In the picture graph, the number of pictures tells you how many of each sport were chosen. In the bar graph, you need a scale in order to know how many each bar shows.

AT A GLANCE

Students revisit the problem on page 194, interpreting the graphs and answering questions about them.

STEP BY STEP

- Read Connect It as a class. Make sure students understand that the questions refer to the graphs on page 194.

- For Problem 3, make sure students describe how they can find this information in the bar graph, not from the other displays shown.

Hand-On Activity

Make a class graph

Materials: chart or construction paper; a 2-inch square of white paper for each student and 2-inch squares of 4 different colors of paper

- Draw a chart on the board like the one on page 194. Ask students to choose their favorite sport from those listed in the chart. Collect data by either a show of hands, selections written on a white board, or by having each student come to the board drawing a tally mark under their favorite sport in the chart.

- Write the sports labels along the bottom of the shorter side of a piece of chart paper or large construction paper. Have students either write their names on the square of paper or draw stick figures. Have them take turns gluing their square on the chart above the sport that they chose.

- Discuss how the picture graph resembles the bar graph. Since the pictures are drawn on squares of paper, they look like a bar.

- Have students cover the picture they glued on the picture graph with a colored square, making sure a single color of square is used for each sport. Add a scale, labels, and a title to the graph.

- Compare the data from your class to that of Martin's class.

Connect It Use the graphs.

2 How do you use the picture graph to find the number of students who chose soccer?

   Count the number of soccer balls.

3 How do you use the bar graph to find the number of students who chose soccer?

   Look at the bar above Soccer. Find the top of the bar and read

   the number on the left.

4 How many students chose soccer as their favorite? ___7___

5 Explain how to use the bar graph to find the total number of students Martin asked.

   Find the number of students who chose each sport and add

   them all together.

6 How many students did Martin ask? ___20___

Try It Try more problems.

7 How many fewer students chose tennis than football? ___3___

8 Two students changed their answers from soccer to baseball. Now how many students chose soccer? ___5___
   Now how many students chose baseball? ___6___

L23: Draw and Use Bar Graphs and Pictographs
©Curriculum Associates, LLC Copying is not permitted.   195

TRY IT SOLUTIONS

7 *Solution:* 3; 6 football − 3 tennis = difference of 3. **(DOK 2)**

8 *Solutions:* 5, 6; 7 soccer − 2 = 5 soccer, 4 baseball + 2 = 6 baseball. **(DOK 2)**

ERROR ALERT: Students who wrote 7 for soccer failed to subtract 2 from those who selected soccer.

©Curriculum Associates, LLC   Copying is not permitted.

AT A GLANCE

Students examine a set of data organized in a tally chart and in a table.

STEP BY STEP

- Read the problem at the top of the page as a class. Discuss that each color Lynn wrote down represents the color of apple she saw in an entire row of apples.

- Ask: *How could you make sure all the colors of apples Lynn saw are recorded in the tally chart?* Listen for responses that indicate students have developed a strategy such as crossing off each color as it is recorded.

SMP Tip: Emphasize the need for precision in recording data when graphing by having students count the total number of rows Lynn saw in the opening problem and compare that to the total number of tallies in the chart and the total number of rows shown in the table. *(SMP 6)*

- Ask the Mathematical Discourse question. Make sure students are aware that both the table and chart are organizing the data. Ask: *Why do you think it is important to organize the data before making a bar graph?* Discuss how to be accurate. Having the data organized and checked first prevents errors in the graph and keeps them from having to redo a graph in which some of the bars were not drawn accurately.

- Ask students which of the organizational tools they think would be easier to use. Discuss with them when it might be easier to make a tally chart than a table. They should recognize that when recording large quantities of data, when they are taking a survey or when they first organize the data, a tally chart is quick and simple.

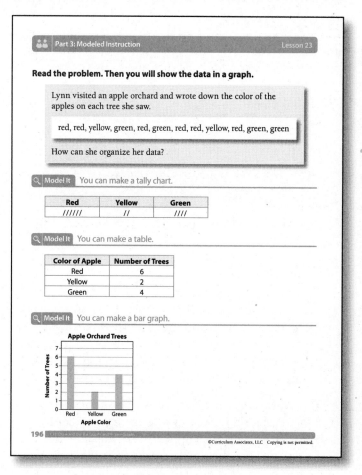

Mathematical Discourse

- *How are the tally chart and the table alike? How are they different?*

  They show the same information. The tally chart uses tally marks to record the data that was collected. The table records the number of each color with a numeral rather than with tallies.

AT A GLANCE

Students revisit the problem on page 196, using the data from the table to create a picture and bar graph.

STEP BY STEP

- Tell students that Connect It will help them learn how to make a graph for the data on page 196.

- Ask: *Why do you think the title you chose is a good title for this graph?* [The graph shows the colors of apples Lynn saw in each row of apples in an apple orchard, so *Colors of Apples in the Orchard* would be a good title.]

- Instruct students to complete the picture graph by filling in the missing information.

- Direct students' attention to Try It. Explain that they will use the information they recorded in the picture graph to complete the bar graph. Tell them to work with their partner, comparing their graphs to make sure they have all the information recorded.

- When they have completed Try It, Ask: *How does the picture graph show one row of a particular color of apple?* [A picture of an apple is used to show one row of a particular color.] *How does the bar graph show one row of a particular color of apple?* [The space (or interval) between each number shows one row of a particular color of apple.]

- Have students analyze the graphs by asking questions such as: *How many more rows of red apples than yellow apples did Lynn see? How many rows of apples were green or red?* Make sure students understand when the word "or" is used, they find the total in both categories.

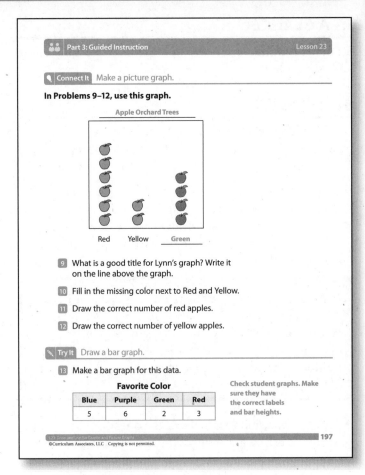

TRY IT SOLUTIONS

13 *Solution:* Bar graphs should correctly show data from the table, and include a title and labels for both axis. **(DOK 2)**

ERROR ALERT: Watch for students who do not include a title with their bar graph. Ask these students how they know what the bar graph shows.

©Curriculum Associates, LLC   Copying is not permitted.

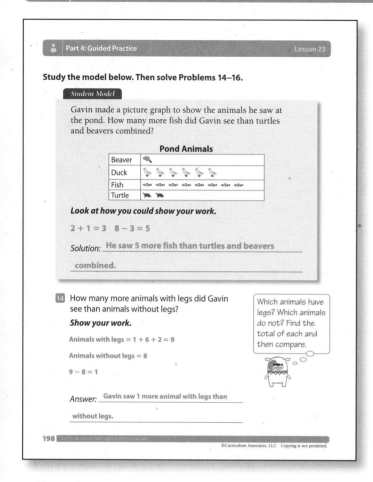

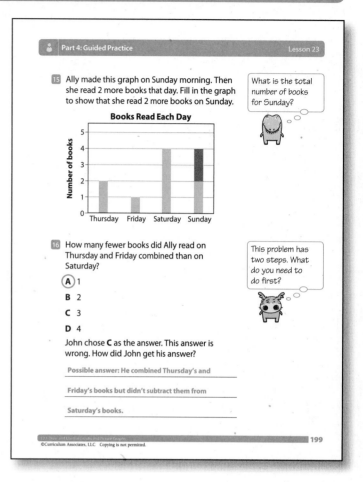

AT A GLANCE

Students analyze data displays, using them to answer questions.

STEP BY STEP

- Ask students to solve the problems individually and show all their work, including the number sentences they wrote.

- For Problem 14, make sure students understand that the word "more" used here is not making a comparison, but tells that an additional 2 books were read on Sunday.

- When students have completed each problem, have them Pair/Share to discuss their solutions with a partner.

SOLUTIONS

Ex A picture graph is shown to display the data collected at a pond. Students should combine the number of turtles and beavers: $2 + 1 = 3$; and then either subtract from the number of fish (8) or add up from 3 to 8 to arrive at the answer: He saw 5 more fish than turtles and fish combined.

14 *Solution:* There is 1 more animal with legs than without legs; Beaver (1) + Duck (6) + Turtle (2) = 9, $9 -$ Fish (8) = 1. **(DOK 2)**

15 *Solution:* The graph should show two additional books drawn above the label Sunday for a total of 4. **(DOK 2)**

16 *Solution:* **A**; $2 - 1 = 1$

Explain to students why the other two choices are not correct:

B is not correct because 2 is the total read on Thursday.

D is not correct because 4 is the number of books Ally read after she added two more on Sunday. **(DOK 3)**

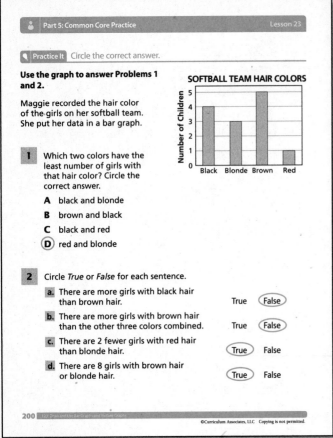

Practice It Circle the correct answer.

Use the graph to answer Problems 1 and 2.

Maggie recorded the hair color of the girls on her softball team. She put her data in a bar graph.

SOFTBALL TEAM HAIR COLORS

1 Which two colors have the least number of girls with that hair color? Circle the correct answer.

A black and blonde

B brown and black

C black and red

D red and blonde

2 Circle *True* or *False* for each sentence.

a. There are more girls with black hair than brown hair.   True   **False**

b. There are more girls with brown hair than the other three colors combined.   True   **False**

c. There are 2 fewer girls with red hair than blonde hair.   **True**   False

d. There are 8 girls with brown hair or blonde hair.   **True**   False

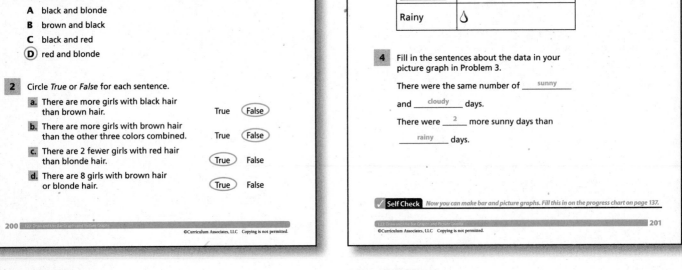

3 Wes recorded the weather for one week in the table at the right.

Complete the picture graph below using the data in Wes's table. Draw a O for sunny days and a ☁ for cloudy days.

Day	Weather
Sun.	cloudy
Mon.	cloudy
Tues.	sunny
Wed.	sunny
Thur.	rainy
Fri.	sunny
Sat.	cloudy

SUNNY, RAINY, AND CLOUDY DAYS

Sunny	☼ ☼ ☼
Cloudy	☁ ☁ ☁
Rainy	💧

4 Fill in the sentences about the data in your picture graph in Problem 3.

There were the same number of ___sunny___

and ___cloudy___ days.

There were ___2___ more sunny days than

___rainy___ days.

Self Check *Now you can make bar and picture graphs. Fill this in on the progress chart on page 137.*

AT A GLANCE

Students use graphs to answer questions that might appear on a mathematics test.

STEP BY STEP

- First, tell students they will use graphs and tables to answer the questions on the next two pages. Draw attention to the graph on the first page and the chart on the second page. Tell them that they should use the graph on the first page for both questions on that page and the chart on the second page for all of the questions on that page.

- After students have completed the Common Core Practice problems, review and discuss correct answers.

SOLUTIONS

1 *Solution:* **D**; Blonde − 3, Red − 1 **(DOK 1)**

2 *Solution:* **a.** False, Black = 4, Brown = 5; **b.** False, Brown = 5, Black + Blonde + Red = 8; **c.** True, 3 − 1 = 2; **d.** True, 3 + 5 = 8. **(DOK 2)**

3 *Solution:* Missing label: Cloudy; 3 sunny and 3 cloudy, pictures drawn. **(DOK 1)**

4 *Solution:* sunny, cloudy, 2, rainy **(DOK 2)**

©Curriculum Associates, LLC   Copying is not permitted.

Assessment and Remediation

- Show students a tally chart containing information about glasses of lemonade flavors sold at a lemonade stand: 6 strawberry, 5 pink, 9 regular, 5 kiwi. Have them make a bar graph to display the data including labels and a title.

- For students who are still struggling, use the chart below to guide remediation.

- After providing remediation, check students' understanding by changing the numbers and/or flavors used on the lemonade stand chart asking students to create a graph using the new data.

If the error is . . .	Students may . . .	To remediate . . .
The bar does not correspond to the number of glasses sold	not understand how to create a scale.	Provide students with paper squares. Have them use one-to-one correspondence to display the data. Remind them that each square represents one glass so all the numbered intervals need to be the same distance apart.
Labels are missing or inaccurate	not recognize the importance of appropriate labels or know how to write them.	Ask the students to describe in words what the scale and categories represent. Have students write their description in the appropriate position on the graph. Discuss how someone who hasn't seen the data would not know what the numbers or bars mean if they are not labeled.

Hands-On Activity

Organize and display data.

Materials: concrete objects to sort and graph such as 4 different shapes of dry pasta, 4 different colors of buttons or beads, etc.; 4 different colors of 1-inch squares (Activity Sheet 3, page 310); plain white paper

- Provide each student with a small cupful of objects and ask them to sort them.

- Demonstrate and have students count and record the number of each group in a table.

- Show students how to fold the paper into 4 sections the long way. Have them write a label at the bottom of each section.

- Tell students to use a ruler to mark 1-inch intervals along the left side of the paper.

- Have students use the paper squares to create a bar graph on the paper and add a title.

Challenge Activity

Collect and display data.

Challenge students to collect data that can be organized in a picture or bar graph. You may want to help them with survey ideas such as favorite game or favorite type of playground equipment.

They must:

- collect the data.

- organize the data in a tally chart and/or table.

- display the data in a graph.

- tell how they (or someone else) might use the data to make a decision.

Lesson 24 (Student Book pages 202–209)

Tell and Write Time

LESSON OBJECTIVES

- Read time to the nearest 5-minute interval.
- Write time using proper notation.
- Show time on an analog clock using proper hand placement.
- Determine when a digital clock should read AM or PM.

PREREQUISITE SKILLS

- Tell and write time in hours and half hours.
- Skip count by 5s and 10s.
- Understand concept of half.

VOCABULARY

There is no new vocabulary. You may want to review the terms:

THE LEARNING PROGRESSION

In Grade 1, students explore time by reading an analog and digital clock telling time in hours and half hours. They write time using a colon to separate the hours and minutes.

In Grade 2, students expand on their understanding of time and reading a clock as they explore duration and passage of time. **In this lesson,** students read an analog and digital clock to the nearest 5 minutes. They recognize the structure of an analog clock that enables them to use skip counting to read or place the minute hand. Students differentiate between and draw clock hands to indicate the time is between two hours and to show the number of minutes that have passed. Students explore the concept of AM and PM and determine when an event occurs in an AM or PM time.

In Grade 3, students tell time with increased precision to the nearest minute. They read and solve problems involving intervals between two times. Students expand their ability to read minutes by reading the minutes shown on a clock as the minutes that follow an hour or as the number of minutes before the next hour.

Ready *Teacher Toolbox*   *Teacher-Toolbox.com*

	Prerequisite Skills	*2.MD.C.7, 2.NBT.A.2*
Ready Lessons	✓	✓
Tools for Instruction	✓ ✓	✓
Interactive Tutorials	✓	✓ ✓

CCSS Focus

2.MD.C.7 Tell and write time from analog and digital clocks to the nearest five minutes, using AM and PM.

2.NBT.A.2 Count within 1000; skip count by 5s, 10s, and 100s.

STANDARDS FOR MATHEMATICAL PRACTICE: SMP 2, 3, 7, 8 *(see page A9 for full text)*

©Curriculum Associates, LLC   Copying is not permitted.

Time Relationships

Objective: Understand concept of time relationships.	**Materials for each student:** • none

Overview

Students explore the concept of a minute and relate it to an hour. They relate time to activities in their lives.

Step by Step (15–20 minutes)

1 Explore one minute.

- Have students put their heads on their desks and close their eyes. Tell them to stay in that position for one minute and when they think one minute has expired, put up a thumb for you to see.

- After one minute, have students put up their heads and discuss if they thought one minute was a long time or a short time and why. Ask when one minute might *seem* like a long time (waiting for something like your turn or a friend to come over) and when a minute seems like a short time (playing a fun game).

2 Explore one hour.

- Ask: *How long is one hour?* [Some may respond: a long time; longer than a minute; 60 minutes; etc.]

- Write the headings: *Longer than one hour* and *Less than one hour* on the board.

- Have students generate ideas of activities in their lives that last longer than one hour and shorter than one hour. For example: recess, lunch, reading a book, playing a game, and going home after school take less than one hour; Watching a movie or a sporting event, driving to grandma's house or to a vacation spot, or playing a game of baseball might take longer than one hour. As students list, write their ideas on the board.

3 Using a clock to tell time.

- Ask the class how they know an activity takes longer than an hour or less than an hour. They should respond that they can watch the clock.

- Show the students an analog and a digital clock or watch and tell them that this lesson will help them tell time.

©Curriculum Associates, LLC   Copying is not permitted.

AT A GLANCE

Students read the time shown on an analog clock by analyzing the placement of the two hands.

STEP BY STEP

• Read the problem at the top of the page.

• Use the Hands-On Activity to help students make sense of reading an analog clock.

• Point out the time notation used in parts C and D.

• Complete Explore It as a class.

Hands-On Activity

Make an analog clock

Materials: a paper plate, 1/4 × 4 inch and 1/4 × 2 inch tag board, and a brad fastener for each student

• Have students gently fold the paper plate in half and in half again. Tell them to write 12, 6, 3, 9 in the appropriate places. Fill in the remainder of the numbers.

• Have students cut a tip at one end of each cardboard "hand". Fasten the hands to the center of the plate with the fastener: long hand on top of the short hand. (You may need to use a thick needle to start the hole.)

• Demonstrate and have students follow showing 4 o'clock on their clocks.

• Ask: *What does the long hand have to do to get to 5 o'clock?* [Move all the way around the clock back to the 12] Remind students that while the minute hand is moving the hour hand is also moving very slowly towards the five.

• Have students move the minute hand to the six and ask how far around the clock it has moved. [half way] Ask: *How far do you think the hour hand should move?* [Halfway to the 5]. Have them model the time 4:30.

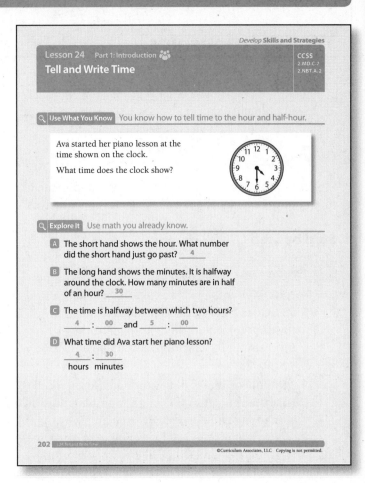

202   L24: Tell and Write Time   ©Curriculum Associates, LLC   Copying is not permitted.

Real-World Connection

• Ask: *When might it be important to know what time it is on a clock?*

  Discuss how it is important to know when it is time for recess, when you are supposed to be ready to go to your ballgame, etc. Encourage students to generate ideas of their own.

• Ask: *What might happen if you don't know how to read a clock?*

  Students may share experiences when they were late for an event, or didn't go home when they were supposed to because they didn't know what time it was.

©Curriculum Associates, LLC   Copying is not permitted.

AT A GLANCE

Students explore reading time and skip count by 5s to count minutes on an analog clock.

STEP BY STEP

- Read Find Out More as a class.

- Ask students how many little tick marks they see between each number on the clock shown. Have them add the tick marks to the clocks they made.

- Ask students what they think each of the marks shows. Ask how many minutes are between each number. [5] Say: *I don't get it! There are only 4 marks, how can there be 5 minutes?* [Students should respond that you count the spaces, not the marks; or that the last mark you count is the next number.] Make sure students understand that the interval indicates the minute, not the mark itself.

- Ask: *Why is the hour hand going toward the 5 and not the 4 when it is 4:30?* Students should remember that the hour hand moves slowly as the minute hand moves. Show this movement with a demonstration clock, if available.

- Ask the Mathematical Discourse question.

- Write 7:30 on the board. Have students model the time on their clocks. Ask students to justify why they modeled it the way they did. Then ask them to read the time out loud.

- Have students discuss the Reflect question and then write about it in their own words. Encourage students to use their clocks to count around the clock.

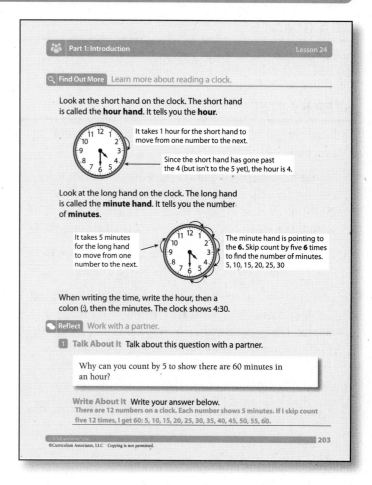

Mathematical Discourse

- *Is it possible for a clock to read 5:75? Explain.*

  Students should respond that it is not possible. A clock is divided into 60 minutes. It keeps starting over once it gets to 60 minutes.

SMP Tip: Sketch a clock on the board and draw curved lines (jumps) to each number emphasizing that the spaces or intervals on the clock that are between each number are what are being counted, not the number itself. Discuss how the structure of a clock enables us to read it easily, using counting strategies. *(SMP 7)*

©Curriculum Associates, LLC   Copying is not permitted.

AT A GLANCE

Students relate time shown on an analog clock to a digital clock.

STEP BY STEP

- Read the problem at the top of the page together as a class.

- In the first Picture It, make sure students can read the 4 intervals past 7 o'clock indicating the time is 20 minutes past 7. Have them recall the two ways of saying the time 7:20: 7 twenty or 20 minutes past 7.

- Direct students' attention to the second Picture It. Ask the first Mathematical Discourse question.

- Direct attention to the AM, PM notation on the digital clock and ask students if they know what that means. Discuss how they know when it is morning or afternoon. For those who do not, tell them that the AM and PM come from a foreign language and mean it is morning or afternoon. Tell them they can think of PM as "**P**ast **M**orning" so AM is in the morning.

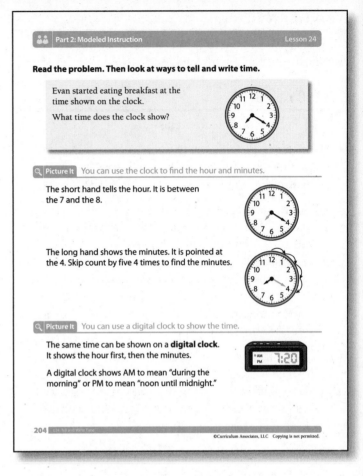

Concept Extension

- Show students a demonstration clock with the hands positioned at 4:59. Write 4:59 on the board.

- Ask: *What time will it be when the hand moves one more minute?* [5:00] Write 5:00 on the board.

- Write 29 on the board. Ask students to describe what happens when one more is added. They should remember that the ones are grouped into another ten making the number 30.

- Discuss how working with time is similar. One minute after :59 is the next hour, :00.

Mathematical Discourse

- *How is a digital clock like an analog clock and how are they different?*

  Students may respond that the digital clock shows the time like an analog clock, but it shows it the way we write the time instead of with hands.

- *When might a digital clock be more helpful than an analog clock?*

  Students should share situations when it is easier to read the clock or times when it is important to know when it is morning or afternoon. They should note that the digital clock tells you when it is morning or afternoon, but the analog clock does not.

©Curriculum Associates, LLC   Copying is not permitted.

AT A GLANCE

Students revisit the problem on page 212, reading and analyzing time on an analog and digital clock.

STEP BY STEP

- Read Connect It as a class. Make sure students understand that the questions refer to the problem on page 204.

- Have students model with the clocks they made the time Evan started and ended breakfast. Ask students what tells them that they are still in the 7 o'clock hour. They should notice that the hour hand is still between 7 and 8 so it is still past 7 not past 8 o'clock.

- Once completed, you may want to use the Concept Extension to engage students in using the intervals to determine how much time has expired between two events.

- Tell students to complete the Try It problem on their own. Discuss their representations to ensure they all understand how to show time on both an analog and digital clock.

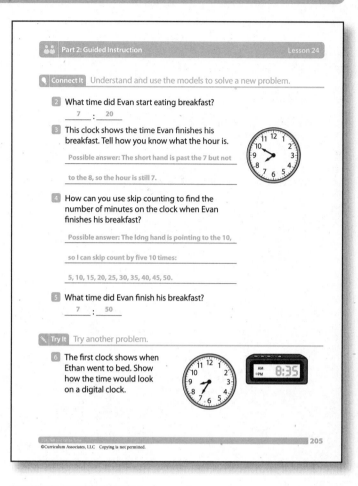

Concept Extension

Explore concept of expired time.

- Challenge students to determine the amount of time it took Evan to eat breakfast.

  Allow students to work in groups to find out how much time it took for Evan to eat. Encourage them to use the clocks they made, or pictures of analog clocks to help them.

- Ask: *Is it easier to figure this problem out using an analog or digital clock? Why?*

  Students may respond that the analog is easier since intervals can be counted. There are no intervals to count on the digital clock. Some students may say the digital because they can count by tens from 20 to 50.

TRY IT SOLUTION

6 *Solution:* The digital clock should show 8:35 PM. *(DOK 1)*

ERROR ALERT: Watch for students who may display 9:35 seeing the 9 as the hour the short hand is moving towards.

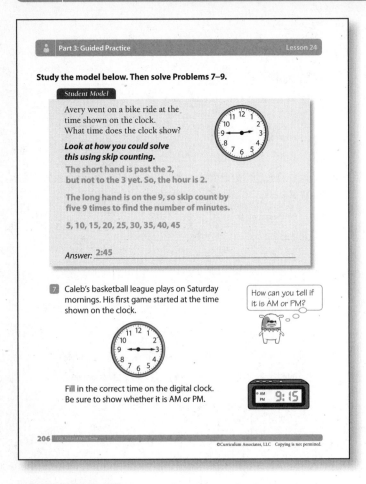

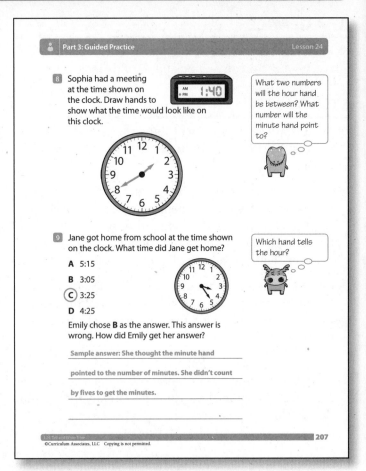

AT A GLANCE

Students show time on analog and digital clocks.

STEP BY STEP

- Ask students to solve the problems independently. Tell them they will use what they learned about telling time during this lesson to complete the problems.

- For Problem 8, remind students that the long hand shows the minutes and the short hand tells the hour. Watch to make sure they all represent the time with hands in the proper position.

- When students have completed each problem, have them Pair/Share to discuss their solutions with a partner.

SOLUTIONS

Ex Analyze that the time is between the hours of 2 and 3 and skip count the minutes to find 45 minutes past the hour of 2.

7 *Answer:* 9:15 AM. The hour is between 9 and 10 and the minute hand is on the 3. Since it is morning, it is AM. **(DOK 1)**

8 *Answer:* The hour hand should be a little more than halfway between the 1 and 2 and the minute hand is on the 8. **(DOK 1)**

9 *Answer:* C: 3:25

Explain to students why the other two choices are not correct:

A is not correct because the hour hand (short hand) is between 3 and 4.

D is not correct because the hour hand is between 3 and 4 so the hour is still 3. **(DOK 3)**

©Curriculum Associates, LLC   Copying is not permitted.

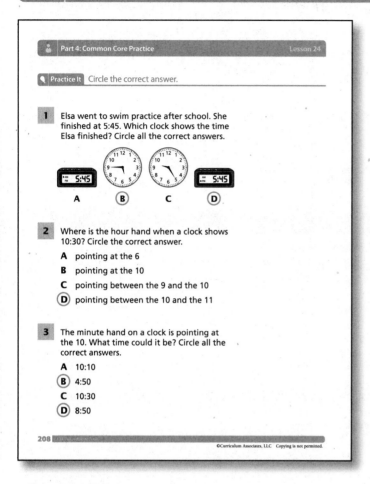

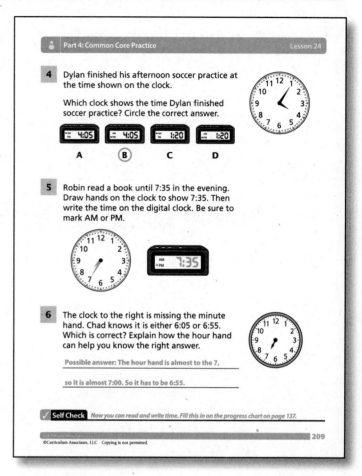

AT A GLANCE

Students use concepts of telling time that might appear on a mathematics test.

STEP BY STEP

- First, tell students they will use what they know about telling time to complete the problems on the next two pages.

- After students have completed the Common Core Practice problems, review and discuss correct answers.

SOLUTIONS

1 *Solutions:* **B**, **D**; The hour hand is between the 5 and 6, the minute hand is at the 9 and it is in the afternoon so it is PM. (*DOK 2*)

2 *Solution:* **D**. (*DOK 1*)

3 *Solutions:* **B** and **D**; The minute hand would denote 50 minutes past an hour. (*DOK 2*)

4 *Solution:* **B**; The clock shows 5 minutes past 4 and is in the afternoon. (*DOK 2*)

5 *Solution:* The analog clock should show the hour between 7 and 8 and the minute hand is on the 7. Digital clock should show 7:35 PM. (*DOK 2*)

6 *Solution:* The hour hand tells if it is closer to 6 o'clock or to 7 o'clock. Since it is closer to 7 o'clock, the minutes must be 55 since that is almost the next hour. (*DOK 2*)

©Curriculum Associates, LLC   Copying is not permitted.

Assessment and Remediation

- Tell students the long hand on the clock is pointing at the 10 and the short hand is between the 3 and the 4. Ask: *What time is it?* [3:50] Show it on a digital clock. [check for accuracy]

- For students who are still struggling, use the chart below to guide remediation.

- After providing remediation, check students' understanding using the following problem:

Display the time 4:15 on a digital clock. Have students say the time and show it on an analog clock face. [hour hand just after the 4, minute hand on the 3]

If the error is . . .	Students may . . .	To remediate . . .
10:15	have read the minute hand as the hour and the hour hand as the minutes.	Show students an analog clock. Ask which hand moves faster than the other. Ask if hours or minutes go by faster. Lead them to see that the short hand displays the hour.
3:10	have read the number on the clock face as the minutes.	Show students an analog clock. Ask how many minutes are in an hour. Model how 60 minutes are counted as the minute hand moves around the clock.
Any other answer	have misinterpreted the hour or misread the minutes.	Tell students to show the time on a demonstration analog clock. Point out the placement of the hour hand and count the minutes together.

Hands-On Activity

Materials: a student-made clock, paper divided to replicate a digital screen, and digit and AM PM cards (Activity Sheet 14, pages 322–323; or blank paper squares for students to make their own cards) for each pair

- Have students work in pairs.

- One of the student pairs shows a time on the analog clock (make sure the student knows what is shown) and tells what might be happening at that time (it should be evident whether it is morning or afternoon/evening.)

- The partner uses the digit cards, or writes digits on paper squares to place on the digital clock showing the time including AM or PM.

- Students analyze whether the digital clock is correct, say the time and switch roles.

Challenge Activity

- Challenge students to search on the computer or in the library to find out about how people told time long ago.

- Give them a list of time-keeping devices including: hour glass, sundial, obelisk, candle clock, time stick.

- Have students:

  - learn everything they can about the timepiece.

  - print a picture to display.

  - report to the class explaining how the device was used to tell time.

©Curriculum Associates, LLC   Copying is not permitted.

Lesson 25 (Student Book pages 210–219)

Solve Word Problems Involving Money

LESSON OBJECTIVES

- Recognize and name the coins penny, nickel, dime, and quarter.
- Know the value of coins and paper denominations.
- Count the amount of money represented by a set of coins or bills.

PREREQUISITE SKILLS

- Count by 5s, 10s, 20s, and 25s.
- Fluently add within 100.

VOCABULARY

There is no new vocabulary.

THE LEARNING PROGRESSION

In Grade 1, students do not formally explore money concepts, however may informally have experiences with coins and their values.

In Grade 2, students explore concepts of money including coins and denominations of bills. **In this lesson,** students recognize, name, and count the values of pennies, nickels, dimes, and quarters. They combine coins to equal the value of other coins, determine the coins needed to equal one dollar, and use notation to label dollars and cents. Students use counting strategies to find the value of a set of bills in denominations of $5, $10, $20, $50, and $100.

In Grade 3 and beyond, students will solve problems involving money. They recognize that coins represent a fraction of a dollar and use the decimal point to separate dollars from cents.

▪Ready *Teacher Toolbox*		Teacher-Toolbox.com
	Prerequisite Skills	*2.MD.C.8 2.NBT.A.2*
Ready Lessons		✓
Tools for Instruction	✓	✓ ✓
Interactive Tutorials	✓	✓

CCSS Focus

2.MD.C.8 Solve word problems involving dollar bills, quarters, dimes, nickels, and pennies, using $ and ¢ symbols appropriately. Example: If you have 2 dimes and 3 pennies, how many cents do you have?

2.NBT.A.2 Count within 1000; skip-count by 5s, 10s and 100s.

STANDARDS FOR MATHEMATICAL PRACTICE: **SMP 1, 2, 3, 4, 6, 7, 8** (*see page A9 for full text*)

Add on a Hundreds Chart

Objective: Explore strategies for adding on a 1–100 chart.	**Materials for each student:** • hundreds chart (Activity Sheet 2, page 309) • one counter

Overview

Students add groups of 1, 5, 10, and 25. They devise, share, and analyze strategies that will prepare them to add coin values.

Step by Step (15–20 minutes)

1 Add tens on the hundreds chart.

- Provide students with a hundreds chart and a counter.

- Write 10 + 10 on the board and have students show and describe how they would perform the addition on the chart. They should place the counter on 10 and then move down one row to the 20.

- Write 25 + 10 on the board and ask students to model and describe how they would perform the addition on the board. The counter starts on 25 and jumps down one row to 35.

- Discuss adding ten on a hundreds chart. If necessary, have children model several more additions of ten to solidify the concept. Have students start at 15, add 3 tens and describe their actions.

2 Add a series of numbers.

- Write 5 + 10 + 10 + 1 + 1 + 5 on the board and have students model the addition on the hundreds chart, moving the counter to the proper position for every number they add on.

- Discuss the ways in which students performed the addition on the chart. Some students may have grouped the tens, the fives, and the ones to add. Some may have combined the two fives to make a ten to add.

- Write 5 + 10 + 1 + 1 + 25 + 1 + 5 + 25 on the board and allow students to model on the hundreds chart. (For those who prefer to calculate in their head, tell them that modeling may help them with the lesson and ask that they show on the chart what they thought about in their head.)

3 Share strategies.

- Discuss strategies. Make sure a variety of strategies are shared with the class. Ask questions like: *Why did you do that? How did that help you find the sum? Is there another way of thinking of the addition? How might you combine numbers differently?*

4 Relate the problem situation to money.

- Discuss how the numbers they added on the chart are like the values of coins. Tell them that this lesson will help them count money.

Note: You may want to refer to or allow students to use the hundreds chart to aid in counting coins during this lesson.

©Curriculum Associates, LLC   Copying is not permitted.

AT A GLANCE

Students explore and count the value of the coins penny, nickel, and dime.

STEP BY STEP

- Read the problem at the top of the page together.

* Ask students what they notice about each group of coins. Discuss that each coin has a front and a back. You may want to display real coins, flipping them around for students to see that they are still the same coin regardless of the side that is shown.

- Work through Explore It as a class. Make sure students understand that they are counting the value of each coin. You may want to practice counting by 5s and 10s before completing the tasks.

- Ask the Mathematical Discourse question. This connection will be valuable when they learn to represent dollars and cents using a decimal point.

- Say: *Susan says the coins are confusing. A nickel is bigger than a dime, but it is only 5 cents and a dime is 10 cents. Shouldn't the bigger coin be worth more?* Discuss this situation with students. You may want to use an analogy such as jewelry. If you have a diamond ring or other jewelry containing a diamond, display it along with a cut glass gem. Discuss that although the diamond is much smaller than the cut glass, it is worth more because it is harder to find. Tell students that a dime is made of silver which is more precious than nickel, so a smaller amount is worth more.

ELL Support

Discuss how the money used in the child's native culture compares to ours. If possible, correlate their money to ours, such as peso = 1; penny = 1.

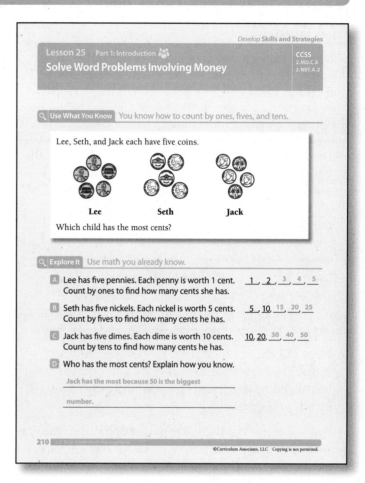

Mathematical Discourse

- *How is finding the value of coins like using base blocks?*

  When finding how much hundred flats, ten rods, and ones are, you don't only count how many of each block you have, but you count by 100s, 10s, and 1s to find the total value.

SMP Tip: Show students a base ten flat, rod and unit. Place a penny, dime and dollar below each block. Ask students to tell how many pennies make a dime and how many dimes make a dollar and how the base blocks can help them decide. Discuss the similarities in the structure of money and our base ten system of numeration. This structure will be used in later grades when the decimal point separates dollars and cents. *(SMP 7)*

AT A GLANCE

Students examine the value of coins and bill denominations and the notation used to represent dollars and cents.

STEP BY STEP

- Draw attention to the chart in Find Out More. Point out that each coin has a distinct front and back. You may want to show the class special coins such as buffalo head nickels and state quarters, reminding them that even though the image on them is different the value is the same.

> **SMP Tip:** Use the Visual Model to help students make sense of the relationships among the values of coins and find ways of combining them. *(SMP 2)*

- Point out the notation used to show dollars and cents. You may want to model the signs on the board and have students practice drawing them on white boards.

- Draw attention to the value of one dollar in cents. Ask: *How many nickels do you think it takes to make a dollar? How many dimes? How many quarters?*

  Allow students to discuss and/or model each situation. Ask the Mathematical Discourse question.

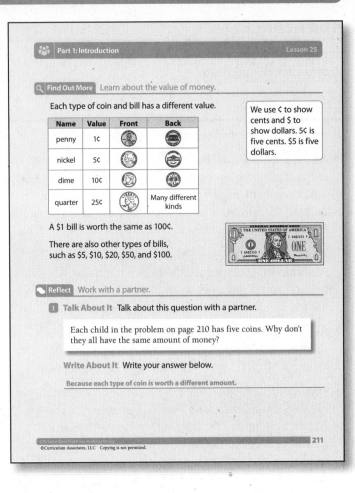

Visual Model

Make a table.

- Have student pairs divide a piece of paper into 4 vertical sections. They should trace the creases and label the sections: 25¢, 10¢, 5¢, and 1¢. If available, give each pair a set of play coins for modeling.

- Tell students to find as many ways as possible to make 25¢. They record in the columns the number of each coin used, separating each row with a line.

- Have students compare lists. Point out any groups that organized their lists and discuss how that can aid in finding all the combinations.

Mathematical Discourse

- *Why does it take more dimes to make a dollar than it does quarters?*

  Listen for responses that indicate that students recognize that since a dime is worth less than a quarter, it takes more of them to equal a dollar.

- *How does knowing that 1 dollar is 100 cents help you to know how many cents are in 2 dollars or 5 dollars or any number of dollars?*

  Students may make the connection to base ten models. Since one flat equals 100 units, 2 flats equal 200 units and 5 flats equal 500 units. Money is the same. Since one dollar equals 100 pennies, the number of dollars is that number of a hundred pennies.

©Curriculum Associates, LLC   Copying is not permitted.

AT A GLANCE

Students use counting strategies and a bar model to determine the value of a set of coins.

STEP BY STEP

- Read the problem at the top of the page as a class. Ask students to identify each coin shown and tell its value.

- Draw students' attention to Picture It. Ask them to describe what the picture shows.

- Have students write the value of each coin below it. Discuss how they might use counting strategies to count Erik's money.

- Examine the bar model in Model It. Ask students how the size of each section of the bar relates to the coin it represents. They should notice that the 10 sections are twice as long as the 5 sections and 10 times as long as the 1 sections.

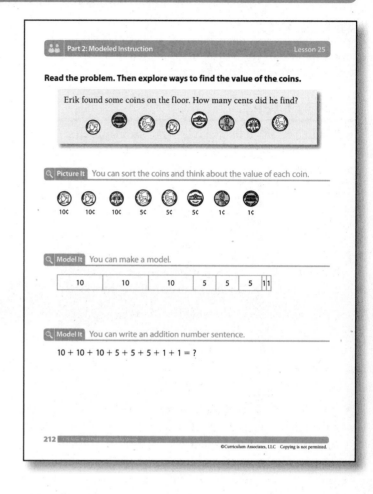

Hands-On Activity

Materials: A bag of play money and cards with money amounts less than one dollar written on them for each student pair (Activity Sheet 15, page 324)

- Give students the play money and money cards. Tell them to place the cards face down on the table/desk.

- Students turn a card face up and use the money to represent the amount of money in at least 2 different ways.

- Have students record on paper the amount shown on the card and the coins they used.

- You may want students to share solutions with the class discussing the varied ways of organizing the coins.

Mathematical Discourse

- *How is the bar model shown in Model It like the coins in Picture It?*

  The bar model shows tens, fives, and ones that are like the 10¢, 5¢, and 1¢ coins.

©Curriculum Associates, LLC   Copying is not permitted.

AT A GLANCE

Students revisit the problem on page 212 by using counting strategies to determine the value of the coins.

STEP BY STEP

- Read Connect It as a class. Make sure students understand that the questions refer to the problem on page 212.

- For Problem 2, make sure students understand that they are to write the cumulative total under each coin to demonstrate a counting-on strategy.

- Ask: *How does organizing coins help you to count them?* [Students may respond it is easier to keep track of where you're at if you count using big numbers first.]

- Draw attention to the way the coins are grouped in Problem 2. Ask: *Does it matter how you group the coins to count them? Explain.* [Students should recognize that neither the order nor the way coins are grouped affect the total value.]

- Have students complete Problem 4 using open circles with values written inside for coins. Share and count solutions together to check for accuracy. Encourage students to give reasons for coin selection. Some may have substituted two nickels for a dime, or two dimes and a nickel for a quarter, etc. Help students clearly articulate their reasoning, articulating the organizational strategy that was used.

- Say: *I notice that all the ways to make 47¢ have at least 2 pennies. Is it possible to make 47¢ with fewer than 2 pennies? Explain.* [Students should notice that the only way to make 7¢ is with 7 pennies or a nickel and 2 pennies.]

- Read Try It together and have students complete the problem independently. Discuss solutions counting each one to ensure 85¢ is displayed.

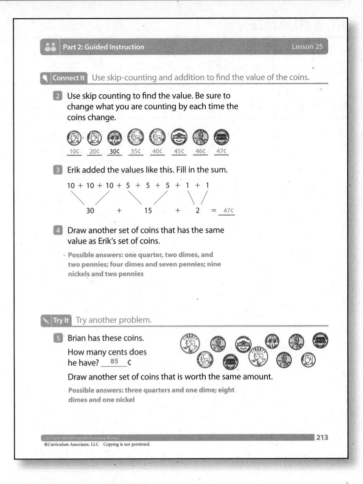

TRY IT SOLUTION

5 *Solution:* 85 cents; Solutions will vary. Possible solutions include: 3 quarters and 1 dime; 8 dimes and 1 nickel; 2 quarters, 3 dimes, and 1 nickel. **(DOK 2)**

ERROR ALERT: Check students' drawings for accuracy.

Note: Students may need extensive practice counting sets of coins. Have play coins available for students to handle and count. You may want to allow them to use a 1–100 chart for the development of visual strategies.

©Curriculum Associates, LLC   Copying is not permitted.

AT A GLANCE

Students solve a word problem involving denominations of bills using a tape diagram and open number line.

STEP BY STEP

- Read the problem at the top of the page as a class. Ask students to describe the problem and explain what they need to find out.

- Ask students to examine the tape diagram in Model It. Ask: *What does the tape model in the second picture remind you of?* [a number bond]. Ask the first Mathematical Discourse question. Discuss how the number bond indicates that a part is missing. Ask: *What number sentences could we write to find the missing part?* [45 + ? = 100; 100 − 45 = ?]

- Have students examine the open number lines and describe what they are showing. Ask the second Mathematical Discourse question.

- Use the Hands-On Activity to provide students another alternative for counting bills.

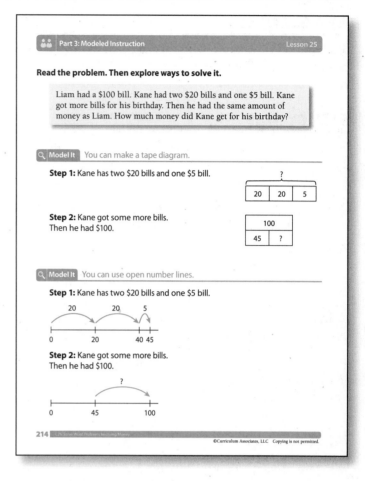

Hands-On Activity

Materials: 10 × 10 grid and colored pencils or crayons for each student

- Ask: *If one of the small squares on the grid is one dollar, what might represent a ten dollar bill?* [a row or column of 10 squares.] *A five dollar bill?* [half of a row of ten or a group of 5 squares] *A twenty dollar bill?* [two rows of ten]

- Show students how to trace around two rows of ten and color them in to represent a $20 bill. Have them write 20 in that block. Then repeat for a group of 5.

- Ask students how they could use the grid to find the amount of money needed to get to $100. Discuss the various strategies students may use to calculate.

Mathematical Discourse

- *Why is the whole 100?*

  Lian has $100. Cade is supposed to get as much as Lian. The total he is supposed to get is $100.

- *How are the tape model, open number line alike?*

  They both show that you first add what Cade has. He has $45. Since he is supposed to get to $100, the missing part in each model shows how much more he needs to get from 45 to 100.

AT A GLANCE

Students revisit the problem on page 214, writing number sentences and determining the bills needed to represent the solution.

STEP BY STEP

- Tell students that Connect It will help them learn how to write number sentences for the problem on page 214.

- Work through the problems together. Note that in Problem 7 the addends may be ordered in any way.

- For Problem 10, remind students that subtraction is one way to solve. Ask if they prefer to use addition or subtraction and why. For some students counting up may make more sense or be easier to think about. Remind them how they learned to use that strategy, even when the operation shown is subtraction.

- Have students draw open rectangles with the denomination written in each one to represent the bills in Problem 11.

Mathematical Discourse

- *Jordan says, "I have 9 bills and Trina only has 3 bills, so I have more money. Is Jordan right?*

  Students should note that 9 − 3 = 6. They should realize that Jordan just subtracted the two numbers shown without paying attention to the value of the bills.

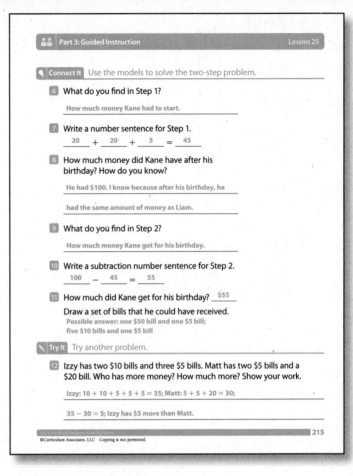

Part 3: Guided Instruction — Lesson 25

Connect It Use the models to solve the two-step problem.

6 **What do you find in Step 1?**

How much money Kane had to start.

7 **Write a number sentence for Step 1.**

20 + 20 + 5 = 45

8 **How much money did Kane have after his birthday? How do you know?**

He had $100. I know because after his birthday, he

had the same amount of money as Liam.

9 **What do you find in Step 2?**

How much money Kane got for his birthday.

10 **Write a subtraction number sentence for Step 2.**

100 − 45 = 55

11 **How much did Kane get for his birthday?** $55

Draw a set of bills that he could have received.
Possible answer: one $50 bill and one $5 bill;
five $10 bills and one $5 bill

Try It Try another problem.

12 Izzy has two $10 bills and three $5 bills. Matt has two $5 bills and a $20 bill. Who has more money? How much more? Show your work.

Izzy: 10 + 10 + 5 + 5 + 5 = 35; Matt: 5 + 5 + 20 = 30;

35 − 30 = 5; Izzy has $5 more than Matt.

L25: Solve Word Problems Involving Money · 215
©Curriculum Associates, LLC   Copying is not permitted.

TRY IT SOLUTION

12 *Solution:* Izzy has more: 10 + 10 + 5 + 5 + 5 = 35; 20 + 5 + 5 = 30. **(DOK 2)**

SMP Tip: Discuss with students the importance of accurate calculations in counting money and how failure to count correctly can negatively affect them. Have students discuss situations where not counting accurately can pose a problem such as: planning to purchase something and finding at the checkout stand that you don't have enough money. *(SMP 6)*

©Curriculum Associates, LLC   Copying is not permitted.

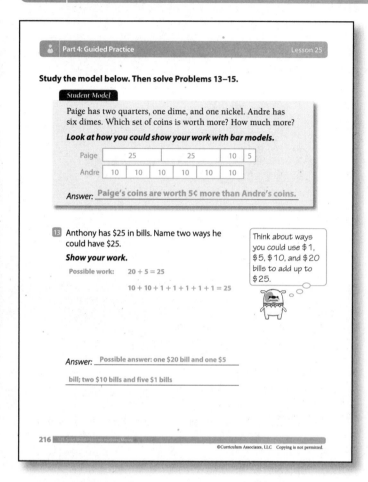

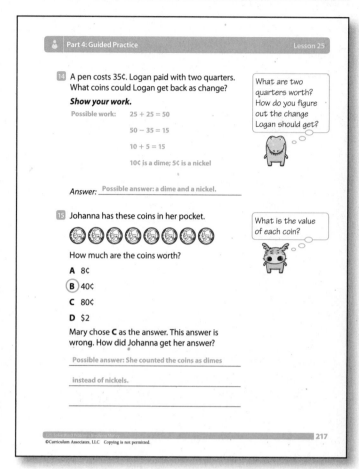

AT A GLANCE

Students solve problems involving coins and bills.

STEP BY STEP

- Ask students to solve the problems individually and show all their work, including the number sentences they wrote.

- In the sample problem, students may notice that the bar model clearly shows a difference of 5¢. Have them also write a subtraction that could be used to solve this problem.

- Problem 14 refers to "getting change." Discuss with students that you may not always have the exact amount of money to pay for an item. When you give the store clerk too much, they give you back the difference between the cost and what you gave them.

- When students have completed each problem, have them Pair/Share to discuss their solutions with a partner.

SOLUTIONS

Ex A bar model is shown representing the problem situation. Students should write the subtraction $65 - 60 = 5$ to model the situation.

13 *Solution:* Possible answers: $20 + 5$; $10 + 10 + 5$; $20 + 1 + 1 + 1 + 1 + 1$; $10 + 5 + 5 + 5$. (**DOK 2**)

14 *Solution:* Possible answer: a dime and a nickel; $25 + 25 = 50$, $50 - 35 = 15$, $10 + 5 = 15$. (**DOK 2**)

15 *Solution:* **B**; eight groups of 5 is 40.

Explain to students why the other two choices are not correct:

A is not correct because 8 represents the number of coins, not their value.

D is not correct because a nickel is 5 cents, not 25 cents. (**DOK 3**)

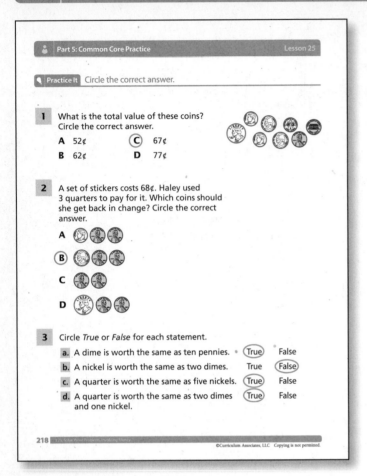

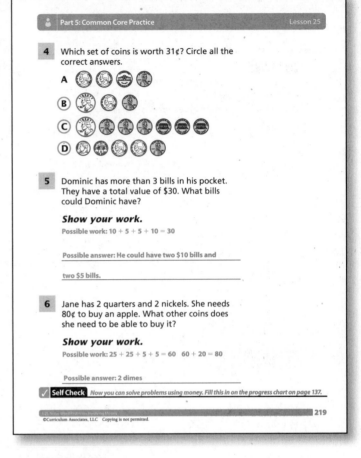

AT A GLANCE

Students find the value of a set of coins or bills that may appear on a mathematics test.

STEP BY STEP

- First, tell students they will count coins or bills to solve problems. Then have students read the directions and answer the questions independently.

- In the first question, encourage students to cross out the coins as they count to aid in keeping track of what has been counted.

- Make sure students read Problem 5 carefully to note that Dominic has **more than** 3 bills. There are sets of 2 or 3 bills whose sum is 30, but the problem asks for more than that so those would not be correct.

- After students have completed the Common Core Practice problems, review and discuss correct answers.

SOLUTIONS

1 *Solution:* **C**; $25 + 10 + 10 + 10 + 5 + 5 + 1 + 1 = 67$. **(DOK 2)**

2 *Solution:* **B**; $75 - 68 = 7, 5 + 2 = 7$. **(DOK 2)**

3 *Solution:* **a.** True; **b.** False, a nickel is worth 5 pennies; **c.** True; **d.** True **(DOK 2)**

4 *Solution:* **B, C, D**; $25 + 5 + 1 = 31$ (**B**); $25 + 6 = 31$ (**C**); $10 + 10 + 5 + 5 + 1 = 31$ (**D**). **(DOK 2)**

5 *Solution:* Possible answers: $10 + 10 + 5 + 5$; $10 + 5 + 5 + 5 + 5$; $10 + 10 + 5 + 1 + 1 + 1 + 1 + 1$. **(DOK 2)**

6 *Solution:* Possible answers: 2 dimes; 1 dime, 2 nickels. **(DOK 2)**

©Curriculum Associates, LLC   Copying is not permitted.

Assessment and Remediation

- Jewel has 2 quarters, 2 dimes, 3 nickels, and 4 pennies in her purse. How much money does she have? [89¢]

- For students who are still struggling, use the chart below to guide remediation.

- After providing remediation, check students' understanding using the following problem: Tony counted 77¢. What coins might he have counted? [3 quarters, 2 pennies; 2 quarters, 2 dimes, 7 pennies; 2 quarters, 2 dimes, 1 nickel, 2 pennies, etc.]

If the error is . . .	Students may . . .	To remediate . . .
79¢	have calculated the quarters as 20¢ rather than 25¢.	Remind students that a quarter is 25¢ and have them calculate again.
11¢	have added the number of coins rather than their values.	Show students 2 flats, 3 rods, and 4 units from a set of base ten blocks. Ask the student if that shows a total of 9. Relate to values of coins. Review the value of each coin and help students count them.
any other number	have calculated the value of the coins incorrectly.	To assess the error, have the students show you how the coins were counted. If the error is simple calculation, have the student recount to find the error. If the error involves coin values and skip counting, provide more practice using a buddy to help the student.

Hands-On Activity

Race for a dollar.

Materials: a die and a bag of play coins for each student pair or group of three

- Have students take turns rolling the die and taking the amount of money matching the number on the die.

- On a player's turn, coins may be exchanged for a coin of greater value.

- Make sure all players monitor a player's exchanges to make sure they are accurate.

- Play continues until the value of a player's coins reaches one dollar. Have players count the coins together to make sure one dollar has been reached.

Challenge Activity

Making change.

Materials: a bag of play coins and one dollar bills, cards with various amounts of money less than one dollar written on them (Activity Sheet 15, page 324)

- Have students work in pairs.

- One student is the "cashier" and the other is the "customer."

- The customer gives the cashier a card with the cost of an item written on it and an amount of money that is not the correct change. The cashier counts back the change.

- Challenge students to find easy ways to count back the change. You may want them to record the strategies they use.

©Curriculum Associates, LLC   Copying is not permitted.

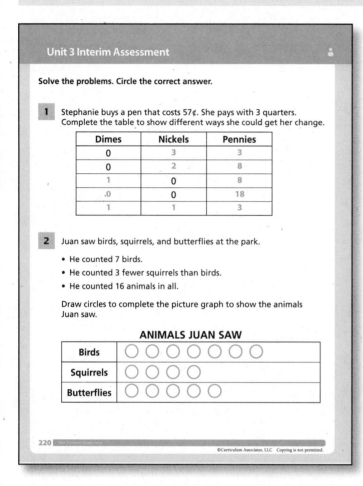

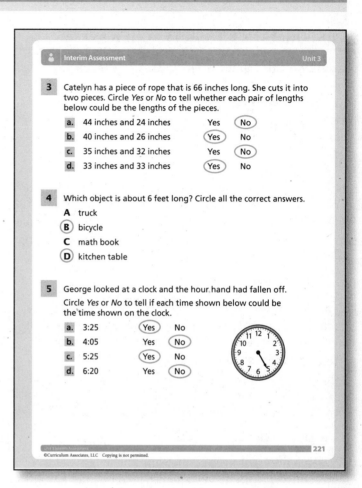

SCORING GUIDE AND ANSWER ANALYSIS

1 *Solution:* 3; 3; 2; 8; 1; 8; 0; 18; 1; 1; 3; Three quarters have a total value of 75¢; $75 - 57 = 18$; Rows should show coins with a total value of 18¢. **(DOK 2)**

2 *Solution:* 7 circles; 4 circles; 5 circles; Bird: 7; Squirrel: $7 - 3 = 4$; Butterfly: $16 - (7 + 4) = 5$ **(DOK 2)**

3 *Solution:* No; Yes; No; Yes; $44 + 24 = 68$ and $68 > 66$; $40 + 26 = 66$ and $66 = 66$; $35 + 32 = 67$ and $67 > 66$; $33 + 33 = 66$ and $66 = 66$ **(DOK 2)**

4 *Solution:* **B, D**; Correct objects are about 6 feet long: bicycle and kitchen table **(DOK 1)**

5 *Solution:* Yes; No; Yes; No; The minute hand is pointing to the 5, so the number of minutes after the hour is 25. The times 3:25 (**A**) and 5:25 (**C**) show 25 minutes after the hour. **(DOK 2)**

PERFORMANCE TASK TEACHER NOTES

Common Core Standards: 2.OA.A.1, 2.MD.A.1, 2. MD.A.2, 2.MD.A.4, 2.MD.D.9
Mathematical Practice Standards: SMP 2, 3, 4, 5, 6, 7
DOK: 3
Materials: inch and centimeter rulers

About the Task

Students measure the lengths of objects in both inches and centimeters and then display the data on a line plot. Students will use addition and subtraction to solve problems about the lengths and will explain measuring in different units.

Getting Started

Read the task out loud with your students. Review the table with students and point out the information that needs to be gathered to complete it. You may want to point out some sample objects for measurement and place some parameters on the objects students should measure. You could, for example, limit the lengths of objects to less than the length of one ruler. **(SMP 5)**

Completing the Task

Students first will need to measure the lengths of five objects using both inches and centimeters. Review with students how to use a ruler to measure the length of an object. Point out that the zero mark of the ruler should be placed at one end of the object and then students should find the whole unit mark nearest the other end of the object. Demonstrate the correct use of the ruler for students who are having trouble with it. Remind students that they will need to measure each object in both inches and centimeters. **(SMP 5)**

Once students have completed the table they will need to display the data in the line plot. Students should recognize that they first will need to label the scale of the line plot. Remind them that their scales may differ based on the lengths of the objects they measured. **(SMP 4)**

Students next will need to add the measures in both inches and centimeters to find the total lengths of the objects, and then compare the numbers. Encourage students first to compare the numbers in the table for each object. Students should recognize that each number of centimeters is greater than the corresponding number of inches. Guide students to think about the sizes of the units and how that might affect the numbers of inches and centimeters. **(SMP 2, 3, 6, 7)**

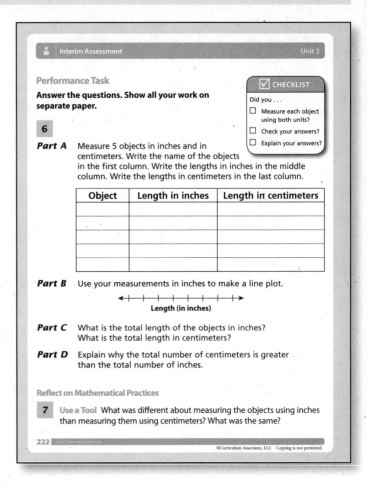

Extension

Have students try this problem:

Suppose you measured the lengths of the objects instead to the nearest foot and the nearest meter. How would that change the numbers in your table? How would it change your line plot? What does that tell you about which units are better to use when measuring those objects?

©Curriculum Associates, LLC   Copying is not permitted.

PERFORMANCE TASK SAMPLE RESPONSES AND RUBRIC

6 Sample 4-Point Solution

Part A Possible answer:

Object	Length in inches	Length in centimeters
Shoe	7	18
Pencil	6	15
Marker	5	13
Book	11	30
Pencil box	8	20

Part B Possible answer:

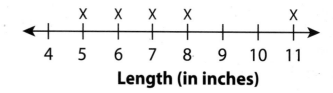

Part C Possible answers: 37 inches; 96 centimeters

Part D Possible explanation: Centimeters are smaller than inches, so the same length gives a greater number of centimeters than inches.

REFLECT ON MATHEMATICAL PRACTICES

7 Possible answer: The number of centimeters was greater than the number of inches; it was easier to find the nearest inch because inches are larger than centimeters. I measured the same way for both units—I lined up one end of the object with the zero mark and then found the nearest whole mark to the other end of the object.

SCORING RUBRIC

4 points The student's response is accurate and complete and all calculations are correct. The table of measures is complete, and all measures are correct. The line plot is complete and correct. All explanations are complete and correct and exhibit an understanding of measuring with different units.

3 points Student has completed the table, and all measures are correct. The line plot is correct and complete. Student has attempted all calculations with the lengths but has made limited minor errors. Explanations are correct, though some might not be complete.

2 points The table is not complete, or there are some incorrect measures. The line plot accurately reflects most of the data from the table. Student makes some errors in calculations. Responses show limited understanding of measuring with different units.

1 point The student's response contains an incorrect solution. The table is only partially correctly completed, and the student does not correctly complete the line plot or make calculations comparing lengths. Explanations are missing or incorrect.

SOLUTION TO THE EXTENSION

Possible explanation: All of the numbers in the middle column of the table would be either 0 or 1, and all of the numbers in the last column of the table would be 0. The line plot would have entries only for 0 and 1. It is better to use the smaller units of inches and centimeters because it tells more about the real lengths of the objects.

©Curriculum Associates, LLC   Copying is not permitted.

Which lessons are students building upon?

Grade 1, Lesson 26
Understand Shapes
1.G.A.1

Grade 1, Lesson 27
Understand Putting Shapes
Together
1.G.A.2

Grade 1, Lesson 26
Understand Shapes
1.G.A.1

Grade 1, Lesson 27
Understand Putting Shapes
Together
1.G.A.2

Grade 1, Lesson 26
Understand Shapes
1.G.A.1

Grade 1, Lesson 27
Understand Putting Shapes
Together
1.G.A.2

Grade 1, Lesson 28
Understand Breaking Shapes
into Parts
1.G.A.3

©Curriculum Associates, LLC   Copying is not permitted.

Unit 4

Which lessons are students preparing for?

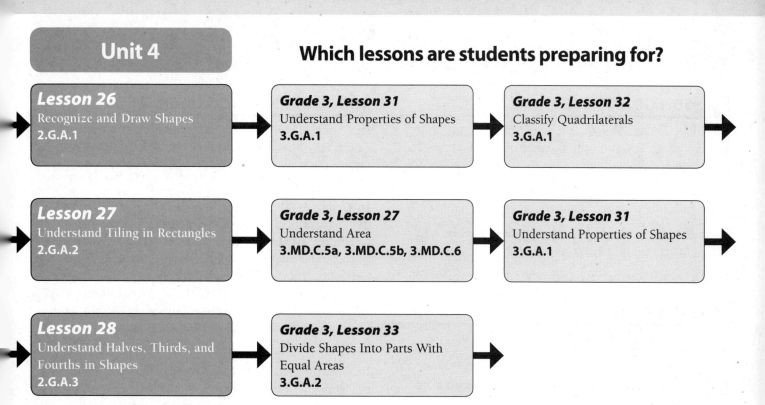

Lesson 26
Recognize and Draw Shapes
2.G.A.1

Grade 3, Lesson 31
Understand Properties of Shapes
3.G.A.1

Grade 3, Lesson 32
Classify Quadrilaterals
3.G.A.1

Lesson 27
Understand Tiling in Rectangles
2.G.A.2

Grade 3, Lesson 27
Understand Area
3.MD.C.5a, 3.MD.C.5b, 3.MD.C.6

Grade 3, Lesson 31
Understand Properties of Shapes
3.G.A.1

Lesson 28
Understand Halves, Thirds, and
Fourths in Shapes
2.G.A.3

Grade 3, Lesson 33
Divide Shapes Into Parts With
Equal Areas
3.G.A.2

©Curriculum Associates, LLC   Copying is not permitted.

Lesson 26 (Student Book pages 224–233)

Recognize and Draw Shapes

LESSON OBJECTIVES

- Identify triangles, quadrilaterals, pentagons, and hexagons based on the number of sides and angles they have.

- Recognize that one shape can be formed from a composite of other shapes.

- Distinguish among triangles, quadrilaterals, pentagons, and hexagons based on their attributes.

- Draw a shape based on specific attributes.

PREREQUISITE SKILLS

- Identify the sides and angles of a polygon.

- Sort objects based on attributes.

- Identify and name triangles, circles, squares, and rectangles.

VOCABULARY

There is no new vocabulary. You may want to review the terms:

side: a straight line or segment that is part of a shape.

angle: the place where two straight lines or segments of a shape meet.

THE LEARNING PROGRESSION

In Grade 1, students explore geometric shapes by examining attributes that distinguish one shape from another and by composing polygons from another set of polygons.

In Grade 2, students become more sophisticated in distinguishing among shapes and in their use of attributes. **In this lesson,** students use the number of sides and angles to identify, name, and classify polygons. They compose and decompose one polygon from a set of other polygons. Students reason logically when they generalize attributes to sets of shapes, and in determining when an attribute can be applied to all of one kind of polygon, some of them, or none of them.

In Grade 3, students expand their understanding of polygons by categorizing sets within sets. They recognize that within the set of quadrilaterals there are shapes such as squares, rhombuses, trapezoids, etc. that all have four sides, yet possess other distinguishing features that set them apart from other four-sided figures.

Ready *Teacher Toolbox*   Teacher-Toolbox.com

	Prerequisite Skills	2.G.A.1
Ready Lessons	✓ ✓	✓
Tools for Instruction	✓ ✓	✓ ✓
Interactive Tutorials	✓ ✓	✓ ✓

CCSS Focus

2.G.A.1 Recognize and draw shapes having specified attributes, such as a given number of angles or a given number of equal faces. Identify triangles, quadrilaterals, pentagons, hexagons, and cubes.

STANDARDS FOR MATHEMATICAL PRACTICE: *SMP 3, 5 (see page A9 for full text)*

©Curriculum Associates, LLC   Copying is not permitted.

Sort Polygons

Objective: Recognize similarities and differences among polygons.

Materials for each student:
- a set of polygons (3–4 each of triangles, quadrilaterals, pentagons, hexagons; one or two shapes of more than 6 sides, and a circle cut from a single color of construction paper or tag board.)

Overview

Students sort polygons by attributes and describe the distinguishing attribute for each set of shapes.

Step by Step (20–30 minutes)

1 Examine and sort shapes.

- Label each shape with a number 1, 2, 3, … or a letter a, b, c, … . Tape the polygons randomly on the board reserving the shapes with more than 6 sides for later use.

- Tell students to work in pairs to find shapes that belong together in some way. Have them record the label of the shapes that have a common attribute and tell how they belong together.

2 Describe sets created.

- Invite pairs of students to tell you what shapes they put together and why. Move the shapes they identify to one side of the board as a group and write the defining attribute above or below the group.

- Invite students to comment on the grouping, discussing their observations.

- Ask for pairs who have a different group and attribute. Display their suggestions and allow others to discuss. Continue until you have a few different groups and attributes displayed.

3 Analyze sets.

- Ask the class to analyze the groupings and the attribute. Ask: *Do all the shapes in this group have (the attribute listed)? Are there other shapes that could fit into this group? Explain.*

- If the description of a set is not clear, have students think of ways to make it more specific so there is no doubt what might fit into the set. If there are multiple ways of describing a set, analyze which description is most clear. Tell students that often there is more than one way to describe a set. Discuss attributes that may be distinguishing (all have 4 sides) to those that are not (all small).

4 Apply set descriptions to new shapes.

- Display one of the reserved shapes and ask if it belongs to one of the sets they made. Discuss why it does or does not belong. Repeat with the remaining shapes.

©Curriculum Associates, LLC   Copying is not permitted.

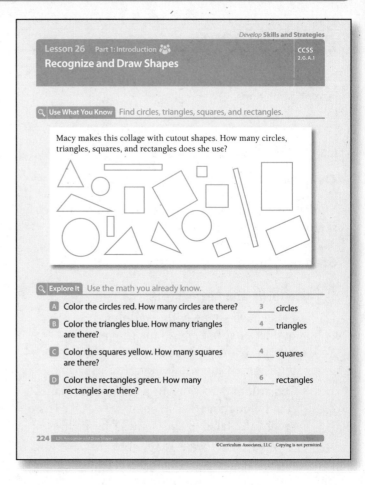
AT A GLANCE

Students identify circles, triangles, squares, and rectangles from a set of shapes.

STEP BY STEP

- Read the problem at the top of the page. Tell students that a collage is an organized group of pictures or objects that all have something in common. Ask what is the same about all the pictures shown [they are all shapes].

- Complete Explore It together. For Part D, a student may ask if the squares should be colored green also. This child may have learned that squares are special kinds of rectangles. Discuss how the squares are like a rectangle [4 sides, 4 angles, square corners (90° angles)]. Ask how they are different [squares have sides all the same length, the rectangles don't]. Tell them that squares are a special kind of rectangle, but for this activity they are to color the rectangles that are not squares.

- Complete the Real-World Connection activity to provide students with a sense of geometry in the world around them. Discuss with them how the shapes they found were each a face of a solid figure. In our world, all two-dimensional figures are faces, not objects themselves.

Real-World Connection

- Make a chart on chart paper or on the board with the headings *circle*, *square*, *triangle*, and *rectangle*.

- Give each student 4 squares of blank paper. Tell them they will be going on a shape hunt around the room.

- Students are to find objects in the room that fit each of the labels on the chart. Draw a sketch of the object and tape or glue it on the chart under the appropriate label. They should find one of each shape, preferably one that no one else has found.

AT A GLANCE

Students identify polygons based on number of sides and number of angles.

STEP BY STEP

- Read Find Out More as a class. Review the terms *side* and *angle*. You may want to use the first part of the Hands-On Activity to reinforce these terms.

- Display labels and pictures of each shape on a bulletin board or chart to help students with visual recognition of the words.

- Have students discuss the Reflect question and then write about it in their own words.

Hands-On Activity

Materials: 2-foot lengths of string, straws cut in various sizes

- Give each student a length of string and 8–10 straws of varying lengths.

- Have students string 3 straws together and tie the ends together in a bow, making sure they are close together.

- Identify the *sides* as the straight pieces of straw and the *angles* as the place where the sides meet.

- Tell students to move the straws around to form different shapes. Ask: *What shape did you all make?* [triangle] Discuss how it doesn't matter how long the straws are or how they are moved on the string. The shape is always a triangle.

- Repeat for the quadrilateral, pentagon, and hexagon. Encourage students to try unusual formations such as concave shape.

- String 6 straws together to form a hexagon. Have students identify the shape. Reorganize the straws so that two of them form a straight line. Ask if the shape is still a hexagon and why. Students should notice that although there are six straws, two of them form a single side making the figure a pentagon.

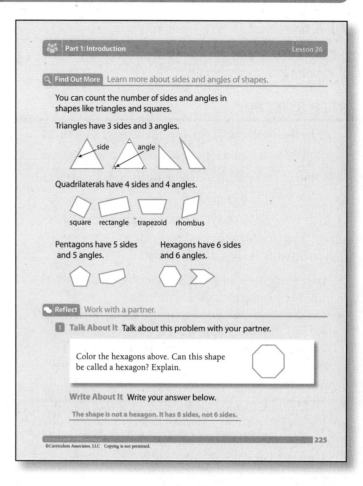

Mathematical Discourse

- *Would a circle belong to any of the groups listed on this page? Explain.*

   No. All the shapes on this page have sides and angles. A circle has neither sides nor angles.

©Curriculum Associates, LLC   Copying is not permitted.

AT A GLANCE

Students examine pictures of real objects and name the shape based on attributes.

STEP BY STEP

- Read the problem at the top of the page together as a class.

- Connect this problem to the Real-World Connection activity from the Introduction.

- Ask: *Where can you find the shape that has 5 sides and 5 angles?* [on the soccer ball]. Ask the Mathematical Discourse question.

- Have students name each of the shapes described. Say: *The pentagon is the shape with 5 sides and 5 angles.* Ask: *What do you notice about the triangle that has 3 sides and the rectangle with 4 angles?* Guide students to recognize that a triangle has 3 sides **and** 3 angles and a rectangle has 4 sides **and** 4 angles.

> **SMP Tip:** Ask: *Do you think it is possible for a shape to have 4 angles, but not 4 sides? Why?* Engage students in discussion about this question. Encourage them to justify their reasoning and question the reasoning of classmates. *(SMP 3)* If there is unresolved disagreement, give students strings and straws and challenge them to make a figure that has 4 angles, but not 4 sides. They will find that, if the shape is closed, it is impossible.

- Have students look at the drawings. Discuss how drawing shapes of more than 4 sides can be challenging. Tell them that a drawing doesn't have to be perfect.

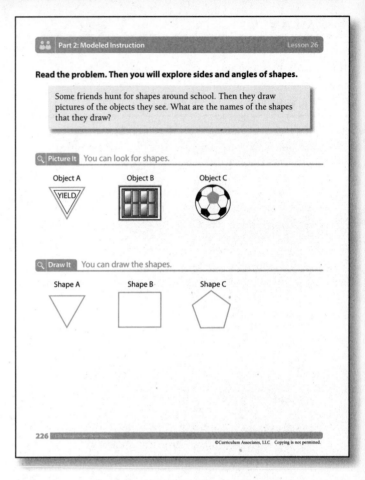

Mathematical Discourse

- *Would it make sense to say a soccer ball has 5 sides and 5 angles? Why?*

  Students should respond that although the pentagon is printed on the ball, the ball itself is not in the shape of a pentagon. When identifying shapes in the world, it is important to be exact in describing where they are found.

ELL Support

The extensive vocabulary used in this lesson may be overwhelming to an ELL student. Make a card listing the terms triangle, quadrilateral, rectangle, square, pentagon, hexagon, side, and angle. Next to each term draw an example of the term. Allow students to keep the card at their desks for visual reference. (Activity Sheet 16, page 325)

©Curriculum Associates, LLC   Copying is not permitted.

AT A GLANCE

Students revisit the problem on page 226, analyzing and naming each shape. Then students draw shapes based on attributes.

STEP BY STEP

• Read Connect It as a class. Make sure students understand that the questions refer to the problem on page 226.

• Some students may identify shape B as a quadrilateral. Tell them that the shape is a quadrilateral, but that it has another name. The Concept Extension can be completed at this time or following Problem 4.

• Tell students that in the Try It problem, their drawings do not need to be exact, but they should try to make the sides as straight as possible.

Concept Extension

Explore subsets of quadrilaterals.

• Display a pattern block square, trapezoid, rhombus, and rectangle (composed of two or more squares).

• Tell students that all quadrilaterals have 4 sides and 4 angles, but some of them belong to a group of quadrilaterals that have their own name. To develop the concept of subset, you may discuss that they are all second graders. "Second grade boys" is a special group of second graders. Ask: *Is everyone in the room is a second grader? a second grade boy?* Tell them that (Jackson) is a second grader, but he is also a boy so he also belongs to the special group of second grade boys. Repeat for the girls.

• Name each of the pattern block pieces and have students compare them based on observations such as: The rhombus has 4 sides that are all the same length. Listen for attributes that set one shape apart from another.

• Students will learn more about quadrilaterals in third and fourth grade.

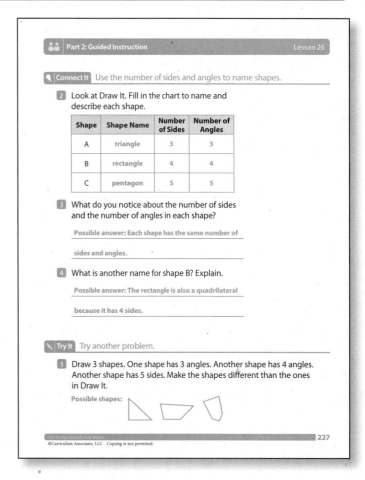

TRY IT SOLUTION

5 *Solution:* See possible shapes above. Accept any shape that fulfills the requirements even though it may be uncommon. **(DOK 2)**

ERROR ALERT: Watch for students who may draw a shape that is not closed such as

The shape has 3 angles, but since it is not closed, it is not a polygon, therefore not a triangle.

AT A GLANCE

Students explore ways to compose a hexagon from trapezoids and triangles.

STEP BY STEP

- Read the problem at the top of the page together as a class and describe the shapes shown.

> **SMP Tip:** Have students construct the composite hexagons shown using pattern blocks. *(SMP 5)* By physically organizing the shapes into a hexagon, students develop spatial reasoning skills and explore part/whole relationships as well as area concepts.

- Ask the Mathematical Discourse question and then have students use pattern blocks to cover a trapezoid with triangles.

- Ask students how many triangles they think will cover the blue rhombus (diamond shape). Ask: *Can you use what you know about the number of triangles that cover a blue rhombus to figure out how many blue rhombuses it will take to cover the hexagon?* Instruct students to discuss the question without using the blocks. They should recognize that, since it takes 2 triangles to cover the rhombus and 6 triangles to cover the hexagon, they will need 3 groups of 2 triangles or 3 rhombuses to cover the hexagon.

- Allow students to test their reasoning by covering the hexagon with rhombuses.

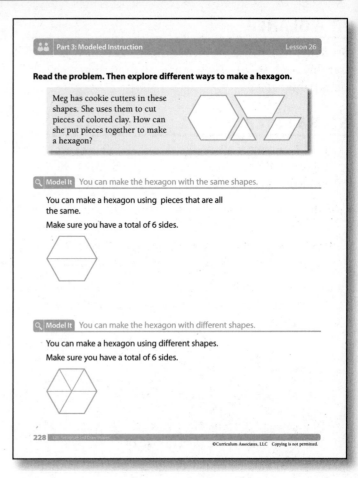

Mathematical Discourse

- *How is it possible for the same size hexagon to be made with either 2 or 6 pieces?*

  The shapes used are different sizes. Three triangles make up one of the trapezoids.

©Curriculum Associates, LLC   Copying is not permitted.

AT A GLANCE

Students revisit the problem on page 228, evaluating the composite hexagon. They then explore ways to cover a hexagon and a new shape.

STEP BY STEP

- Read Connect It as a class.

- For Problems 8 and 9, allow students to use pattern blocks to find ways to cover a hexagon. Remind them that the shapes shown at the top of page 228 are the shapes they can use. Tell students they may use the term *diamond* to refer to the blue rhombus.

- For Problem 9, remind students to draw as best as they can. If there is enough space on the page, allow them to trace the pattern block configurations made.

- For the Try It problem, remind students that the small shapes they should use are the triangle, trapezoid, and (rhombus) diamond shape.

Concept Extension

- Display the two configurations shown here and ask if they are the same arrangement of blocks.

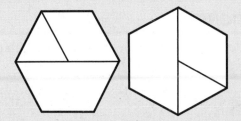

Although the orientations are different, the blocks used are the same and in the same positions.

- Challenge students' spatial abilities by asking them if it is possible for the two figures to exactly match up. You may want to copy the figures onto lightweight paper and cut squares of paper apart containing each shape for each student or student pair to manipulate. Allow students time to flip and turn the figures either mentally or physically. Demonstrate using a transparency or interactive white board how one shape can be flipped and turned to fit exactly over the other figure. This builds the concept of congruence.

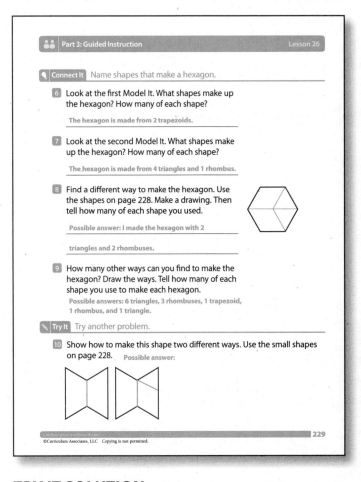

TRY IT SOLUTION

10 *Solution:* Sample answers are shown. Accept any configurations that meet the given requirements. **(DOK 2)**

ERROR ALERT: Students may leave gaps or spaces that are not in the shape of one of the polygons shown.

©Curriculum Associates, LLC   Copying is not permitted.

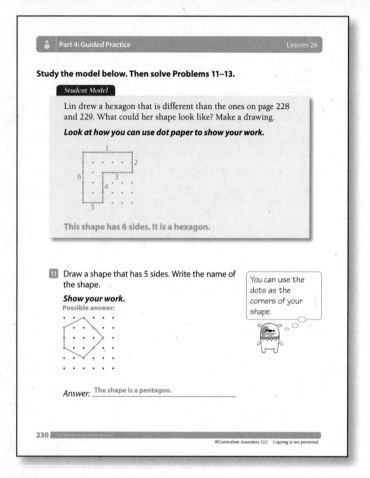

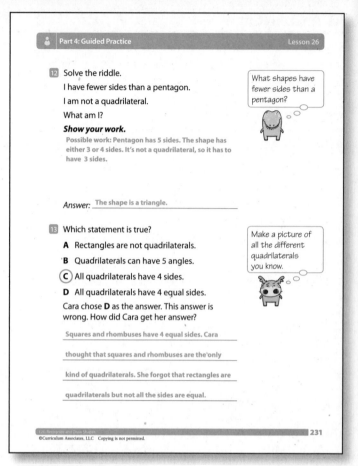

AT A GLANCE

Students use attributes and logical reasoning to answer questions about polygons.

STEP BY STEP

- Ask students to solve the problems independently. Tell them they will use what they learned about shapes during this lesson to complete the problems.

- When students have completed each problem, have them Pair/Share to discuss their solutions with a partner.

SOLUTIONS

Ex Six dots are connected to draw a non-regular hexagon.

11 *Solution:* A 5-sided pentagon should be drawn. **(DOK 2)**

12 *Solution:* A triangle has fewer sides than a pentagon and it is not a quadrilateral. **(DOK 2)**

13 *Solution:* **C**; a quadrilateral is a 4-sided polygon.

Explain to students why the other two choices are not correct:

A is not correct because a rectangle has 4 sides so it is a quadrilateral.

B is not correct because quadrilaterals have exactly 4 sides and 4 angles. **(DOK 3)**

©Curriculum Associates, LLC   Copying is not permitted.

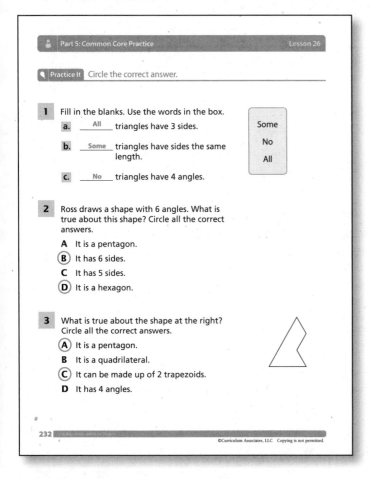

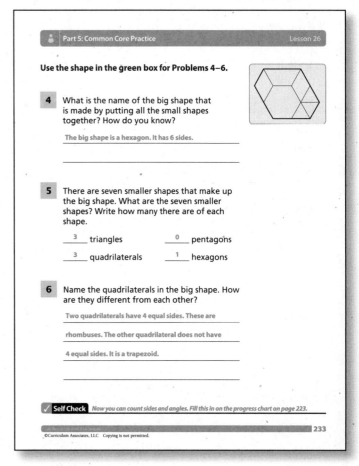

AT A GLANCE

Students use concepts dealing with attributes of polygons that might appear on a mathematics test.

STEP BY STEP

- First, tell students they will use what they know about polygons to complete the problems on the next two pages.

- After students have completed the Common Core Practice problems, review and discuss correct answers.

SOLUTIONS

1 *Solutions:* **a.** All; **b.** Some; **c.** No. *(DOK 2)*

2 *Solutions:* **B** and **D**; A hexagon has 6 sides. *(DOK 2)*

3 *Solution:* **A** and **C**. *(DOK 2)*

4 *Solution:* It is a hexagon. It has six sides and six angles. *(DOK 2)*

5 *Solution:* 3 triangles, 3 quadrilaterals, 0 pentagons, 1 hexagon. *(DOK 1)*

6 *Solution:* Students may respond that two of the quadrilaterals are diamond shaped (rhombuses) and one is like the red pattern block shape (trapezoid). The rhombuses have sides that are the same length and the trapezoid has sides that are different lengths. *(DOK 2)*

©Curriculum Associates, LLC   Copying is not permitted.

Assessment and Remediation

- Tell students you have a rectangle, square, trapezoid, and diamond shape (rhombus). Ask what name can be used for all of the shapes you have and have students tell why. [They are all quadrilaterals. They have 4 sides and 4 angles.]

- For students who are still struggling, use the chart below to guide remediation.

- After providing remediation, check students' understanding using the following problem: Show students a variety of triangles, quadrilaterals, pentagons, and hexagons and ask them to name them and organize them into groups. [Check for accurate labels.]

If the error is . . .	Students may . . .	To remediate . . .
pentagons or hexagons	not have learned the vocabulary word *quadrilateral* yet.	Ask the student to tell you what all the shapes have in common. If the student can tell you that they all have 4 sides and 4 angles, remind them that the name for that group of shapes is *quadrilateral*. Ask if they have ever heard of someone having quadruplets (4 babies). "Quad" means 4, so quadrilateral is a 4-sided shape.
rectangles	have misinterpreted rectangles as any 4-sided figures.	Show students several quadrilaterals. Have them identify similarities and differences. Help them to recognize that only some of the shapes share the attributes of a rectangle.

Hands-On Activity

Materials: a set of tangrams for each student pair or a tangram puzzle copied on heavy paper for students to cut apart

- Draw a chart on the board with the headings and a picture of a triangle, square, rectangle, trapezoid, and parallelogram. Have students replicate the chart on plain paper.

- Give each student pair a set of tangrams and tell them they are to work together to try to make each of the shapes shown with their puzzle pieces. Tell them that there are more than one way to make most shapes.

- After students build the shape, they should draw it on their chart showing the pieces they used. Emphasize that exactness is not necessary.

- When everyone is finished, share solutions.

Challenge Activity

Materials: a set of tangrams for each student pair or a tangram puzzle copied on heavy paper for students to cut apart

- Challenge students to extend the activity done by the class.

- Students should attempt to construct each of the shapes on the chart using 1, 2, 3, 4, 5, 6, and 7 tangram pieces.

- Have them record each set of solutions on a separate sheet of paper showing the tangram pieces they used.

- When finished, compare their solutions to others and display them, if desired.

- When everyone is finished, share solutions.

©Curriculum Associates, LLC   Copying is not permitted.

Lesson 27 (Student Book pages 234–239)

Understand Tiling in Rectangles

LESSON OBJECTIVES

- Analyze a tiling as an array of squares with no gaps or overlaps.
- Determine the number of squares used to tile a rectangle.
- Create a tiling of squares to fit a rectangular shape.

PREREQUISITE SKILLS

In order to be proficient with the concept/skills in this lesson, students should:

- Know that an array is organized in equal sized rows and columns.
- Compose a shape from a different shape.
- Know the attributes of a square and a rectangle.

VOCABULARY

There is no new vocabulary.

THE LEARNING PROGRESSION

In Grade 1, students identify and explore attributes of triangles and squares. They compose two-dimensional shapes to create a composite shape.

In Grade 2, students extend their understanding of shapes and attributes by grouping them into broad categories of triangle, quadrilateral, pentagon, and hexagon. They compose a polygon with other polygons and explore the concept of an array as a rectangular shape. **In this lesson,** students build on the concept of an array and composing shapes as they tile a rectangular shape using congruent squares.

In Grade 3, students utilize the concept of an array as rows and columns of equal sized squares as a tool for understanding multiplication and division, and in exploring concepts of area.

■ **Ready** *Teacher Toolbox*		*Teacher-Toolbox.com*
	Prerequisite Skills	*2.G.A.2*
Ready Lessons	✓ ✓	✓
Tools for Instruction	✓	
Interactive Tutorials	✓	✓

CCSS Focus

2.G.A.2 Partition a rectangle into rows and columns of same-sized squares and count to find the total number of them.

STANDARDS FOR MATHEMATICAL PRACTICE: SMP 1, 2, 3, 4, 5, 7 *(see page A9 for full text)*

©Curriculum Associates, LLC   Copying is not permitted.

Tile a Rectangle

Objective: Explore tiling a rectangle with congruent squares.	**Materials for each student:** • a 5" × 6" construction paper rectangle • 2-inch squares cut from construction paper (Activity Sheet 17, page 326), (different color than rectangle, if possible) • color tiles (1-inch squares; Activity Sheet 3, page 310)

Overview

Students cover a rectangular shape with 1-inch and 2-inch squares, having no gaps or overlaps. They analyze the tiling to determine the reason one size of square will tile and the other will not.

Step by Step (15–20 minutes)

1 **Tile a rectangle.**

- Distribute construction paper rectangles and color tiles to students.

- Ask students to cover the rectangle with 1-inch color tiles, making sure there are no gaps. Point out how the squares cover the paper, perfectly lining up with each side of the rectangle.

2 **Try another tiling.**

- Distribute the 2-inch squares to students. Have students cover the rectangle with the 2-inch squares in the same way they covered it with the 1-inch tiles. They may notice that there is difficulty in tiling since the squares don't fit perfectly in both directions.

3 **Talk about the tilings.**

- Compare the two tilings. Ask: *What is the same about the two tilings?* [They are both made of squares of the same size.] *What is different about the two tilings?* [The 1-inch squares all fit perfectly, the 2-inch squares hang over on one side.]

- Help students make sense of the concept of a tiling and self-correct faulty reasoning through yes/no questions. Ask: *What would you need to do to make the squares fit?* Students may respond that they would need to cut off

part of some of the squares. Ask: *Would all the tiles still be squares?* [No.] *Would it still be a tiling of squares?* [No.] Some students may respond that they would have to make the rectangle bigger. Remind them that the rectangle cannot change. Some students may respond that they could make one row of 1-inch tiles. Tell them that the idea is a good one, but this kind of tiling must be made of squares that are all the same size. Ask: *If we used some of the 1-inch tiles, would they all be the same size?* [No.]

- Project a tiling where a row of 2-inch tiles overlaps another row. Ask: *What do you think about this strategy?* Guide students to see that it won't work because when you covered some of the squares, it made them into rectangles. You can only use squares to tile.

- Summarize the activity by discussing that in order to tile a rectangle, you need to use tiles that are the same size squares. You have to arrange the tiles so that there are no gaps and no overlaps.

©Curriculum Associates, LLC   Copying is not permitted.

AT A GLANCE

Students explore tiling as a series of equal rows of congruent squares.

STEP BY STEP

- Introduce the question at the top of the page. Remind students of how, in the last lesson, they composed a hexagon with equal sized triangles, equal sized rhombuses, and equal sized trapezoids.

- Use the Hands-On Activity to engage students in the process of building rectangles.

- Reinforce the concept that the squares cover each rectangle completely. There are no gaps and no extra spaces at the end of a row or column.

- Use the Mathematical Discourse questions to help students connect the concept of tiling to an array.

Hands-On Activity

Materials: colored tiles

- Distribute 12 tiles to each student.

- As students examine the pictures of rectangles, have them build their own rectangles to replicate the ones shown.

- After completing the page, have students use their 12 tiles to create rectangles that are not shown on this page. They should make rectangles with rows of 4, 6, and 12.

SMP Tip: Reinforce the structure of the array and how it applies to a tiling here and throughout the lesson. This prepares students for concepts involving multiplication and the area of rectangles. (SMP 7)

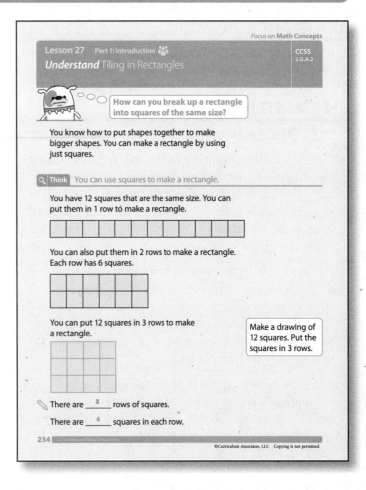

Mathematical Discourse

- *How is the tiling on this page like an array?*

  The tiles are lined up in rows and columns with the same number of squares in each row and the same number in each column.

- *What would happen to the shape if you removed one of the square tiles?*

  It would no longer be in the shape of a rectangle, so it would not be an array. There would not be the same number in each row or each column. Students may respond that the shape would be a hexagon.

AT A GLANCE

Students explore correct and incorrect ways to tile a rectangle with squares.

STEP BY STEP

- Read Think together as a class.

- Direct students' attention to the two ways of tracing the squares to tile. Ask the Mathematical Discourse questions to engage students in thinking about how squares are composed from other squares. You may want to give students grid paper or tiles to help them think about the second question.

- Examine the rectangle that is divided into groups of different sizes of squares. Discuss that since the squares are not the same size, an array was not made. Use the Hands-On Activity to explore this concept and reinforce the impossibility of creating an array with different sizes of squares.

- Read the Reflect question with the class. Ask students to discuss ideas with a partner before writing an answer. Invite students to share responses with the class, demonstrating their reasoning with tiles.

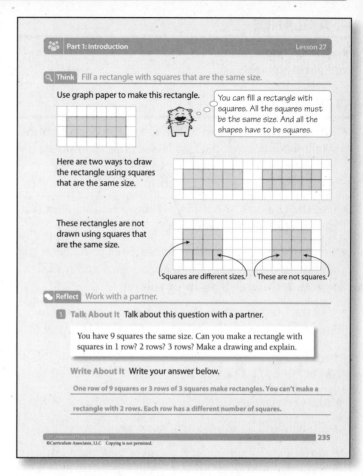

Hands-On Activity

Explore tiling with two different sized squares.

Materials: 12 1-in. squares, (Activity Sheet 3, page 310) and 12 2-in. squares (Activity Sheet 18, page 327) for each student or student pair

- Distribute the paper squares to each student or student pair. Ask them to try to build an array using some of each size of square.

- Ask students if they were able to build a rectangle. Invite a volunteer to display the rectangle that was made.

- Ask: *Is this rectangle an array? Explain.* Allow the volunteer to respond or allow the student to call on a classmate to respond. They should recognize that an array has not been formed since the rows and columns do not each contain the same number of squares.

Mathematical Discourse

- *What other ways might you trace squares in this rectangle? How could you decide if different sized squares could be drawn?*

  Students should respond that there are no other ways to trace squares in this rectangular shape. To make a larger square, there needs to be an equal number of rows and columns of smaller squares.

- *Is there another way of arranging the 12 square tiles so that a different sized square could be used? Explain.*

  No. If we arranged the tiles in a 1×12 rectangle or a 3×4 rectangle, the only size that can be used is the single square.

SMP Tip: Encourage students to attempt varied configurations in exploring answers to questions. This promotes perseverance in problem solving and stimulates spatial reasoning skills. *(SMP 1)*

©Curriculum Associates, LLC   Copying is not permitted.

AT A GLANCE

Students determine the number of tiles used to make up rectangles.

STEP BY STEP

- Work through Problem 2 with the class. Drawing individual squares may be challenging for students. Encourage them to take care in drawing the missing squares to make sure they all fit inside the rectangle. For students with fine motor challenges, it may be easier for them to use a straight edge to extend each line creating a grid inside of the rectangle.

- Tell students they will have time to work individually on the rest of the Explore It problems on this page and then share their responses in groups.

- As students work individually, circulate among them. This is an opportunity to assess student understanding and address student misconceptions. Use the Mathematical Discourse questions to stimulate thinking.

- Watch for students who are still having difficulty. See if their understanding progresses as they work in their groups during the next part of the lesson.

> **SMP Tip:** When students are finished, say: *I'm wondering why the same size rectangle can be made with 24 squares or 6 squares. It doesn't seem to make sense. What do you think?* Engage students in a discussion of how a larger sized square covers more of the rectangle than a smaller square so you don't need as many of them. This prepares students for concepts of equivalencies of fractions and measuring area using different sized units. *(SMP 2)*

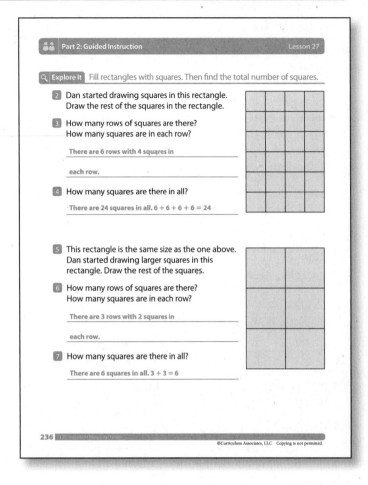

Mathematical Discourse

- *How do you know where to draw the missing squares?*

  I can follow the way the squares were started and make it like an array.

- *What strategy did you use to find the number of squares in each rectangle?*

  Possible responses: I added 6 together 4 times; I added 4 together 6 times; I counted them all.

AT A GLANCE

Students answer questions based on the activities from page 236.

STEP BY STEP

- Instruct students to work in groups to complete Problems 8–10. Walk around to each group, listen to, and join in on discussions at different points.

- Have students discuss ways in which they could draw squares in Try It Another Way with a partner.

Concept Extension

Materials: dot paper, colored pencils, scissors

- Tell students to draw a line connecting dots to form a 6 unit sized square. Have them cut it out.

- Instruct students to find as many ways as possible to divide the large square into smaller squares.

- Have them trace around each group of squares using a different color for each size.

- Ask students to compare their squares with a partner. Make sure they have found squares of 1 unit, 2 units, and 3 units.

- Tell them to put their squares together to form a 1 × 2 rectangle and ask: *Is it possible to find the number of squares of one size in the entire rectangle by knowing how many of that size square are in your square? Explain.* Provide time for students to discuss this question with their partner. Students should respond that since there are two large squares in the rectangle they can double the number of smaller squares found in the large square to find the number in the entire rectangle.

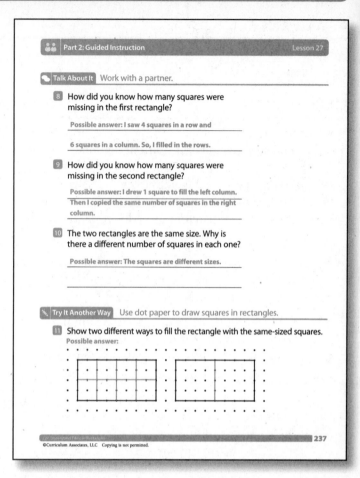

Mathematical Discourse

- *How does thinking about these rectangles as arrays help you find a strategy for counting all the squares?*

  An array is organized in rows and columns just like the rectangles. There are the same number of squares in each row and each column so you can add up the number of squares in all the rows or the number in all the columns.

©Curriculum Associates, LLC   Copying is not permitted.

AT A GLANCE

Students demonstrate their understanding of how to tile a rectangle with squares.

STEP BY STEP

- Discuss each Connect It problem as a class using the discussion points outlined below.

Explain:

- Discuss with students how a tiling is organized like an array. Ask: *Is there more than one way to find the total number of squares used? Explain.* Students should recognize that they might add 6 three times or 3 six times. You can either add the rows or the columns since there are an equal number in each row and in each column.

Evaluate:

- Ask students why Tim might have divided the rectangle as he did. Engage them in a discussion of the similarities and differences between squares and rectangles. They both have 4 sides and 4 angles. They both have 4 "square" angles. The rectangles have two sides that are longer than the other two sides while all the sides of the square are the same size.

- Ask: *How should Tim have divided his rectangle?* [He should have divided it into all squares.] *How many squares would he count?* [12] *How do you know?* [Each of the rectangles could be divided into two squares. There would be 6 squares there and 6 squares that he already made. That makes 12 squares.]

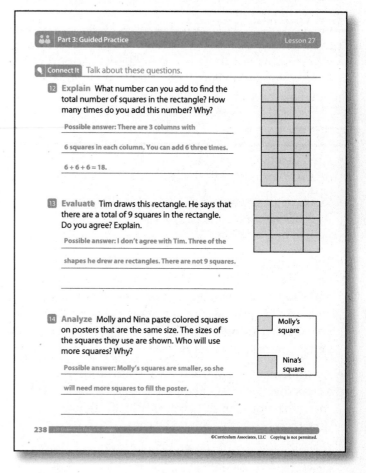

Analyze:

- Remind students that this situation is like the one that was discussed on the previous page.

- Ask: *What do Molly and Nina need to remember when filling their poster board with squares?* [They need to remember to use all the same sized squares for the whole tiling and make sure there are no empty spaces or pieces that overlap each other.]

©Curriculum Associates, LLC   Copying is not permitted.

AT A GLANCE

Students demonstrate their understanding of a tiling by determining the size of squares that will cover a specific rectangular shape. They justify their choices and explain why they would prefer one over another.

STEP BY STEP

- Direct students to complete the Put It Together task on their own.

- Read the directions with students and make sure they understand each part of the task before proceeding.

- Tell students that their drawings need not be the exact size of the paper. They can draw any rectangle and show how the squares will fit on it. You may want to demonstrate drawing a rectangle on the board using straight lines to divide it into 3 rows and 4 columns of squares.

- As students work on their own, walk around to assess their progress and understanding, to answer their questions, and to give additional support, if needed.

- If time permits, ask students to share the square sizes they chose and justify their choices.

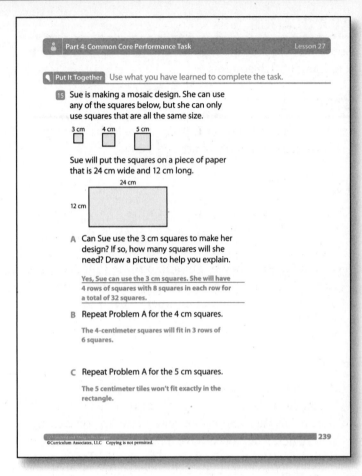

SCORING RUBRICS

A

Points	Expectations
2	The student selects 3-cm and 4-cm squares and draws rectangles showing 32 and 18 squares respectively. The student uses words to explain reasoning.
1	The student may select 3-cm and 4-cm squares, but the drawings are inaccurate. Words may or may not be present to explain reasoning.
0	The student may select all of the square sizes or inaccurate combinations. The rectangles drawn do not reflect the size of square selected.

B

Points	Expectations
2	The student clearly articulates a reason for the selection based on size/number of squares needed comparisons.
1	The student makes a choice but may articulate a reason such as "It is easier" with no other justification.
0	The student does not provide a justification for a size selection.

©Curriculum Associates, LLC   Copying is not permitted.

Intervention Activity

Create a mosaic tiling.

Materials: 6 × 8 inch grid paper with 1-in. squares (Activity Sheet 3, page 310), at least 24 2-in. squares (Activity Sheet 18, page 327) in varied colors, and glue for each student

Note: Tiling with no gaps or overlaps is challenging for students at this level. Providing grid paper as a guide enables all students to successfully complete a tiling.

• Provide each student with the rectangle grid paper and cut out squares.

• Tell students they are to make a tiling of squares to cover the rectangular grid paper.

• Help them notice that each of the cut out squares covers 4 squares on the grid paper.

• Suggest that they arrange the squares on the grid paper before gluing to ensure they like the design.

• Glue the squares on the paper staying within the grid lines.

• Provide a place for students to display their tilings when completed.

On-Level Activity

Create a mosaic tiling.

Materials: a 6 × 8 inch rectangle, at least 24 1-in. or 2-in. squares (Activity Sheets 3 and 18, pages 310 and 327) in varied colors, and glue for each student

• Provide students with the rectangle and cut out squares.

• Tell students they are to make a tiling of squares to cover the rectangular sheet of paper. They may use either size of square, but the entire rectangle must be covered with the same size square.

• Students may arrange the colored paper in any way they choose. Suggest that they place the squares on the rectangle in the way they would like before gluing.

• Glue the squares on the rectangle to create a tiling that has no gaps or overlaps.

• Provide a place for students to display their tilings when completed.

Challenge Activity

Materials: 12 × 18 sheets of construction paper

• Distribute the sheets of construction paper, but do not tell them the size of the paper.

• Tell students that their challenge is to find out what size of squares they could use to tile this rectangle. They need to find **all** the possible sizes of squares that would work and justify why those are the **only** sizes that will work.

• Provide them with further challenges by telling them to find all the sizes of squares that could tile a 16 × 24 inch rectangle, a 21 × 35 inch rectangle, a 24 × 48 centimeter rectangle and justify.

Lesson 28 (Student Book pages 240–245)

Understand Halves, Thirds, and Fourths in Shapes

LESSON OBJECTIVES

- Identify and name halves, thirds, and fourths as parts into which a shape is divided.

- Recognize that fractions parts are equal in size.

- Understand that the more parts a whole is divided into, the smaller the size of each part.

PREREQUISITE SKILLS

In order to be proficient with the concept/skills in this lesson, students should:

- Recognize halves of a whole.

- Know the meaning of ordinals third and fourth.

VOCABULARY

There is no new vocabulary.

THE LEARNING PROGRESSION

In Grade 1, students explore halves and fourths by partitioning circles and rectangles into two and four equal shares. They recognize that the more parts a shape is divided into, the smaller each of the parts.

In Grade 2, students extend their understanding of fractions to thirds. **In this lesson,** students partition squares, circles, and rectangles into halves, thirds, and fourths recognizing that an equal share of congruent shapes need not be identical. They name fractions and compare equal shares based on the shape of the fractional part and on the amount of the whole it consumes.

In Grade 3, students focus on fractions as equal areas of a shape in preparation for calculating areas in grade 4. They read and write fractions numerically and explore fractions on a number line. Students expand their understanding of fractions to sixths and eighths. They compare fractions in varied ways and find equivalencies preparing them for future study of addition of fractions.

■ **Ready** *Teacher Toolbox*		*Teacher-Toolbox.com*
	Prerequisite Skills	*2.G.A.3*
Ready Lessons	✓ ✓ ✓	✓
Tools for Instruction	✓	✓
Interactive Tutorials		✓

CCSS Focus

2.G.A.3 Partition circles and rectangles into two, three, or four equal shares, describe the shares using the words halves, thirds, half of, a third of, etc., and describe the wholes as two halves, three thirds, four fourths. Recognize that equal shares of identical wholes need not have the same shape.

STANDARDS FOR MATHEMATICAL PRACTICE: SMP 1, 3, 5, 6, 7 (*see page A9 for full text*)

©Curriculum Associates, LLC Copying is not permitted.

Half of a Square

Objective: Find multiple ways of dividing a square into two equal parts.	**Materials for each student:** • grid paper and pencils

Overview

Students divide a 4 × 4 square into arrangements of halves. They compare ways of dividing the square, justifying that the division represents one half of the whole square.

Step by Step (20–30 minutes)

1 **Show half of a square.**

- Ask students to trace around a 4 × 4 square on grid paper.

- Tell students to draw a line that will divide the square in half. If necessary, remind them that half means two equal parts. Expect horizontal, vertical, and diagonal divisions, but accept any division that can be justified.

- Have students display the way they divided the square and tell how they know they have divided it in half. Listen for reasons such as: The two parts look the same; If I folded the paper they would be the same or one would fit on top of the other. Some students may use area to justify rather than relying on visual comparisons. They will notice that each half contains the same number of little squares.

2 **Extend the concept of half.**

- Ask students to trace another 4 × 4 square.

- Challenge students to be creative in finding another way that no one has thought about to divide the square in half. Allow students who have no ideas to collaborate with a partner.

- Provide students time to struggle with ideas. Once a student finds a way to divide, have them project their solution for all to see. Ask questions like: *How do you know the two parts are the same size? Does everyone agree they look the same? Is there something you could do to be sure?* Listen for justification that is becoming more sophisticated. Students should

begin focusing on ways to count the little squares, think of folding, seeing a reflection, or identify that a shape has been turned.

3 **Analyze half.**

- If no student has divided the square in one of the following ways, project one and ask students if they think the square has been divided in half. These divide the square into visually congruent parts so if students have not thought in terms of area, they can still reason accurately.

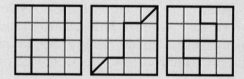

- Ask: *Is this square divided into half? How can you tell?* Listen for reasons listed above. If necessary, have students replicate the square and then cut it out to compare the two halves.

AT A GLANCE

Students explore the concept of halves as taking up an equal amount of space in a whole.

STEP BY STEP

- Introduce the question at the top of the page. Remind students that in the opening activity they explored different ways of dividing a square into halves. Ask: *What is important when showing half of a square?* [Both parts must cover the same amount of the square.]

- Draw attention to circles shown. Ask the Mathematical Discourse questions.

- On the board, draw examples of circles that are not divided into equal parts and discuss how these are different from the ones on the student page.

- Draw attention to the two squares and ask: *Are these squares cut in half?* [The first two are, the third one is not.] *How can you tell?* [In the first two, the parts are the same, but in the third one, the parts are not the same.]

- Make sure students understand that when the terms half, third, and fourth are used, equal sized parts are implied.

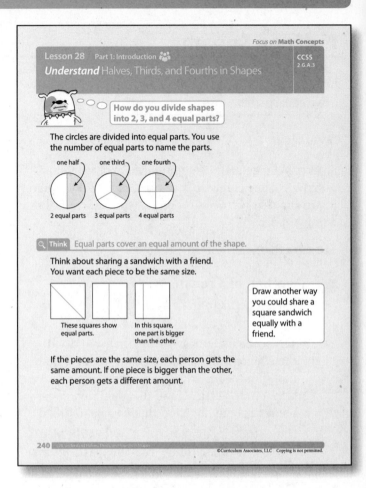

Real-World Connection

Materials: paper cut into circles, squares, and rectangles

- Ask students to think of things they have seen or used that are in the shape of a circle, square, or rectangle and are divided into equal parts.

- Encourage students to share some of their ideas to stimulate the thinking of the class. Expect them to name pizza, pie, cake, brownies, graham crackers and other food items. Steer them to other things such as windows divided into panes, a square game board folded into two parts, etc.

- Have students draw things that are divided into equal parts on paper cutouts making them look like the object.

- Display the pictures under the heading "Fractions in Our World."

Mathematical Discourse

- *How are dividing a shape into thirds and fourths like dividing it into halves?*

  The parts all have to be the same size so they take up the same amount of the shape.

- *What could you do to make sure the thirds or fourths are the same amount of the shape?*

  I could cut out the pieces or fold the paper to see if they matched up.

ELL Support

Students may struggle with the vocabulary, thirds and fourths. Provide situations in which ordinal numbers are used such as: *You are the third person to come to the board. How many people have come to the board?* [3] *You take the fourth cookie. How many cookies are taken?* [4]

©Curriculum Associates, LLC   Copying is not permitted.

AT A GLANCE

Students explore thirds and fourths of shapes in which the fractional parts are not the same shape.

STEP BY STEP

- Draw student attention to Think. Compare the three ways in which the square is divided. Ask students how they could be sure each of the parts is one fourth of the shape. Listen for suggestions such as cutting one of the fourths into smaller pieces to see if they fit on each of the other fourths.

> **SMP Tip:** Ask the first Mathematical Discourse question to engage student thinking and encourage articulation of a concept. *(SMP 6)* Encourage students to be clear and accurate in describing half of a half by asking questions such as: *What does it mean that they are the same?*

- Draw the following on a 4 × 4 dot paper square, display it and ask: *Is this square divided into fourths? How do you know?*

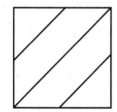

Students should notice that the parts don't have an equal area. The two middle sections contain at least 2 small squares while the triangles at the ends contain only one square.

- Analyze the way in which the squares shown on the student page are divided into thirds by focusing on the amount of space that is consumed by each part.

- Have students work together to discuss the Talk About It question. Make sure they draw the squares before answering the question. Tell them to draw squares as close as they can to the same size as the ones shown.

- Discuss student responses to the question and ask the second Mathematical Discourse question.

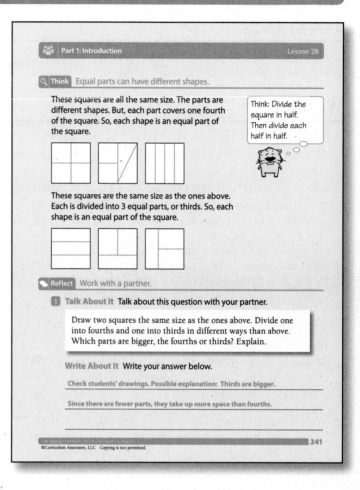

Mathematical Discourse

- *Why does it make sense that dividing a half in half makes a fourth?*

  When you divide a shape in half, you know those parts are the same. If you divide the half in half again, it makes two equal sized parts that take up the same amount of space. Now there are 4 parts that each take up the same amount of space.

- Bridger says, "I don't get it! Four is greater than three, so why aren't fourths bigger than thirds?" *What will you tell him?*

  Listen for suggestions that reflect student understanding of the concept of fractions. Fourths and thirds tell the number of parts into which a whole is divided. The more parts, the smaller each one is.

AT A GLANCE

Students divide a rectangle into halves, thirds, and fourths and identify the parts by name.

STEP BY STEP

- Discuss Explore It with the class. Tell students to divide each rectangle as carefully as possible. Thirds are more challenging to visualize and draw than halves or fourths. Suggest that students check their thirds using a nonstandard measure such as a length on their pencil or finger to ensure the divisions are close to being equal.

- Tell students they will have time to work individually on the rest of the Explore It problems on this page and then share their responses in groups.

- As students work individually, circulate among them. This is an opportunity to assess student understanding and address student misconceptions. Use the Mathematical Discourse questions to stimulate thinking.

- Watch for students who are still having difficulty. See if their understanding progresses as they work in their groups during the next part of the lesson.

Part 2: Guided Instruction — Lesson 28

Explore It Follow the directions for each rectangle.

2. Divide this rectangle into two equal parts.

   Possible answer:

3. Circle the word to the right that makes this sentence true about the rectangle in Problem 2.

   Each part is a ___half___ of the whole rectangle.

   (half)
   third
   fourth

4. Divide this rectangle into three equal parts.

   Possible answer:

5. Circle the word to the right that makes this sentence true about the rectangle in Problem 4.

   Each part is a ___third___ of the whole rectangle.

   half
   (third)
   fourth

6. Divide this rectangle into four equal parts.

   Possible answer:

7. Circle the word to the right that makes this sentence true about the rectangle in Problem 6.

   Each part is a ___fourth___ of the whole rectangle.

   half
   third
   (fourth)

242 L28 Understand Halves, Thirds, and Fourths in Shapes

©Curriculum Associates, LLC   Copying is not permitted.

Concept Extension

Explore fraction/size relationships.

- Say: *Josie is confused. She said she know a half is bigger than a third, but a half of a mini pizza is smaller than a third of a family sized pizza. Why?*

- You may want to draw a picture on the board of the two pizzas described.

- Discuss that a fraction describes a part of a whole. Even though the amount of pizza is smaller in the pizza divided in half, it is a bigger part of THAT pizza than the third is of the larger pizza. Emphasize that when comparing fractions using more than one whole, each whole should be the same size to avoid confusion.

Mathematical Discourse

- *What tells you the name of the fraction?*

  Third is like three, so when I divide into 3 parts they are thirds. Fourth is like four so when I divide into four parts they are fourths.

- *How do you know the parts you drew are equal?*

  Listen for responses such as: I measured to make sure they are all the same size; They all look the same.

SMP Tip: Focus on the structure of fractions and how that structure relates to the name of the fraction part. (*SMP 7*)

©Curriculum Associates, LLC   Copying is not permitted.

AT A GLANCE

Students describe a whole in terms of the number of fractional parts it contains.

STEP BY STEP

- Instruct students to work in pairs to complete Problems 8–10. Walk around to each group, listen to, and join in on discussions at different points.

- As students work on Problem 10, ask the Mathematical Discourse questions to reinforce the relationship of fractional parts to the name of the fraction.

- Have students discuss Try It Another Way with a partner. Tell them to divide each rectangle differently from each of the other rectangles in this problem.

- Invite volunteers to justify that the fractional parts they made within each rectangle are equal in size. Discuss whether this would be a good way to demonstrate that a half is greater than a third, and that both a half and a third are greater than a fourth. Students should respond that since the rectangles are all the same size, it is clear to see which parts are larger in size than the others.

Part 2: Guided Instruction   Lesson 28

Talk About It   Work with a partner.

8 How many halves are in the big rectangle in Problem 2?

    There are 2 halves in the whole rectangle.

9 How many thirds are in the big rectangle in Problem 4?

    There are 3 thirds in the whole rectangle.

10 How many fourths are in the big rectangle in Problem 6?

    There are 4 fourths in the whole rectangle.

Try It Another Way   Show a different way to makes halves, thirds, and fourths.

11 Show another way to divide a rectangle into halves.

    Possible answer:

12 Show another way to divide a rectangle into thirds.

    Possible answer:

13 Show another way to divide a rectangle into fourths.

    Possible answer:

           243

©Curriculum Associates, LLC   Copying is not permitted.

Hands-On Activity

Materials: geoboards, bands

- Instruct students to use a single band to outline a 3 × 3 square on the geoboard. Have them divide the square into halves, thirds, and fourths. Discuss how halves cannot be made vertically or horizontally on the geoboard for this square because of the placement of the pegs.

- Ask students to use a band to outline a rectangle. Have them discover which of the fractions they can make and share observations with the class. Challenge them to find a rectangle that can be divided into the other fractional parts on the geoboard.

Mathematical Discourse

- *Would it be possible to have 5 fourths in a rectangle? Explain.*

    No. Fourths means the rectangle is divided into 4 parts. If there were 5 parts they would not be fourths.

- *What if I divided one of the fourths into two equal parts? There are still fourths, but 5 pieces.*

    If you divide a fourth into two parts, each of the parts is not a fourth because it is not the same size as the other fourths. Fourths all must be the same size.

AT A GLANCE

Students demonstrate their understanding of the fractions half, third, and fourth.

STEP BY STEP

- Discuss each Connect It problem as a class using the discussion points outlined below.

Explain:

- Allow students to work with a partner to share ideas. Encourage them to explain their thinking clearly, using pictures to help justify.

- As students share their ideas with the class, listen to each explanation helping students clarify thoughts and descriptions.

Compare:

- Ask students how they could be sure the divisions are equal. They should focus on the concept of congruence: matching the parts up; or area: making sure the parts take up the same amount of space.

- Have students justify that the parts in circle B are not equal. They may suggest that if you cut the circle apart, the end pieces would fit into the middle piece with some left over. You may want to cut out a circle to demonstrate for those who lack the visual reasoning skills to "see" this.

- Make sure students understand that even though two of the parts in circle B are the same size, they can't be thirds since all three are not equal in size.

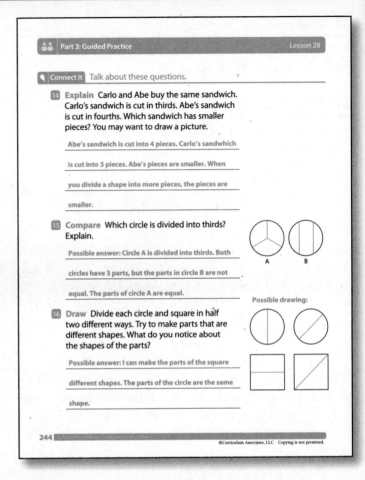

Draw:

- Some students may be creative and divide a circle in a way similar to what is shown.

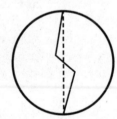

- Ask how they could be sure the two parts are the same size. Listen to their reasoning, then suggest the following. One way would be to use a single line to divide it in half (see dotted line). Compare the triangles on each side of the line. They show how much has been "cut out" of each half. If the triangles are the same size, the halves are equal. If not, the halves are not equal.

- Discuss how, when a single line is used to divide, the two parts of the circle always look exactly the same.

©Curriculum Associates, LLC   Copying is not permitted.

AT A GLANCE

Students demonstrate their understanding of fractional parts by dividing wholes into halves, thirds, or fourths and then analyzing equality of the parts.

STEP BY STEP

- Direct students to complete the Put It Together task on their own.

- Read the directions with students and make sure they understand each part of the task before proceeding. Remind students to divide pizzas into halves, thirds, or fourths.

- As students work on their own, walk around to assess their progress and understanding, to answer their questions, and to give additional support, if needed. If students are concerned that all the pieces they are making are not the same size, tell them that within each pizza, the parts should be the same size, but the problem doesn't say that all the pieces must be equal.

- If time permits, ask students to share the divisions they chose and justify their choices.

Put It Together Use what you have learned to complete this task.

17 Shara and her mom make the 3 pizzas shown for a party.

A Shara will have 10 people at the party. Draw how she could cut each pizza so every person gets 1 piece.

Possible answer:

B Shara counts again and there will be 12 people at the party. Draw how she could cut the pizza so each person gets 1 piece.

Possible answer:

C Do you think each person gets an equal amount of pizza? Explain.

Possible answer: No; each person does not get an equal amount of pizza. The pizzas are different shapes and divided into different numbers of parts.

245

©Curriculum Associates, LLC Copying is not permitted.

SCORING RUBRICS

A

Points	Expectations
2	The student accurately divides into halves, thirds, or fourths to make exactly 10 pieces.
1	The student may cut 10 pieces, but the fractional parts within each shape are not equal or the fractional parts are equal, however there are not a total of 10 pieces.
0	The student was not able to accurately divide shapes into fractional parts and either more or fewer than ten pieces were made.

B

Points	Expectations
2	The student accurately divides each shape into 4 equal parts.
1	The student may cut 12 pieces, but the fractional parts within each shape are not equal or the parts are equal, but 12 parts were not made.
0	The student was not able to accurately divide the shapes into fractional parts or divide into a total of 12 pieces.

C

Points	Expectations
2	The student's response demonstrates a clear understanding of fractions. They recognize that a fourth of one shape may not be equal in size to a fourth of another shape.
1	The student's response shows some understanding of fractions. They may respond that each person gets a fourth of a pizza, but may fail to recognize that a fourth of one may not be equal to a fourth of a different shape.
0	The student was not able to articulate an understanding of fractional parts or their relationship to each other within a single shape or among different shapes.

Intervention Activity

Fraction puzzles.

Materials: rectangles, circles, and squares cut apart from heavy paper into halves, thirds, and fourths (cut the fractions of rectangles and squares differently from each other)

- Provide each student or student pairs with a set of cutouts.

- Tell students to find the pieces that when put together will make rectangles all the same size. Repeat for the circles and squares. Study each set of shapes comparing the size of halves to thirds to fourths. Allow students to physically place a half, third, and fourth of one shape next to each other and order them from largest to smallest. Reinforce the concept that the more pieces a shape is divided into, the smaller each piece will be.

- Have students glue their puzzle pieces onto another sheet of paper and display them under the headings half, third, and fourth.

On-Level Activity

Paper folded fractions.

Materials: 3 rectangles and 3 circles drawn on paper or cut out

- Put students in pairs and provide them with the rectangles and circles. Ask them to cut them out if necessary.

- Tell students to fold one rectangle into halves. Encourage a variety of ways to fold. Compare the ways students folded.

- Repeat for thirds and fourths discussing strategies students used in folding such as: fold in half and in half again for fourths. Have students shade one of the fractional pieces on each shape.

- Repeat the above activity for circles. For thirds, have students fold a circle in half and then fold that piece into three equal parts from the center of the fold. It will make 3 wedges (sectors). Open it all up and notice that two of the folded parts is a third of the whole.

- Display the fractions under the headings half, third, and fourth.

Challenge Activity

Challenge students to find ways of dividing a rectangle into sixths, eighths, ninths, and twelfths.

Have students use plain paper and paper folding to show the fractions. They should then describe how they found each fraction and justify that the parts are the same size.

Ask students to tell how knowing halves, thirds, and fourths can help them find sixths, eighths, ninths, and twelfths.

©Curriculum Associates, LLC   Copying is not permitted.

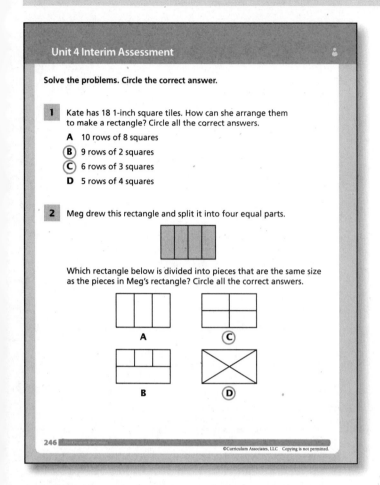

Unit 4 Interim Assessment

Solve the problems. Circle the correct answer.

1 Kate has 18 1-inch square tiles. How can she arrange them to make a rectangle? Circle all the correct answers.

   A 10 rows of 8 squares

   B 9 rows of 2 squares

   C 6 rows of 3 squares

   D 5 rows of 4 squares

2 Meg drew this rectangle and split it into four equal parts.

Which rectangle below is divided into pieces that are the same size as the pieces in Meg's rectangle? Circle all the correct answers.

   A   **C**

   B   **D**

246

©Curriculum Associates, LLC   Copying is not permitted.

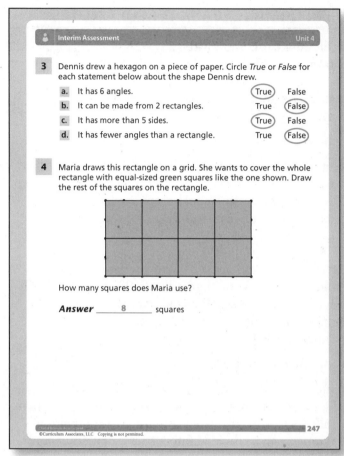

Interim Assessment   Unit 4

3 Dennis drew a hexagon on a piece of paper. Circle *True* or *False* for each statement below about the shape Dennis drew.

   a. It has 6 angles.   (True) False

   b. It can be made from 2 rectangles.   True (False)

   c. It has more than 5 sides.   (True) False

   d. It has fewer angles than a rectangle.   True (False)

4 Maria draws this rectangle on a grid. She wants to cover the whole rectangle with equal-sized green squares like the one shown. Draw the rest of the squares on the rectangle.

How many squares does Maria use?

Answer _____8_____ squares

©Curriculum Associates, LLC   Copying is not permitted.

247

SCORING GUIDE AND ANSWER ANALYSIS

1 *Solution:* **B**, **C**; Add or skip count to find the totals.

$8 + 8 + 8 + 8 + 8 + 8 + 8 + 8 + 8 + 8 = 80$ (**A**);
$2 + 2 + 2 + 2 + 2 + 2 + 2 + 2 = 18$ (**B**);
$3 + 3 + 3 + 3 + 3 + 3 = 18$ (**C**);
$4 + 4 + 4 + 4 + 4 = 20$ (**D**) (***DOK 2***)

2 *Solution:* **C**, **D**; The shaded rectangle is divided into fourths. The answer choice rectangles are identical wholes, so those with fourths are correct. **C** and **D** show fourths. **A** shows thirds and **B** shows 4 unequal sections. (***DOK 2***)

3 *Solution:* True; False; True; False; A hexagon has 6 angles and 6 side. It can not be made from 2 rectangles, so B is false. A rectangle has only 4 sides. (***DOK 1***)

4 *Solution:* 8; A total of 8 squares that are 2 units on each side can fit in the larger rectangle that is 8 units long and 4 units wide. (***DOK 2***)

PERFORMANCE TASK TEACHER NOTES

Common Core Standards: 2.G.A.3
Mathematical Practice Standards: SMP 2, 3, 4, 5, 6
DOK: 3
Materials: (optional) square and regular rectangular sheets of paper, scissors

About the Task

Students reason with shapes and their attributes. This task calls for students to identify geometric shapes and divide rectangles into equal parts. Students also will reason about the sizes and shapes of equal parts.

Getting Started

Read the problem out loud with your students. Have students identify the shapes they will be working with on the page. Guide students to understand that each shape is being used to model a rectangular field at the school. **(SMP 4, 5)**

Completing the Task

Students first should recognize that they need to divide the shape into 2 equal parts to make halves. Encourage students to see that there are multiple ways that the rectangle can be divided into halves. Some students might see division using only horizontal or vertical lines, but miss dividing the shape across diagonals. This could be because they don't recognize the parts as being the same size. You could illustrate the equivalence of halves formed by a diagonal line by cutting a sheet of paper diagonally into halves and turning one piece to match the other. **(SMP 4, 5)**

Students will need to identify the shapes of the halves they form in the rectangle and explain how to find different shapes. Dividing the shape vertically should result in squares, horizontally in rectangles, and diagonally in triangles. **(SMP 6)**

The same process will be repeated to divide the two squares into fourths. Dividing lines will divide each shape into squares, rectangles, or triangles. Students should recognize and be able to explain that fourths of equal wholes also are equal. You could demonstrate this by cutting a square sheet of paper into fourths in two different ways. Then cut the sections of one model again into appropriate pieces so that they can be matched with fourths from the other model. **(SMP 2, 3)**

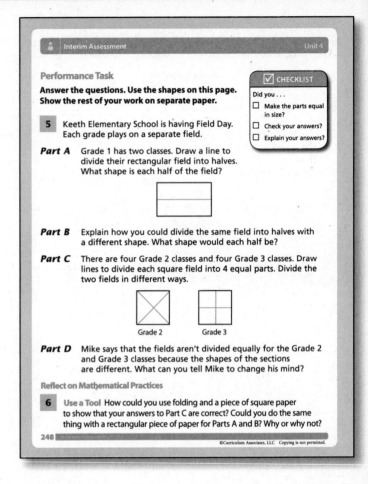

Extension

Have students try this problem:

The two Grade 4 classes will be playing in a circular area at the school. Explain how to divide the circular area into halves. Can you divide the same area into halves that are a different shape? Why or why not?

©Curriculum Associates, LLC   Copying is not permitted.

PERFORMANCE TASK SAMPLE RESPONSES AND RUBRIC

5 Sample 4-Point Solution

Part A The field could be split into equal-sized squares, rectangles, or triangles.
Sample Answer:

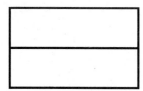

rectangles

Part B Possible explanation: The rectangle could be split by a line between opposite corners. Each part would be a triangle.

Part C Sample answer:

Grade 2   Grade 3

Part D Possible answer: The parts for both Grade 2 and Grade 3 are fourths of equal wholes, so their sizes are equal, even if the shapes are different.

REFLECT ON MATHEMATICAL PRACTICES

6 Folding a shape into two parts that match exactly shows that the parts are halves. Folding the shape again into equal parts will make fourths. I could fold a square piece of paper along the two lines that I drew to make sure that each piece matched exactly. I could confirm Parts A and B using a rectangular piece of paper only if the dividing line is horizontal or vertical. If it is diagonal, a fold along that line will not make two matching parts.

SCORING RUBRIC

4 points   The student's response is accurate and complete. All shape identifications and divisions are correct. All explanations are complete and correct.

3 points   Student has attempted to identify and divide all shapes, but the shapes of the sections given in Parts A and B or in Part C are not different. Explanations are correct, though one might not be complete.

2 points   The student correctly identifies the shapes of the sections, but makes several mistakes in dividing one or more of the shapes. Explanations contain some errors or are mostly incomplete.

1 point   The student's response contains incorrect solutions. Two of the three shapes are not divided into the correct number of equal parts. Explanations are incorrect or incomplete.

SOLUTION TO THE EXTENSION

Possible solution: Divide the circle along a line that passes through its center. There is only one possible shape for the halves, which is a half-circle. The shape of the parts does not change with different orientations of the dividing line.

©Curriculum Associates, LLC   Copying is not permitted.

Activity Sheets

These activity sheets are provided for use with the Opening Activities, Hands-On Activities, and Intervention Activities found in the **Ready**® Teacher's Resource Book. These masters may be photocopied for classroom use. Refer to the activity in the lesson for a full list of materials and instructions.

0	1	2	3
4	5	6	7
8	9	+	−
=	⬜	<	>

©Curriculum Associates, LLC

Hundreds Chart

1	2	3	4	5	6	7	8	9	10
11	12	13	14	15	16	17	18	19	20
21	22	23	24	25	26	27	28	29	30
31	32	33	34	35	36	37	38	39	40
41	42	43	44	45	46	47	48	49	50
51	52	53	54	55	56	57	58	59	60
61	62	63	64	65	66	67	68	69	70
71	72	73	74	75	76	77	78	79	80
81	82	83	84	85	86	87	88	89	90
91	92	93	94	95	96	97	98	99	100

©Curriculum Associates, LLC

©Curriculum Associates, LLC

Number Bond Mat

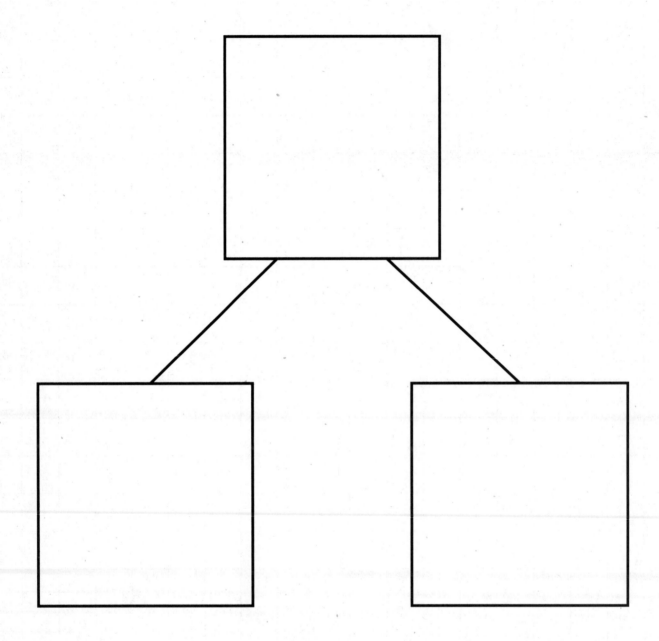

©Curriculum Associates, LLC

	Hundreds
	Tens
	Ones

301	456	729	128
988	506	222	438
793	650	114	269
834	940	175	407

©Curriculum Associates, LLC

20	95	76	44
11	71	53	83
62	39	25	17
41	58	73	50

(continued on next page)

99	78	36	26
19	47	68	91
54	12	30	84
32	65	56	24

©Curriculum Associates, LLC

Measuring Lengths   (For use with Opening Activity, Lesson 18)

Measure each object.

1. Measure the stem.

3. Measure the marker.

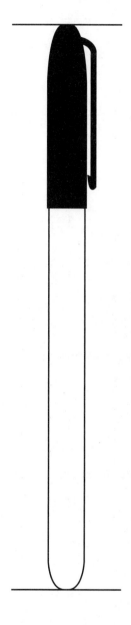

2. Measure the slanted side of the triangle.

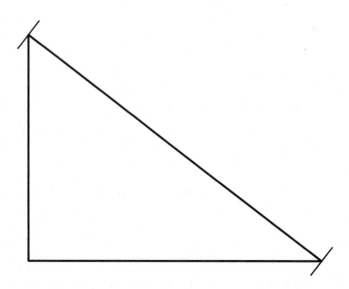

4. Measure the length of the bug.

©Curriculum Associates, LLC

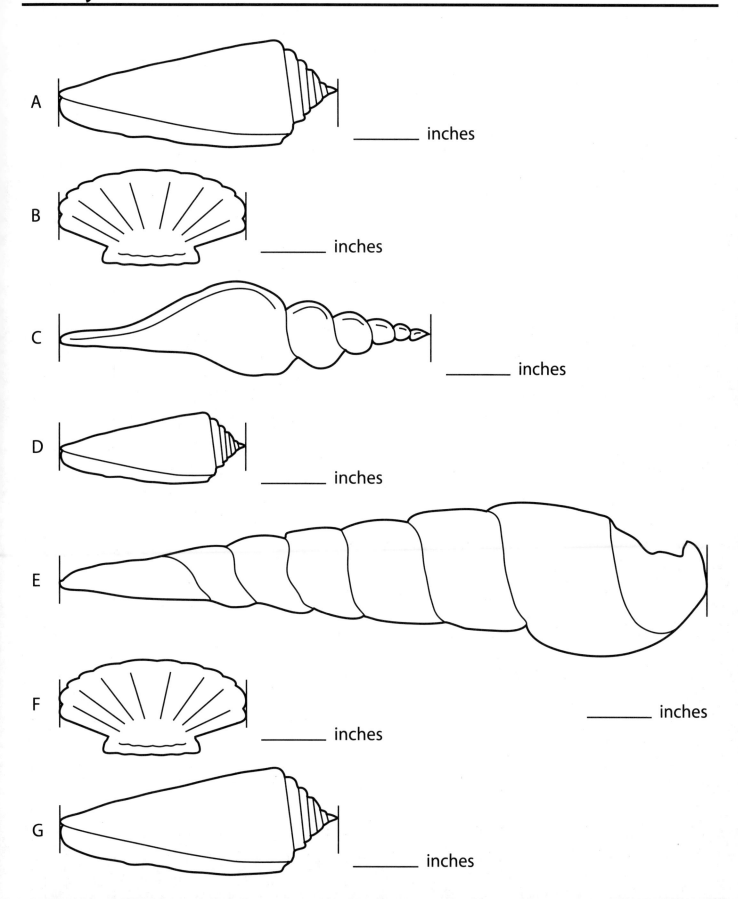

A _____ inches

B _____ inches

C _____ inches

D _____ inches

E

F _____ inches

_____ inches

G _____ inches

Name: _____ Date: _____

Activity Sheet 12   For use with Lesson 22 Intervention Activity

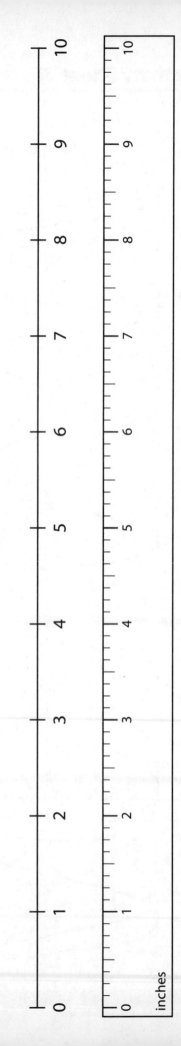

Activity Sheets
©Curriculum Associates, LLC

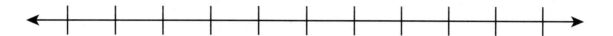

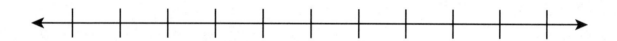

1	2	3	4
5	6	7	8
9	10	11	12
:	AM	PM	

(continued on next page)

©Curriculum Associates, LLC

00	05	10	15
20	25	30	35
40	45	50	55

55¢	38¢	4¢	92¢
49¢	7¢	50¢	61¢
70¢	25¢	13¢	84¢
10¢	15¢	98¢	1¢

©Curriculum Associates, LLC

Triangle

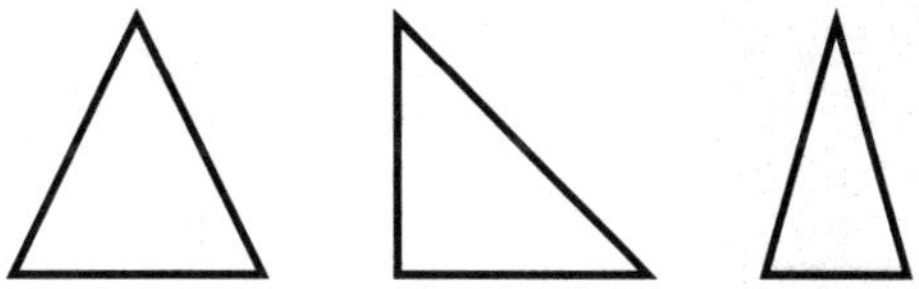

Quadrilateral

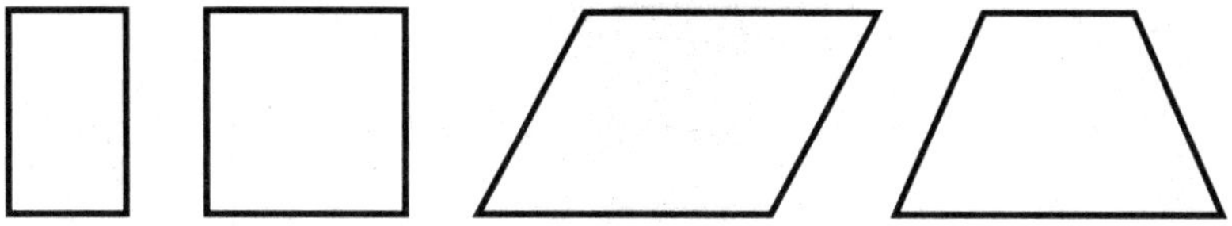

Rectangle

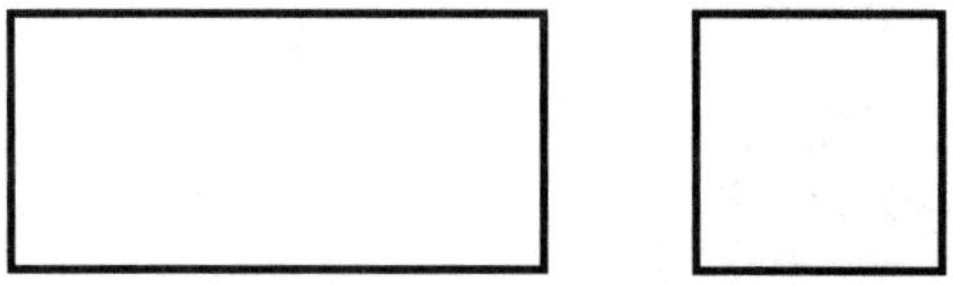

Square

Pentagon

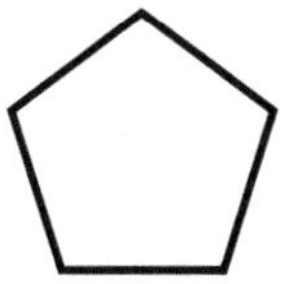

Hexagon

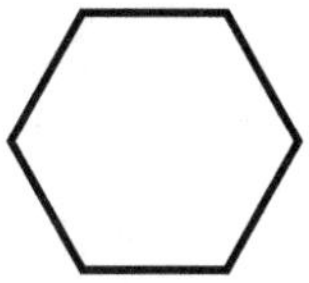

Side

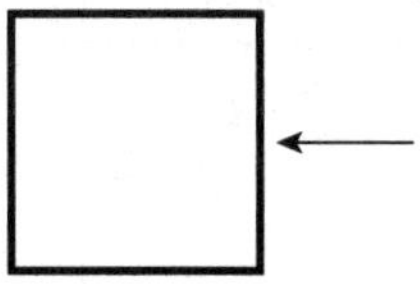

Angle

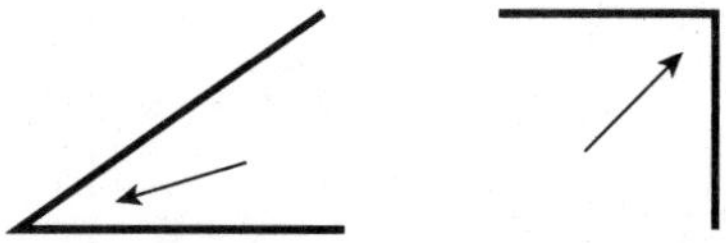

©Curriculum Associates, LLC

©Curriculum Associates, LLC